THROUGH THE BREACH

WYRD MINIATURES PRESENTS

MALIFAUX
RISING POWERS

CREDITS

Creator of MALIFAUX

Nathan Caroland

Creative Direction
Miniature Direction

Nathan Caroland
Eric Johns

Managing Editor

Casey Jones

Game Creation and Design
Graphic Design
Photography

Eric Johns

Rules Development

Dave Bowen
Ambrose Coddington
Drew Littell
Dan Weber

Writers

Dave Bowen
Nathan Caroland
Lenny Glower
Casey Jones
Dave McGuire
Nicholas Volker
Dan Weber

Illustration, Logo, Concept

Alexandur Alexandrov
Melvin de Voor
Stéphane Enjoralas
Hardy Fowler
Kate Laird
Christophe Madaru
Ng Ho Man
Karla Ortiz
Pablo Quiligotti

Office Administrator

Victoria Caroland

Webmaster

Matt Kutchins

Terrain

Jeffrey Andrajack

Playtester Leads

Ambrose Coddington
Eric Johns
Dan Weber

Playtesters

Luke Addison
Michael Basc
Peter Blum
Dave Bowen
Michael Bowsher
Andy Brandt
Tony Branstetter
Ambrose Coddington
Jeremy A. Daniel
Jacob Davis
Glenn Getyina
Evan Gibbs
Justin Gibbs
Steve Hilley
Scott Huber
Andrey Kalugin
Gary Larson
Travis Marg
Keith McCoy
Matthew McDunnell
Mark Muench
Joshua Powers
Nathan Reed
Michael A. Rivera
Daniel Scragg
Thomas Sjöstrand
Aaron Skrivanek
Dan Sulin
Zafar Tejani
Jacob Trewe
Michael Usi
Dan Weber
Steven Zukowski

Additional Help

Krzysztof Żabko-Potopowicz

Wyrd Miniatures is grateful to everyone who enjoyed our first book so much that they jumped right in for the second book and to provide valuable feedback to improve the game. We couldn't have done it without the support and critical eyes, not to mention hard work of our artists, sculptors, painters, and playtesters. It's your energy and enjoyment of all things Wyrd that make the world of Malifaux so much fun for everyone. As always, our families and friends deserve a lot of thanks for believing in this project.

TABLE OF CONTENTS

MALIFAUX STORIES

DESIGNER'S NOTE
STILL A CHARACTER-BASED SKIRMISH GAME

Creating the first Malifaux book was a long process and we had so many ideas for what we thought would make a great game. But we decided that it simply was not a good idea to include them all in the first book. One of the key concepts we removed from the first book was the Henchmen and Special Forces, but they've come back to life in this book.

Henchmen are powerful characters who have the influence to lead their own Crews, which they sometimes do, but they also offer their services to Masters. However, their true powers lie in their influence over the Special Forces that only they can fully command. Even Masters have only limited control over these Special Forces. While Henchmen are introduced in this book, we've presented only a hint of the influence that the Special Forces hold in Malifaux.

We also want Malifaux to continue to be a game of options for the player, giving you as many options, and ways to enjoy the game. As such, we've focused on updating and expanding the existing encounter system to provide nearly endless variation to players. Encounters have been separated into Core and Expanded Strategies. Core Strategies were developed to facilitate an even field for competitive play. Expanded Strategies, which include the Core Strategies, provide players with hundreds of combinations of Strategies and Schemes for encounters to continually challenge gameplay skills. These 13 strategies and nearly 50 schemes kept us busy, and hopefully, they'll provide you with all the options you need to make each Malifaux game different from the one before and always challenging your Malifaux skills.

But as the designer, what I really enjoyed most was in developing the unique characters which make up the bulk of this new book. Malifaux is a world much more than a sideways glance of our Earth. The histories, cultures, and mythologies are designed to be similar enough to our own for everyone to recognize but different enough to draw players into a intriguing new world.

We've drawn influences from many cultures, their myths and legends brought to life in Malifaux. We've also worked hard to give characters abilities that reflect these myriad influences and styles as well as a few that reflect who the characters are. So yes, it was on purpose that one of our new Masters, a timid girl from the Orient, is using hedge clippers. I mean, what else would a gardener use as a weapon?

Eric Johns

Eric Johns
Game Designer

Sedition

The dark and cold came abruptly upon Malifaux, and the chill proved hard to dispel. As the last of the sun's light disappeared over the horizon and the gaslights along the cobblestone streets were lit by roving sentries, the Governor General thrust open the doors of his study and stepped onto the balcony that encircled the upper level of his mansion.

Built in haste, and largely with materials he had imported from Earth, it served as a great testament of his power and authority to the settlers travelling past his residence on the final leg of their journey from the Breach and into Malifaux. The mansion stood beside the main road on a hill overlooking the city. Newcomers to this world had two great sights on either side of the road, the looming Governor's mansion, reminding them both of home and of the man that would tame this place, or the massive Hanging Tree whose legend had traveled beyond Malifaux and back Earthside. It might have been a native knotwood tree though it had grown well beyond the typical height, easily surpassing oaks. The bark was smooth and grayish-black with sharp ridges twisting up its trunk to its leafless branches. Silhouettes of rope and the faint outline of bodies swayed in the darkness. Upon cresting the hill, however, the great city of Malifaux consumed everyone's attention as her towering structures stretched high before them.

No settlers rode by at the late hour, however, and the Governor had pressing matters to attend to, even so late. Down the gently sloping hill, more than a mile distant, torches were held above the heads of a growing mob near the Guild Security offices leading into Malifaux. Judging by the hostile shouts that carried across the distance, they intended to riot. "Lieutenant," he commanded to one of the Guardsmen behind him. "Report!" His breath left him in a fog upon the cold air.

"Sir," the Guardsman said, stepping behind him. "The mob consists of miners, mostly, and other settlers sympathetic to their complaints. They number near sixty. Our intelligence failed to detect the planning for this attack."

"Of course not. Hoffman had better be able to change that," he said of his latest recruit, a man placed in a high position specifically to break the nonsense that cost him manpower and resources, but mostly represented a loss of control the Guild had over the rabble.

Across the distance, he watched the mob's torches bob as they marched upon the Guild's buildings along the north side, heralding a night of murder and destruction. *Sedition*. He stood safely upon the balcony of his mansion, knuckles whitening as he gripped its ornate wooden railing in agitation. He had no doubt that his commands would be fulfilled and order would be restored, but the actions of the mob spoke to him in a tone no man would dare. He would make examples of these rioters. A bloody example makes for a strong teacher, he'd often instruct his Marshals.

The fireplace within the study cast a warm glow upon his shoulders, and four dark shadows of men stretched around him. One man stepped to his side, the iron on his heels ringing on the hardwood like horseshoes. The Governor continued staring at the mob, now mobilizing and marching through the cobblestone streets. "Captain Gideon," he said.

"Sir. My men and I can ride hard and engage the mob before damage is done."

"I'm sure you could, Captain. But Guards are already moving to handle this *nuisance*. It is time for you and me to finalize the arrangements for the contract we discussed."

"Yes. My contract. I appreciate you giving me the opportunity to, well, my family, sir, back Earthside. We need-"

The Governor General cut him off. "That mob, Captain Gideon. What do you make of it?"

Gideon followed his gaze toward the city and the mob marching upon the Security Facility at the gates of the Guild Enclave. "They're just men. Confused. Angry. Desperate to do something to change circumstances they do not understand."

"Yes," the Governor said gravely. "You would understand desperation, would you not?" Gideon did not respond, though his teeth gnashed audibly. He continued. "They're angry because we abandoned their colleagues, friends, in the northern mountains."

Gideon nodded. "The Ice Witch. I've heard. I'm sure the Witch-Hunters will bring her to justice soon. Re-open the mountain pass. We'll save those miners up there."

"To hell with the miners."

"Sir?"

"That damned unnatural storm rages, closing every path for miles around. The miners up there are already dead or soon will be. Assess the situation for me, Captain."

Gideon's training allowed no hesitation. "Tactically sound decision. She has the upper ground and weather is clearly on her side. The loss of a small group of miners is acceptable against the additional loss of our Guardsmen and Witch-Hunters."

"Very good, Captain Gideon. And the mob down there?"

"We'll break them up. Send them on their way. Interrogate those in command."

"And loss of life?"

"Minimal. But we do what we must."

The Governor nodded. "We do what we must," he agreed. "That group is well organized, don't you think?"

"Yes. Militant. Focused."

"We've not been able to infiltrate their ranks. They are a strangely organized and disciplined lot. Far more disciplined than a typical mob. They have a clearly well-defined objective in their movements, direct and purposeful. What disturbs me is not their ability to organize. It is their ability to remain silent. Even under rigorous interrogations by the Judge and an eager Executioner nearby, they do not break. What does this mean, Captain?" he asked, continuing the odd testing of Gideon's judgment.

Again, Gideon did not hesitate. "Absolute loyalty to strong leadership. Fervent. The Union leaders?"

"More. There must be more to it than that."

"Like an army. To beat an army you must break the soldiers or take out the command structure."

"And these soldiers fighting against us?"

"Miners. We must find their leadership."

"And then?"

Gideon said simply, "Kill him."

The Governor General smiled, still staring at the transgression about to befall across the valley and within the city. "It's that easy?"

"Necessary. Minimize casualties. End the conflict. Make a point to stave off further rebellion."

The Governor waved his hand, dismissing the others with the gesture. They left through the study, and the Governor turned away from the view of the mob descending upon *his* security buildings. Gideon, however, could not pull his eyes from the revolt in the city below, agitated that he could not be there, himself.

"You and I have been brought together by fate, it seems, Captain. You have an urgent need for your family – your wife still Earthside. When you approached me regarding my desire to hire a mercenary for an urgent and discreet mission, you pleaded for the position, yourself. I believe you used the term 'desperate'?" Gideon fidgeted uncomfortably. "That's why we're fortunate that fate brought us together: so that we might help one another. You will operate outside of the jurisdiction of the Guild." Gideon nodded. "There is a girl. A prostitute. I need her eliminated."

"A girl, sir?"

"Kirai Ankoku. A groundskeeper by day. Kill her."

"A groundskeeper? A prostitute? Our contract is worth this one girl?"

"If you can fulfill this agreement before the sun sets again. With discretion."

Gideon nodded and left to begin his search for this prostitute, Kirai Ankoku.

Fire lit the northern perimeter of the city, quickly and hungrily engulfing the surrounding buildings as the flames from the Security Facility spread while the Guard dealt with those that brought the fire rather than the fire itself. The Governor sighed in frustration, the fog of his breath developing around him in the crisp air, and he watched a building burn.

The crack of gunfire echoed across the distance.

For the Guild deputies that killed the rioters that night, it was hell. The miners mounted into a maddened frenzy, hurling their torches to feed more of the city to their insatiable fire. In contrast, the Guild marshals were coolly efficient and surgical where the mob was rage and fire. That zealous rage could not be extinguished as easily as the lives of these miners, and the marshals contained the mob systematically, corralling them into a narrow street to quickly eliminate the threat in crossfire.

Three buildings burned. The Guild Security Offices had become engulfed. Windows burst from the pressure within, and the internal structure growled as the fires consumed the support timbers. As the building collapsed, the compromised foundation crumbled and the force of the fire and material of the building fell in, sinking beneath the surface. The cobblestone street about the perimeter of the building fell in as well, the entirety of it becoming a great sinkhole. It gave with a grinding of stone upon stone, and the structure fell through to the great open chasm of the intricate sewer system below. The burning buildings to either side of the sinkhole faced similar demise and, if the infrastructure below them gave way, too, the whole section of town might find itself fallen into the cesspit beneath them.

A Guild sergeant leapt atop a pile of rubble beside the expansive hole, watching the structure's burning remains fall through the open space into the sewer's water channel several stories below. He cried, "Circle 'round! Hedge them off! They're not going to raze this City on my watch!"

Men darted between columns of fire, unable to discern the difference between enemies and Guardsmen in the smoke. Cries and gunshots rang out, echoing off the towering buildings. Within minutes, the buildings immediately adjacent to the Guild Security Offices fell. The City's townspeople, having nothing to do with the riot, were in the streets amidst the turmoil, handing buckets of water to one another in a feeble attempt to stop the fire's devastation. Some were mistakenly gunned down by Guardsmen.

The miners' frenzy intensified despite their dwindling numbers. Their voices were a chorus that praised the virtue of the Union and slandered the rule of the Guild. Their labor now was revenge, a display of loyalty for their abandoned comrades. The fiery death they visited upon these Guild officers were, to them, a merciful fate compared to that unfortunate end they imaged those miners suffered at the hands of cannibals rumored to inhabit those mountain passes.

The turmoil continued until the loud wailing cry of a young boy in their midst stopped the conflict. Every settler in Malifaux knew that their protection against the encroaching threat of the Neverborn was tenuous at best, and paternal instincts to protect the children ran high. Like an unspoken gentleman's agreement, everyone paused in their anger and violence to protect the truly innocent endangered by their irresponsibility.

It took no time to find the crying youth, sobbing in the middle of the street, "Owie, owie, owie!" while holding his skinned knee to his chest and rocking back and forth, a long shock of blond hair matted to his forehead and across his eyes. No one had seen this boy enter the conflict; it was as if he had simply materialized among them.

"Hey kid," one rather protective old man said, approaching him quickly. "We've got to get you to safety."

"What?" the boy said around breathless sobs.

"The fire," the old man said urgently, motioning to the burning buildings just a stone's throw beyond them. He gestured in an arc to the angry men gathered about them. "And these men are fighting!" His voice grew gruff, and he went to snatch the boy up and find the fool parents that brought the kid out into the bedlam. As he reached out, the boy jerked away from the old man.

The boy brushed the hair from his eyes and realized his surroundings with clear distress and obvious

confusion. "Why are they looking at me?" he asked, the panic mounting within him as the expression on his face conveyed that he didn't know where he was.

The boy's expression flashed from pain to anger as he shrieked, "Stop looking at me!"

The old man repeated, "Come on now," with impatience. The boy jerked away, again, as the old man got his hands on the boy's nightshirt.

The boy turned upon him in rage. "I said, stop looking at me!" His eyes flashed with powerful magic unheard of in one so young. He shrieked in a tantrum of rage, "Stop looking at me!" He bent the very rules of reality, twisting the man's face so that his eyes ceased to be, smooth flesh and bone replacing eyes and sockets in a blink. The man reeled backward, howling in shock, falling down and writhing in terror as he grabbed at his suddenly eyeless face.

The miner's revolt was quickly forgotten as the men stared at the scene in mute confusion. One Guardsman, however, stepped forward to assert his authority, intending to bring this anomaly to Sonnia Criid and demonstrate his leadership all at once. He held his Peacebringer, leveled at the child's back, afraid of his incredible power, hoping to scare the child into quick submission. As he approached, though, he stopped short as the boy abruptly stood and turned to face him. The boy spoke to someone who wasn't there.

"I'm sick of this game," he said to the empty space on his left. "I'm not having any fun! Oh, yeah, I guess that's a funner one. Yeah, I could do that."

"Do what?" the Guardsman said, suddenly uncomfortable at the mischievous grin upon the boy's face, his pistol shaking in a suddenly trembling hand. Shooting the child was something he couldn't bring himself to do. That hesitation would be his greatest mistake.

The boy turned to his right to address another imaginary friend. "Oh, good idea!" The Guardsman took a cautious step back. "Flying pink horses?" he asked with a face of disgust. "No way! I ain't no girl. I'm not gonna do rainbows and fairies, either! No girl stuff. Blech." He turned to his other side, eyes beaming. "Better idea!" he said with a nod. "That's way funner! But should we play 'Monster' or 'Tag'? Both together?" He nodded and said to the people gathered around him, "Alright, friends! I'm'a gonna be the monster first. When I catch you, you are O-U-T, out!"

Tall flames cast long, deep shadows between the buildings. Within these shadows countless twinkling eyes appeared. They glowed red and yellow, peering from dark forms that became quickly more substantial, coalescing into hundreds of nightmare shapes.

An inky tendril shot from the darkness between buildings to wrap around the Guardsman with the temerity to confront the boy. More shadowy arms, long and twisted like ropes of darkness grabbed hold of him and tore his limbs from his torso in an effortless jerk. "Got him!" the boy said gleefully. "He's out! I'm gonna get you all! I'm the monster named 'Lord Chompy Bits'!" and he ran at a miner who screamed and bolted. Nightmare visions came alive around them, pouring in an endless wave from the shadows.

Squat creatures with great toothy mouths snapped at them while others with long tentacles strangled the stunned men. Those who had waged conflict against one another just moments before now ran in confused chaos, shooting or swinging upon anything that moved. Fat creatures of burlap and strange humanoid faces shambled about as grotesque mockeries of giant horrible dolls, snatching running victims in their huge open mouths, their swallowed bodies pressing visibly against the cloth in their desperation to escape.

Darkness was the only quality these creatures shared. Each was composed of a seemingly random assortment of limbs with inky tentacles or knifelike talons, representing the collective nightmare images each person had visualized since earliest childhood, all come alive to feed upon them.

Fear gripped the crowded men who stood motionless in disbelief. In gruesome concert, these terrible monsters lunged upon the humans that stood in their midst. The sounds of battle resumed, and shouts and gunfire filled the night. Now, however, the humans fought not against one another but against the dark assailants. Each person fought only for his own survival against the great and unbelievable amassed horde. Just as quickly as the sound of violence erupted, the screaming and gunfire vanished as the men were torn asunder and left dead or dying in the middle of the street.

Blood pooled beneath the fallen corpses of Guardsmen, rioters, and townspeople caught in the wrong place at the wrong time. It drained into the gutter and ran through an open sewer grate.

The living nightmares finished their carnage, slowing the assault as they ran out of victims. The boy, still scampering about, seemed oblivious to the carnage, blood, and gore about him. He yelled, "Boogedy! Boogedy!" pretending to be the monster. The smile waned as his "playmates" fell, leaving him alone amidst the true monsters he created.

This throng gathered around the boy, countless eyes all focusing on him for direction. The boy lifted his arms into the air, and one of the creatures, very different than the others, stepped toward him. This creature, double the size of the largest human in Malifaux, was covered from top to bottom in thickly matted fur. It turned its massive head toward the humans as one man moaned with his last breath. The light of the fire reflected off the shiny black of its huge eyes sewn to the creature's face as if they were colossal buttons, each as large in diameter as a man's chest. The shambling monster pulled back its fabric lips, exposing great jagged teeth across a mouth wide enough to swallow a man whole if the teeth, each as long as a butcher's knife, didn't cut him in half first. The boy looked up lovingly and said, "Teddy!" ignoring its gruesome mouth. And the creature did resemble a nightmarish teddy bear, though no one was there to witness it. Hunkering down, the monster reached out with its thick paw, careful not to harm the boy with its dagger-like claws and pulled him toward its chest.

Yawning, the boy softly whispered, a voice barely audible over the sound of crackling flames all around, "Take me home, Teddy. I'm too tired to keep playing."

As the boy and his great imagined teddy bear blinked out of sight, returning to the comfort of his bed beyond the aether separating the worlds, the nightmares melted back into the shadows from which the boy had drawn them. With his control over their physical form gone, they returned to the dark depths of imagination and the narrow boundary between sanity and insanity.

One great nightmarish creature remained, however. Having lived for countless centuries, far before the amazing child was born, it needed no external magical force to hold him in the physical world. He had been called many names through that time; the Beast, a Bogart, the Boogeyman, and the Nytmare, among many others. Although many thought he was from the same horrible place as the other nightmare creatures, the truth was that he merely emulated them, for they had found a nearly endless sustenance – the fear and anxiety of the human psyche. Like the nightmares disappearing around him, he tormented children, feeding off the bountiful energy of their fear.

He had found this boy, the Dreamer, quite accidentally. The Dreamer was not afraid of him,

could not feed him. But the Dreamer had a greater power that lured this creature to him. This boy had power over the spiritual nightmare world which could sustain him beyond all imagination.

A glimpse into that great world was a portent heralding war. The insignificant life forms of this world would be mere casualties, quickly consumed and forgotten by a greater being that had begun the war so many years before.

The key to his survival and power would be with the boy that could bend reality to his will.

Lesser Breaches

Despite what propaganda the Guild spews, The Breach of The Great Boundary is neither the first nor the only Breach to link Earth and Malifaux. Smaller tears, referred to as Lesser Breaches, have occurred over the centuries, bringing the two realms together for random periods of time.

The realms are separated by what Guild theoreticians have dubbed the 'in-between', through which Earth and Malifaux drift much like soap bubbles caught in a lazy air current. From time to time, the realms wander close enough to one another to "rub". This rubbing generates areas of aetheric disturbance wherein magic is stronger and dreams and visions are more vivid than normal. When the friction between the realms is violent enough, a small rip can form, allowing passage from one to the other through the newly-created Lesser Breach.

The Breaches are unpredictable openings, lasting brief seconds or longer, sometimes for years, before snapping shut once again. Their sizes vary as well; a Lesser Breach may be only large enough to accommodate a pebble or sizable enough to drive a stagecoach through. No pattern seems to exist as to where these rifts will appear on either side of the in-between. They have been known to appear not only in densely populated areas but also in remote locations.

While the Guild works actively to suppress their existence, turning reported sightings of Lesser Breaches into faerie tales among the populace, a few individuals know the truth. Smugglers use a practice they call rift dowsing, as an inexact method to search Lesser Breaches and use them to transport their cargoes out of Malifaux before they close. The Lesser Breaches are popular with Arcanists who have been known to import arms and material from their shadowy contacts Earthside. And even the Neverborn sometimes wander through them, seeking to sow discord and destruction on Earth, much as they do in Malifaux.

Dark Treasures

Hamelin knelt to wipe his blade clean on his victim's shirt. The metal rang as he pressed a button on the handle of the knife to quickly retract the blade. The sharp sound reverberated throughout the vast channel of the sewer tunnel. In the distance, he could hear a colony of rats react to the echo, scattering into the river of filth that ran down the center of the tunnel. No one else would have even noticed it, no doubt, much less understood that the shift of the small splashing echoes were rats jumping into the thick water rather than the constant dripping and splashing of water from every adjoining tunnel, but he certainly did. No one knew rats, nor the sewers, quite like Hamelin. He could even envision the size of the colony and had an instinctive notion of the several twists the tunnels made to bring the sound of their scattering to him. At his side, his faithful canine companion sniffed at the corpse.

"Aye, let's see what we've got, Nix."

Reaching into the dead man's coat, he pulled out the wallet. Hamelin found a fistful of Guild scrip and several greenbacks, all but worthless in Malifaux. He could trade them in, but the effort was more trouble than they were worth. Toilet paper still cost the last time he checked, so he was sure they would come in handy one way or another. He shrugged, stuffing them in a pocket on the inside of his coat. Those Earthside bills painted a picture that this stranger was a new arrival upon Malifaux soil, no doubt here to make his mark like so many other lost souls. Now, instead of making his mark, he was one, lost and very soon forgotten. One more victim for Malifaux's void, another tragic tale of failed ambition and shattered hope Hamelin loved to hear told in the bars. The few Guild notes that did have value weren't as much as he'd hoped for but were more than enough to buy him some Malifaux gin and the warm company of girl at the Qi and Gong. Standing, he stuffed the money into his pocket and raised his gaslight lamp. He glanced back down the tunnel to ensure his isolation, although he knew no one could approach him without his sharp ears noticing. Certainly Nix would have alerted him. "Welcome to Malifaux, friend!" he said loudly to the corpse at his feet. With a swift kick, Hamelin sent the body of the man he'd robbed and murdered tumbling into the water. "Enjoy your stay!" The slowly moving sludge enveloped the body, dragging it below the fetid depths and carrying it away. His voice dropped and resonated with sinister purpose. "Be sure to tell them Hamelin sent you."

He guffawed and snorted. Clearing his throat, he spat a thick plug of mucus into the cesspool. "Come along, now," he said, beckoning for Nix to heel. "Let's head back."

Overly slender and of modest stature, Hamelin was not an imposing figure. Not only was he physically on the frail side, but his knees and elbows had a particularly knobby edge that matched his hooked nose and jutting chin. People had a natural tendency to turn away from the sight of him, afraid they might embarrass him by staring at his strange looking features. His apparent frailty served him well, allowing him to slink through the alleyways of Malifaux and prey on the unaware. As one who lived in the shadows and subsisted on the waste of society, Hamelin felt a certain natural kinship with the vermin of the sewer. It was an environment he felt welcome in, preferring the company of the city's pests to its people, who he never understood. His only companion was the bull terrier that trotted at his side. The dog remained at the edge of the small circle of illumination provided by Hamelin's lamp, ever alert.

If Malifaux was an immense and indecipherable labyrinth of streets and alleyways, its sewer was far beyond the genius of the ancient builders Earthside. Hamelin's gaslight illuminated his path but was unable to reach the top of the passage high overhead. Cyclopean in scale, the sewer had been designed and built to withstand storm drainage of unimaginable intensity. During the tenure of man in Malifaux, no rainstorm had even come close to challenging this sewer, and even when the nearby marshlands swelled with water, the streets of Malifaux remained dry and clear.

This incredible network had evolved into an elaborate ecosystem all its own, and most would-be adventurers avoided it nearly as desperately as they avoided the wilderness beyond what civilization humanity had reclaimed in its short return to Malifaux. Subterranean creatures had become specially adapted to this dark environment. The most ubiquitous example was the Malifaux gray rat, which, while appearing very similar to its Earthside counterpart, was far more suited to braving vast depths of water and could crawl even upside down along the tops of the slippery sewer channels. The dissimilarities between rat species did not end there, however. As with most creatures, Malifaux bred a particularly vicious animal. Most humans had a natural inclination to avoid any rat, and many feared them altogether, though erroneously in most cases. Rats were scavengers and survivors, fleeing from danger whenever possible. Although they occupied the places man would avoid, they fulfilled a necessary role of consuming what man discarded. The Malifaux gray rat, however, did not rely upon scavenging, alone, to sustain itself. They were overly aggressive and wickedly smart. They could hunt, and not only in groups, but sometimes even in isolation. Hamelin often likened them more to wolverines than normal rats, and even pondered why it was said the legendary beast-master, Marcus, could not figure out how to bend them to his will. Hamelin snorted again as he considered that. Better, he decided, for the beast-master to remain in the dark on that count. People tolerated Hamelin because he, alone, could compel whole colonies at once. "The trick," he thought, "is not to dominate them, but to submit to their power."

Holding his lamp over the water, Hamelin noticed how a subtle vibration disturbed it as small ripples moved the water in minute waves against the bricks lining the channel. Although he had nothing to fear from the predatorial gray rat, other creatures existed entirely within the thick, spoiled water of the sewer, and Hamelin knew well to keep clear of the strange creatures that patrolled its fetid murk.

He backed away and pressed against the stone wall of the sewer. The vibration was there, too, and it slowly grew in intensity. Cobblestones and bricks from the street's foundation, far overhead, fell to the water with great splashes. The quake spooked Nix who tugged incessantly at his leash. Dog and owner turned to flee as a glowing fissure opened overhead. Only then did he realize that the quake began above ground rather than below. He quickly placed his subterranean location below the northern quarter of the City, its structures built upon a relatively thin membrane separating the buildings above, and the

expansive sewers below. Where the riot that brewed above provided great cover for this night's dark transgression, the fools had managed to raze a building, and the sudden violence of its collapse threatened him as well. Ironically, then, the same elements he had used to conceal his murder had now compromised him.

Hamelin quickly unhooked Nix's leash and said, "Stay close, boy, but find a way out'a here!" The dog loped ahead, anxious to find safety, but he remained within Hamelin's lamplight, moving as quickly as his spindly legs allowed.

The fissure grew into a jagged, fiery crack, and more cobblestones from the street above collapsed, falling into the sewer below, splashing Hamelin and Nix. Although far overhead, Hamelin could hear the crackle of burning timbers within the building as fire engulfed the exposed bottom, sending some debris, glowing in oranges and yellows down to the foul water. Hamelin and Nix could not traverse the span of the great chamber in time as that building, full of fire and smoke, crumbled into the sewer channel, breaking the stone walls. If he had been safe, the sight of a fully constructed building falling several stories through open air might have been one of the greatest sights of his life. As it was, he feared it might be the last sight of his life. "Faster, boy," he urged, knowing it was he who slowed them. "Go, dog!" he said. "Just go, Nix!" But it was too late. The structure hit the water. The sudden impact of the full building and the remains of its stone foundation displaced the fetid muck, sending volumes of the dark substance up in a great wave that consumed the entire passage while sludge spilled from its channel and poured through the openings. Hamelin was caught in this sudden surge and washed beneath the surface.

All was darkness as the water pulled him under and swept him away. He had lost the gaslight and his companion as well. As he rolled through the thick water, he struck against the side of the channel and turned over and around. Panic consumed him as he struggled to pull himself up for air. There in the dark, beneath the thick waters of the sewer, he kicked madly but no longer knew which way was up. A very dim glow from the burning building illuminated the way behind him, giving him his only notion of direction. The surge of heat from the burning mass was left far behind as his body was cruelly tossed out of the main channel and down a series of narrow tunnels. The torrent bludgeoned him against walls and one particularly severe blow drove the remaining air from him, and he screamed out beneath the water. Bubbles rolled across his face as he clawed and kicked madly, hoping he'd emerge from the watery hell. His lungs ached for air, and just as he was convinced he would drown, his body spilled out into a tall waterfall. Falling more than a dozen yards, he felt the brief air upon his face and inhaled desperately, drawing in both air and the foul water. He refused to choke it out, stifling the gag reflex, knowing he'd again desperately need every breath. He landed in a lake of sludge which saved him from further injury, though the water continued to pour upon him and forced him to the bottom of the reservoir. The air within him was once again driven from his body, and his face and chest were dragged painfully across the roughly hewn stones below. He screamed out again beneath the water and involuntarily drew in the grotesque fluid. He choked and his chest exploded in pain as flashes of light played out before his eyes as he succumbed to drowning.

He passed out, reluctantly accepting the death that had come to claim him. He was unconscious as his body bobbed to the surface and coughed out thick sewage. The density of the water kept him partially

afloat and allowed him to breathe, although cracked ribs and bruised lungs left his breathing shallow and wheezing.

He regained consciousness slowly, unaware of how long he might have lain in that pile of filth. Eventually, though, he managed to blindly grope his way out and pulled himself onto the stone landing at the side of the pool. Completely drenched and his lamp lost long ago, he was blind and cold. He felt the gaping wounds upon his brow and cheek as well as both palms. He didn't need to check to know that several ribs were cracked or broken, and for all he knew, he might be blind as well. Having lived for some time in the black sewers, he had come prepared, and, searching through his coat, he produced a waterproof chemical flare. He struck it on the ground beside him with the last of his strength and the end of the flare erupted with bright red light. He held it up feebly to survey his surroundings.

High above him, a column of water poured down from out of sight, its current slowly returning to its normal volume. Rats, sludge, and garbage all cascaded down into the growing subterranean lake before him. Just as he had crawled out, the rats also scurried out of the muck and into the darkness, equally anxious to end their ordeal. However, they were far less beaten than him, he knew, and not for the first time did he wish he were as resilient. Hamelin also discovered that he was no longer in the sewer, but within an expansive vault beneath the surface fed by the sewer tributary. Although his flare illuminated much of the area around him, it could not penetrate the far depths of the cavern and the moving of the water against rock echoed strangely, disorienting him and confusing his sense of space and depth.

Lifting the flare, the red light illuminated tall, straight walls that contrasted sharply with the cylindrical vaults of the sewer he was accustomed to. Although he initially thought the chamber was a naturally occurring cave that ancient city planners had connected their elaborate sewage system to, he saw that the rough stone was more purposefully carved from the hard rock, as if torn from top to bottom by immense claws, as long recesses gouged into the otherwise flat surface. His breath still coming in labored gasps; he used this oddity of architecture as an excuse to pause before hunting for Nix and a way out. Naturally, if he had survived, his smart dog would surely have done even better. Hamelin ran his hand across the jagged face of the stone and found, very much to his surprise, that set into the wall and in a regular pattern, were a series of tombs. Suddenly very curious, he ignored the pain within his chest and the protesting of his much bruised arms as he pulled and pried at the cap sealing one of the chambers. Although he at first thought he lacked the strength to open one even in an unwounded state, with an accidental push and tug, the stone encasement swung open, groaning against a rock hinge, the door held by almost perfectly balanced and crafted stone. Although the bones within this first tomb were human in size, he could not be certain they were of either human or Neverborn origin. To the scavenger in him, he saw the opportunity to find treasures to be salvaged. He soon found the relatively easy method of opening each vault and hungrily examined tomb after tomb. Very few of the graves held any complete corpse, but many also contained additional accoutrements set to rest with the departed. In lifting himself to inspect these items, Hamelin felt the bruises visited on his body by the rough journey into this chamber and decided he must come back for the treasures after escaping this watery graveyard instead of straining himself, now, in plundering.

He wasn't going to escape the way he came in, as the sewer that deposited him here opened far overhead, and he could certainly not climb out even in the best of his health. The water, here, flowed out of this cavern somewhere, and the rats had certainly seemed eager enough to find the way. If they were able to get out, then he was assured he could as well. What puzzled him most, though, and caused him the greatest fear, was the strange absence of Nix. He worried that the dog might have perished, either by drowning or from a pummeling against the walls. He called, "Nix!", but the effort shook his body, and he fell against one of the outer ribs of the wall next to him, fighting down the urge to cough as bloody bile arose in his throat. He whistled shrilly for Nix to come, certain that the dog would hear it echoing through the chamber and pinpoint him. But Nix did not come.

Hamelin gathered up his courage and fought against the growing dread. He followed along the wall of the crypt, amazed by the uncountable number of graves stacked within, assuming that they went all the way to the top of this already expansive chamber. His fingers felt along the wall as he slowly made his way,

and he discovered the stones were decorated with script between the recessed columns of tombs. The words were indecipherable to him, written, he supposed, in the language of Old Malifaux, but the volume of words crowded between the graves suggested an enormous epic. He began to wonder what manner of men were buried here, if the people of Old Malifaux were so different from the men who inhabited the City today. He heard a strange mewling noise from further along the passage, faint and pitiful.

He moved quietly and carefully toward the feeble noise. To him it sounded like the pitiful whimpering of the dying, yet, other than him, no living thing should be down here. He hated the thought, but reluctantly knew it might very well be Nix crying somewhere ahead. He held the flare before him and steadied his nerves as he crept along the edge of the water as quickly as he dared. Eventually the crypt opened up into a large, vaulted chamber, similar to the massive room it adjoined, but this room's lower ceiling and angular walls bounced his light very efficiently, illuminating the entire expanse. The walls of the chamber were not crowded with graves like the rest of the crypt but were decorated with enormous statues set into wide circular alcoves.

The center of the chamber was ruined. Soil had swelled beneath the stones and had grown into a large mound. A pile of stones had been rolled away and what appeared to be a large sarcophagus had spilled open. The bones of its occupant lay scattered on the ground, but as Hamelin approached, he noticed that the skeleton's hand still clutched some treasure possessively in its grip. Leaning in close, Hamelin held his flare out over the object. It was a flat, thick piece of lacquered metal inlaid with a myriad of interconnected gears. Hamelin was reminded of the inner workings of a music box or the motion of a pocket watch. It was decorated with what appeared to be a crescent moon and a collection of stars with one large red gem in the middle of the others. He imagined the cogs moving and the stars spinning in a dance around the moon, although the red star did seem to sit in the middle of the device's face. In addition, one side of the metal plate was hinged, and it appeared that the device might be opened in a manner similar to a book.

His inspection of the device was interrupted by the faint simpering sound that had drawn him here.

Moving away from the corpse and to the other side of the tumbled sarcophagus, Hamelin discovered the body of his canine partner. It was unmistakably Nix, but, as he rounded the corner, looking for the source of the whimpering, he found only the dog's devoured carcass, only bones and a bit of sinew remaining. He cried out and leapt to the poor creature, at once struggling to accept the great loss of his friend and companion and fighting the great compulsion to flee. He stood, fear and confusion overwhelming him. At the edge of the flare's light, he saw a ripple of movement upon the ground and thrust the light toward it. Fleeing before him were crawling vermin, small blind maggots that carpeted the entire region of darkness just beyond the light.

"What the hell?" he muttered. He thrust his arm forward, and the mass of creatures writhed away as if in agony at the light, but he jumped back, amazed at the great magnitude of the larvae. Still, Nix had been alive just seconds before he came around the sarcophagus.

The ground around him rippled and heaved as the tiny creatures twisted about, just beyond the fading light of his flare. He inched his way forward, using his light to push them away, working his way out of the horrible chamber. As he did, the rippling of the ground in the darkness slowly subsided, and, when he again thrust his flare forward, he found that only a few of the vile maggots remained. They must have burrowed back into the ground, he reasoned, and quickened his step to get out and away, only hesitating for a moment to consider the loss of his canine companion.

As he turned to flee, a tremor below him gave him pause. At the center of the chamber, where the large mound of earth stood, the soil was visibly disturbed, tiny fragments of debris and small pebbles suddenly dancing upon its surface. A thick, sickly white fluid began bubbling up from the apex of the mound and poured over the ground. It appeared to Hamelin like a wound seeping puss, but the bubbling quickly erupted into a geyser gushing into the air. The ground beneath him lurched and rumbled loudly. The liquid surged, and Hamelin suddenly found a flood upon him as he held up his arms to ward off the raining fluid. He was horrified to discover that what appeared to be a thick white fluid was in reality a rolling mass of the maggots that had consumed his dog! He shrieked and flailed his arms as he spun and batted at the endless stream of larvae, spinning and kicking through the room.

They bit into his exposed flesh as he frantically brushed them off, screaming with terror. Despite his attempts, they continued to bite him, feeding upon his flesh, burrowing beneath his skin to devour the soft muscle beneath. As he brushed at his arms, they continued to pour down and quickly crawled beneath his clothing, eating every inch. He fell but scrambled onto his hands and knees, attempting to escape the chamber, but when his hands dipped into the flood of hungry maggots, his flesh was dissolved as if it were acid. He pushed down on the exposed bone of his hands, trying to rise and run, but his legs failed as they, too, were devoured by the creatures, causing him to fall face down into the wriggling mass. He screamed and flailed. They erupted from beneath his skin, consuming him alive, and he fell backward upon the undulating mass of the vermin surrounding him. As his strength and will failed him, he brushed instinctively at the larvae, trying still to stop their voracious feeding. It was futile. They crawled about his exposed bones. He watched, stunned and still alive, as the insect larvae devoured his flesh, the tide of white, putrid maggots slowly working its way toward his head and leaving only the exposed bones of his forearms and ribs behind.

He thrashed and screamed, his raw-throated cries filling the chamber. His flare was doused by the rolling mass of insects, plunging the area into renewed darkness. The creatures flooded into his mouth and down into his lungs to steal his breath and feast on his organs. Hamelin was given only moments to consider the final, brief, moments of his life. The white larvae poured out and through his chest. He heaved upward and thankfully expired.

Ambush

Sonnia and Samael rode side by side. Behind them, four Guild Guardsmen rode at a distance. One said it was so the two senior officers could have privacy. Samael knew it was more out of discomfort and fear. Sonnia could do that to a person. Their horses maintained a leisurely trot, and the slight beat of their hooves against the soft earth allowed for conversation. There was, however, no exchange. Sonnia had a ragged leather-bound book spread open on the pommel of her saddle. Embossed on the front of the book were the words *The Philosophy of Uncertainty*. She read quietly to herself from the book as the horses put miles behind them.

"You're the only person I know that can read in the saddle," Samael said, testing Sonnia's attention.

Sonnia smirked and closed the book. "How many literate people do you know, Samael?" she quipped.

Samael laughed at her sarcastic jab. It wasn't often that the two of them had a moment like this to relax. The grim work of a Witch-Hunter left a person jaded and detached. No other Guild force worked so intimately with the people of Malifaux, and few had to endure the political wrangling that they did. The people of Malifaux would never consider the two of them heroes. Theirs was a thankless job. They were much more likely to be labeled villains for the subtle crimes they policed. The rising influence of the Union only exacerbated the issue. Union propaganda actively campaigned against the Witch-Hunters, calling them thought-police and the martial arm of a fascist dictator.

"You've had your nose stuck in that book for months. You must have read it a dozen times by now. What is it that has you so captivated?"

Sonnia looked at the cover of the journal for a moment before tucking it into her coat. It was true; she had barely put the thing down since she had confiscated it from the witch, Rasputina. It was hard, though, to explain her fascination.

"The things this man experienced, especially in regards to the events at Kythera, the way he explains them, they so mirror my own memories of that place. For Phillip Tombers, his life changed dramatically after witnessing the opening of the Artificial Breach. I felt the significance of that moment, too. It was an epiphany."

"Yeah, of course," Samael said. "Me? Now when the pressure mounts, I just want to go huntin'. Maybe have a few shots of gin or whiskey with the boys. You? Things get heavy and you read a book."

"Well, not just any book. And not exactly normal pressure, either. If we were not there in that crucial moment, this world would be a very different place. If what lies beneath Kythera is truly what Tombers thought, Death, itself, would have been loosed upon us. That is the epiphany. It falls to us to do those things which others cannot or will not. Though we are damned by those we save, it is for us to face the remnants and influence of Old Malifaux and quash them. That we survived, that our sanity persevered where others' failed, this is the proof of our duty."

He had heard such grandiose self-righteousness from Sonnia, before. It was this kind of justification that

allowed her to callously hunt the pitiful fledgling sorcerers of Malifaux's slums before they were recruited by the Arcanists. It was the same kind of justification she used to come to terms with the events of Kythera. For him, the memory was very different. He and Sonnia did not prevent the workings of the device, they enabled it. If it were not for Ramos' intervention and his super-weapon, they would have loosed a plague of unknown potency upon this world. That plague had destroyed people, only a handful of deputies had left it with their minds unbroken.

He didn't condemn her for that self-righteousness, however. He admired her for it. He knew she was not deluded by it but understood the errors that had led to the terrible events of that day. That purity of focus, however, allowed her to pursue her agenda with a single-minded determination and clarity of purpose. The Governor General had chosen well in naming her his Chief Witch-Hunter. Samael knew, too, why the Governor had named him as her aide. Samael had to be her conscience where she had none.

"I think Tombers would have appreciated your penchant for the dramatic, Sonnia, but I agree. We're the best option for Malifaux - the people have no idea just how bad it is."

"I have suspicions that must be confirmed before we act, and there's so many ways this could go wrong. I need allies I can trust, Samael. You sure you want to be part of this?"

"You really have to ask?" he said. "Even if I didn't believe in what we do, riding with you is way more interesting than huntin' three headed sabers."

"As I'd assume. Then our circle of trust will have to tighten a bit. We'll need more Stalkers with us soon. They'll obey us absolutely. I need a Steward. That's you, and you'll answer only to me. You ride where I ride, and no other will command you."

He nodded. "Fine by me. But, 'Witchling Steward' best we can do?" he quipped.

"You have a better title in mind?" she asked with a smile.

"Samael Hopkins, Hero of the People?"

She actually laughed out loud which surprised him. "We'll save that for when you're in charge," and she surprised him again by tossing him a small bag of Soulstones. "Start by mastering those, *Hero*."

He felt the stones within the pouch thoughtfully. "This trip to the Ortega ranch. It's not about delivering those 'witched bullets, is it?"

She glanced back at the Guild Guards, ensuring their privacy. "No, that's just an excuse. Regardless of our moral authority, we must have allies. I know the Ortegas are more ethically flexible than Lady Justice. We'll also need more than Witchling Stalkers if I'm right about Kythera and some of the Arcanum in this book. I think there's a war brewing we know nothing about, by forces that would consider us nothing more than an irritation."

As they rode to the top of a small hill, Samael reined in his horse. "There it is. Latigo, the Ortega stronghold." Samael called out to the Guardsmen. "Be ready!"

The Captain rode to join him. "Sir? Is there a problem?" he asked.

"No. Not yet. Those Ortega maniacs built that damned fortress out here on the edge of the wilds to taunt the Nephilim. Kind of a slap in the face and a constant challenge. Nephilim are pissed and they might be savage, but they sure aren't dumb. They're all through this area looking for a chance to slap the Ortegas right back," he said, sweeping his arm to the sparse wooded areas throughout the landscape surrounding the ranch. Very few men have what it takes to homestead in the Outlands of Malifaux. With a stockpile of high caliber firearms and a constant xenophobic paranoia, the Ortegas created a sprawling villa. The thing was as much a fort as it was a ranch, meant to repel the beasts of the Malifaux wilds and to withstand the siege of determined Neverborn.

Humans in this world clustered together under the canopy of the Guild for protection, seeking sanctuary in civilization. Latigo was an oasis in the wilderness, a fortress in the wastes. It consisted of several large log-constructed buildings arranged in a walled compound. Built on terraced earth, each structure sat higher than the one below. Gathered together, those buildings could have equally been a monastery or military compound. It housed the gathered members of the Ortega clan and served as the unofficial headquarters of the Neverborn Hunter Task Force. It held a very tactically important position, situated in close proximity to the bayou wetlands populated by gremlin raiders and serving as a barrier to their activities.

They rode cautiously, each man with his pistol in hand and cocked at the ready. Sonnia deferred to Samael's lead, experience supporting the notion that his hunting skills would come in handy when an ambush might be around the next bend. As they drew closer to the dense foliage that enveloped both sides of the road, Samael held his clenched fist in the air for them to halt, and the Guardsmen cast nervous glances from him to the undergrowth around them. He remained motionless, listening intently. Finally, with a nod toward Sonnia, he turned his steed and plunged into the thick growth, disappearing from sight. His horse, well trained to move with Samael, passed easily through the brush and trees.

Sonnia pulled the great sword from her back. The magical weapon glowed faintly a deep azure.

Long seconds passed as the men shifted nervously in their saddles, the horses stepping anxiously as they were kept in check. Thundering hooves suddenly erupted within the woods, and they all expected Samael to burst forth, urgent to rejoin them, so they were shocked when a great Nephilim lunged forth, the striking hoof-beats from it rather than Samael's mount. The men were seasoned and trained and should have responded to it bursting out of the trees with a shower of shattered branches. But this creature surpassed anything they had ever heard of or imagined. They saw that the great Nephilim, while a massive creature, was not the thick masculine beast they had all heard tales of,

with broad and sinewy bare chest who could kill a man with its two slashing claws. Instead, barreling toward them was an extremely large Nephilim female.

The Guardsmen barely moved to defend themselves, and the great wings upon her back stretched then snapped back with a clap, propelling her forward. Her lithe body spun as she left the ground, and the creature's great sword, as long as a horse and wider than a man's waist, arced around and caught one Guardsman in the chest, sending his dead body back more than a dozen yards.

Her cloven hooves dug into the earth, and she rose, towering above the nearest man, easily doubling his size. Her spreading wings bathed him in shadow. He lifted his pistol only through instinct of training, but she lunged forward, easily tossing aside both man and horse. Her arm reached out and grabbed a third man. She let her great sword fall, lifting him from his saddle and tore him in half at the waist.

She crouched, and her lower jaw distended and her lips pulled back as her face twisted with rage. She bent and screamed, the howl pulsing and reverberating from deep within her chest. Sonnia, trained and experienced in hunting down the most dangerous men alive, still fought against the terror this great creature instilled and could not focus the magical energies around her in an attack. The Guardsman nearest to her, however, could not control his panic and bolted.

The last Guardsman, knocked from his horse, cowered futilely beneath a shrub at the side of the road. His horse, however, stumbled upright. Samael burst forth from the underbrush on foot and deftly leapt upon the horse even as it began to run away. He shouted over his shoulder, "Sonnia! Ride!"

It was not in her character to flee from battle, yet she made an exception that day as her spurs dug smartly into Ember's flanks. Ember ran faster than she had ever before, urged on by the sudden screams of the last Guardsman found beneath his shrub and mercilessly killed.

Sonnia caught up to Samael and shouted, "You okay? What happened to your horse?"

Samael hitched a thumb back from where he had burst from the woods, and Sonnia turned to see a small swarm of tiny Nephilim pouring forth from the same location. The great female Nephilim casually touched one, and it twisted and writhed at her touch, growing over double its former size in an instant as small wings sprouted from its back. "What the hell is that thing?" Samael shouted back.

"No idea! Nephilim, that's for sure. Most powerful one I've ever seen!"

Although they rode hard toward Latigo, Nephilim were known for their speed and even the youngest tot could pace a horse. They weren't really worried about the Nephilim tots, though, as the great female took up her incredible sword and took flight, quickly closing the distance between them. The seasoned Witch-Hunters had ridden away from dozens of gun battles. They worked in perfect concert. and when Sonnia tugged on the reins of her horse and steered him to the right, Samael matched her, keeping the woman and her giant blade between him and their assailant. They soon emerged from the dense woodlands into more open hills.

Before them, riding atop a sturdy Spanish stallion, a broad-shouldered man emerged from his hiding place and charged toward them. His ragged duster flapped furiously in the wind and his spurs dug cruelly into the flanks of his steed. He guided his

mount with his knees while his hands held two giant pistols. He had narrow eyes and thick muttonchops on his cheeks. The extended clips in his pistols allowed for a devastating hail of fire, and he rained shots down past the two Hunters, at the great Nephilim. They heard it shriek above the thunderous hooves of the horses as bullets sank into its tough flesh.

Santiago Ortega turned his mount and doubled back, joining them as he twisted in the saddle and continued to fire upon the creature. "You did this, Criid!" he shouted to her in accusation.

"Not now, Santiago!"

He continued to fire at the pursuing creature, "You don't come out here unexpected and without warning! You know better than that!"

It's true that Sonnia had broken protocol and had not followed the procedures the Ortegas established. Latigo loomed before them, and she could see a rather young boy perched atop a tall tower, taking aim upon the pursuing creature. The Nephilim shrieked again, followed by one echoing blast from the boy's rifle, then another. The creature broke its pursuit, but they continued to ride hard toward the compound.

At the gates, they pulled to an abrupt stop as Francisco, the family's eldest, strode out to greet them, his own pistol at the ready. Sonnia said, "Thanks. How did you know we needed the help?"

Francisco nodded to a Guardsman's horse within the compound that belonged to the first man that had bolted. Santiago's legendary temper could not be controlled even toward her, however, as he spat, "How many died out there with you, Criid?"

"Mind yourself," she warned.

He snarled at the leader of the Guild Witch-Hunters, saying, "You mind yourself! You endangered your own men, and this compound, too. Don't think your recklessness can be —"

"Boy, you stand down!" The voice was a croak, as dry and brittle as tinder. Somehow it still held the volume necessary to demand immediate obedience.

"Abuelita, get back inside!" Santiago said to the venerable old woman shuffling up behind Francisco.

She hefted a large shotgun and triggered a blast into the air as a kind of warning. It knocked her back without fazing her, and she barked, "The second shell's for backtalk like that! Criid's a guest. Now apologize, boy, and get in and set the table for two more!"

Santiago burned with rage but would never consider defying the matriarch of the Ortega clan. Grudgingly he muttered, "My apologies, Criid." He was frustrated at the danger brought to his door but fought down the anger and nodded at Sonnia with respect. Lashing the reins of his horse, he rode toward the villa.

Sonnia and Samael offered a bow to the wizened woman. "Thank you, kindly, Ma Ortega," was Samael's greeting, "It's our honor to be welcome at Latigo."

Sonnia was silent, sheathing her sword upon her back. Abuela Ortega gave the woman an appraising look, squinting her near-sighted eyes. "Boy, shut up and get inside," she said to Samael. "Dinner's on and I won't tolerate it getting cold."

As they followed the old woman, the savory aroma of the evening meal wafted out to greet them.

Twenty men, women, and children gathered around an enormous table, each one of them quite clearly an Ortega. Those Ortegas who were deputies of the Guild, those who hunted Neverborn while the rest attended to the villa, sat at one end, including Perdita, a dazzling woman possessing the generous curves the Ortega women were known for. Her exterior belied her silent and reserved demeanor and her incredible skill with firearms. She was so young, Sonnia remarked to herself, and she said very little while the room clamored with voices. Yet Perdita studied the two intently. Despite his own great confidence, Samael found himself blushing and turned aside from her penetrating gaze. He found her presence disconcerting.

Francisco possessed a presence of authority and directed the younger members of the clan to find their seats. He was tall and dressed a bit finer than his fellows. His brother Santiago sat at the table, shoveling great quantities of food from the center of the table onto his plate. The youngest Neverborn Hunter, a boy the rest referred to as Niño, pleasantly prepared a plate for his uncle, the legend, Papa Loco, before ever thinking of himself. Still, even in the dining room of the Ortega compound, Papa Loco wasn't trusted with sharp or pointed silverware. He dug into his meal with a blunt wooden spoon, and Niño assisted him, urging him to slow down, and even helped him take a drink.

Abuela Ortega shot an expectant look at Sonnia and Samael and after only a moment of hesitation, they joined the meal, as well. Dinner at Latigo was a boisterous affair accompanied by hefty amounts of food and generous helpings of tall tales. Every story featured a monster bigger than the last or a shot so miraculous that angels in the heavens must have put a hand on the bullet.

The food, drink, and revelry soon reached a lull. Perdita, who had not spoken at all during the meal, cleared her throat. There was immediate silence. She asked for privacy with the Witch-Hunters, and all the rest quickly gathered up the dirty dishes and were gone from the room within a moment. Sonnia had never been with the Ortegas outside of their professional duties, and she respected the young girl even more seeing how quickly those around her deferred to Perdita's authority without hesitation. When only her father and two brothers remained, she asked, "Sonnia, why have you come here?"

Sonnia's own voice had a similar weight and all those at the table knew dire matters were about to be discussed. She said, "First let me answer your hospitality with a gift."

She stood and motioned to Samael at her side. Reaching into a satchel at his hip, the man produced a small oak box inlaid with the Ortega's brand in walnut. He opened the box and inside were twenty rounds. On the frontier, one caliber was ubiquitous. A .45 caliber round was better known as 'mortal caliber,' a round selected specifically for its ability to kill a man. These rounds had been specially prepared by Sonnia's staff and bore the mark of witchcraft upon them.

Each was subtly engraved with a winding serpent, the coils of the snake crafted to engage the rifling of the firearm it was fired from. More curious was the fact that the tip of each was set with a faceted soulstone. Each tiny stone glowed with a sanguine color, like the blood it would draw from its victim. The serpent was the current obsession of Sonnia Criid, and she had commanded the witches in her employ to imbue these rounds with the venomous poison of that creature.

"I offer these witch-rounds so that the enemies of the Ortega clan might know only death." Sonnia spoke much more with the tone of her voice and the motion of her eyes. Perdita simply nodded in acceptance, though she left the box untouched on the table before her.

Sonnia continued, "I know that the Neverborn Hunters have been directed to raid the gremlin encampment to the east of here. Our research has suggested that notable ruins exist in that area. I am interested in recovering artifacts that bear this mark," she said, pointing at the winding serpent.

Samael rose and drew out a piece of parchment from his poncho and rolled it out upon the table. A very simple emblem was drawn on the paper. To Santiago it resembled a cattle brand not unlike the Ortega's own. Everyone around the table crowded in to look at the mark. It was an image of a snake wound around a sleeping eye.

"I'm looking for this," she said. "The snake is used throughout the artifacts I've been studying. It's a key or symbol. Maybe a hieroglyph ancient even to the Neverborn. If we can understand it, I believe we will unlock something no human has ever seen. Something amazing and awful. If you can help me find the serpent we may begin to unlock the secrets. But be wary if you do. There's something . . . unspoken, in the research surrounding the serpent imagery."

Perdita thought for a moment, a finger absently twirling a long black lock of hair. She reached for the box of ammunition and pulled a bullet from within. She had her pistol drawn and the bullet chambered quicker than Samael could follow. Her pistol roared. They followed the trajectory of the bullet to a support beam above the mantle on the other side of the room. The hole the bullet made sizzled, giving off an olive colored smoke that smelled like rotten eggs. Francisco left his seat to examine the hole more closely as Perdita stared at it solemnly.

"Don't touch the hole," Sonnia warned.

"Why's that?"

"It'll burn your skin like acid. 'Bout an hour, I'd guess, and it'll be safe to handle. But we never fired it through a wooden beam to test that."

Francisco winced at the burning of his eyes when he leaned in close to inspect it. Then he nodded in appreciation. "Looks like it punched clean through."

Perdita shifted her gaze to Sonnia. "Search for your serpent in some possible lost ruins in what might be the single most dangerous location on Malifaux? Just between ourselves, of course." Sonnia actually found herself fidgeting. She didn't expect the young woman to be so brazen and strong-willed. "We'll do it. For one hundred more of these bullets."

Samael guffawed. "One hundred? That's crazy. Do you have any idea what's involved in making those? The work, the money, the magic. Hell, the testing alone-"

Sonnia put her hand on his arm, stifling him. "One hundred," she said with a nod. Nothing, it seemed, was free in Malifaux, and Perdita proved she was far more brash and confident than Sonnia realized. It was a good sign.

Perdita nodded and said, "Find a serpent in some Malifaux ruins. Be careful around it cause it's the key to something awful. Keep this between us 'til we sort it out. Got it."

"Ya blamed fools is gonna git yourselves killed," Abuela Ortega scolded from the entry to the kitchen, ignoring the request for privacy. Rules in the Ortega house didn't apply to her.

Francisco nodded and said, "We'll be careful, Abuelita. We'll come back in one piece."

"Hell you will! It'll do you lot some good if you don't, you ask me. Running around the countryside, kickin' up dust," she continued to berate them for their "stupid Ortega stubbornness" though her voice dwindled away as she stamped through the house. "Shooting this, that, and the other thing that moves before checking to see if it's even related to you first...cabrónes locos..." Her voice trailed off though they could hear her cursing for a while.

Construct Intelligence

It is a widely-held belief that Constructs do not possess sentience. The nature of their Logic Engines prevents reasoning on any level higher than that of a well-trained dog. Advanced, though they might be, their programming is still somewhat limited. Machines with Logic Engines follow specific sets of instructions collectively called edicts. Several general edict templates exist: protect, survive, dig, and search are examples of how broad an edict may be written. These general templates are often modified by their designers to allow a Construct some latitude in how it will react to certain situations. Despite assurances that these are not self-aware machines, Constructs sometimes display erratic and unexplainable behavior. Guild Peacekeeper Louisiana (fondly referred to as "Louise" by Guardsmen working alongside the metal brute) gunned down nine civilians in a homicidal rage before being brought down. One of the new Watcher constructs, heavily modified by a new Guild Construct specialist, took flight and refused orders, joining a small flock of ordinary birds, much to their consternation. Oddities that could be explained away by a malfunction or faulty Logic Engine until it was learned that the Soulstone used to fuel Peacekeeper Louisiana had recently been recharged at a public hanging in New Amsterdam. The Watcher's bizarre behavior occurred soon after a nearby mobile ambulatory unit reported the sudden death of a wounded Guardsman.

For most, considering these quirks are faint echoes of the personality which fueled the Soulstone is too grim a thought to bear. Madmen trapped in their own jewel-faceted hells, until finally drained into oblivion, is simply a possibility none are willing to entertain.

Lover's Kiss

Kirai awoke at the feel of cool metal upon her hand, held lovingly by Francis, son of the Governor General. He took her hand and gently slid the ring down her delicate middle finger. It was a perfect fit, and she marveled at its beauty. It was polished silver and studded along its surface with tiny green gemstones, cut at interesting angles so that together they overlapped, forming transparent snake scales that wrapped around her finger. The snake's "head" was a large stone that rested near her first knuckle. The rising Malifaux sun filtered in through the window and lit up the stones so that Kirai thought it looked like a tiny slumbering dragon snuggled against her finger. To her, it was an omen of good fortune Though neither could know it at the time, fate unlocked a door the moment this ring, an ancient talisman of Malifaux, was slipped upon her finger.

The two lovers lay together in bed. Their room was at the Qi and Gong, a tavern in the slums district that catered to illicit deals of contraband and other indiscreet endeavors of the flesh. The district had a minimal Guild presence which made this tavern a popular meeting place for those wishing to avoid its intruding eye. That few of them even spoke English added to the clandestine mystique of the place. Kirai worked for the tavern as an escort and prostitute, and for many visitors to Malifaux, the Qi and Gong was their first taste of the exotic Orient.

Francis held her hand up near her face, looking from her eyes to the stones, pretending to study them gravely. "Ah," he said, feigning disappointment. "Just as I feared."

"What?" she asked, concerned as she looked at the beautiful ring upon her finger.

"I thought I had finally found a gift to equal your beauty, but I've failed again."

Francis smiled at her, and she gazed into his eyes. There she saw his obvious adoration for her, the dreamy-eyed gaze of young love. He marveled at her beauty, the gentle contours of her naked body disguised only by the deep red silk of a single bed sheet. As was the custom for so many peoples, the exchange of such love tokens implied the convergence of two destinies. Although the couple came from different cultures, the forbidden union of the Governor General's son and common harlot represented far more to Francis than a mere rebellion – their connection went deep, and he conveyed to her the nearly desperate need he had to be with her along with a need to demonstrate that eternal devotion. He tried every time he saw her to give her some small token that showed her how much he loved and needed her, to give her something that would bring him one step closer to giving her the happiness she gave him, though he felt it an insurmountable impossibility. Kirai looked down at the ring on her finger, and the weight of that promise overwhelmed her. She, too, felt that devotion and longed to give him the same love and promise, but she never had much to offer other than herself. "It's beautiful...," she said, trying to find the words to convey her love.

Months earlier, she had been hired by the Governor General to escort his son to a gala event. Their romance was something he hadn't bargained on. As if reading the very thoughts from his mind, she said, "What would your father think if he saw you here, giving me this?" she asked dreamily.

"Well, it'd have made things much more difficult if he were here several hours earlier," he answered with a wolfish grin as he pinched the soft flesh above her hip.

"Yes," she said, not afraid to explore that bawdy avenue, either. After all, she was not shy and had greater experiences than Francis could even imagine. "Perhaps he would have been proud of you," she said, adopting a look of consideration. "Although I'd have tried to remain quiet. Just a bit. More ladylike than normal." Her tiny body and face maintained the illusion of youth yet her speech gave no indication that she might even consider the topic embarrassing nor even distasteful. "I wouldn't want to make your father uncomfortable." She nodded at him as though she had come to a very logical conclusion on the matter.

"Okay!" he said, tickling her quickly. "You win. Now you're just making me uncomfortable."

"You knew I would. You cannot play this game with me. You should know better." She nodded sternly although she broke out in a smile and kissed him deeply.

"Yes, yes," he said. "My father always seems to come up in these conversations. I hope we can one day have a day all to ourselves. No talk of the Governor General at all."

"That would be nice. But he is the center of my world as he is yours."

"I know. He governs me as tightly as he does this City."

"It's no worse for me. The workers at the mansion fear for their every mistake. He is very strict. We all worry about displeasing him."

Francis felt so helpless and wanted only to help her. He stroked her dark forearm as he said, "And you more than others, I know. I almost wish he never hired you to escort me to that dinner. We've been so careful, so discreet, but he knows about us. He knows everything."

"Don't say that, *qíng rén*. You're the only thing that gives me hope. The only thing for me, here. My family cannot come to Malifaux. Not until we save enough. I labor all day in your father's gardens and the *shi fu* is very brutal. Maybe more than your father, because he must bear the punishment for all of my mistakes. All the mistakes of the grounds' laborers."

"Kirai, maybe we shouldn't try to bring your family here. Maybe you and I need to get out of here. Go back there and start over. Just you and me."

"And my family?"

"We'll find a way to get them out of the Three Kingdoms. We'll find a way."

"No, *qíng rén*. Your father would find you. He'd find me. He could never tolerate such defiance. The son of the most important man in Malifaux consorting with a lowly prostitute? I would bear him great dishonor."

"I wouldn't let him hurt you," Francis said, squeezing her upper arm tightly. "I could never let anyone hurt you."

She smiled warmly at him. "I am not worried for myself. I am worried for you. You cannot stop him. We know this. And I know it would hurt you if something happened to me. Your father will not know until it is too late. I cannot allow you to be hurt, either." She was, of course, correct. His father would try to remove her

from his life. Although she tried to protect her innocence, and many experiences with her were most certainly exaggerated and bragged upon by those who hired her, a rumor was as powerful as truth.

Francis pulled her closer, and the two lay together in that way that lovers do, basking in the warmth of each other's bodies, neither urgent to begin the day. He pulled her hand into his and held them together between their bare chests, his fingers absently spinning the new ring he had placed on her finger.

The light from around the thin curtains grew, but Francis would not succumb to the growing need for them to part, though he knew she must return to the mansion's grounds within the hour. Still, he spoke to her, relating the tale of the ring, how he had led an expedition into the ruins of Old Malifaux's Quarantine Zone and discovered a most curious structure. A large vault, he explained, whose hemispherical ceiling was painted to mimic Malifaux's night sky, had been filled with what appeared to be a giant astrolabe. Kirai was enthralled by her lover's romantic description of the beautiful structure and was reminded why she loved Francis so much. He could make the most mundane thing look beautiful in another light, and he made beautiful images in his mind come alive before her. He continued to discuss how the place was ruined, however, and there was evidence of a great struggle. Some of the structure had been burnt and much of the equipment had been knocked over and broken. Pock marks in the walls suggested some sort of gunfight. In the process of exploring the scene, he had found the ring. "So many discoveries there, but none as valuable as this," he said. "The green stones glowed like your eyes. I knew it should belong to you."

"Then the union is complete. Now, when I see the serpent upon my finger, I will think only of you as it has made you think only of me." She nodded as if a covenant had been finalized.

A rattling of the locked door jolted them into sudden awareness, and the mechanical sound of metal clicking caused Francis to sit up quickly. His eyes widened in fear. Kirai could not identify the sound, but Francis knew exactly what it was. Their intimacy vanished, replaced with urgency. "Get dressed!" he whispered sharply, and Kirai knew not to question him.

The sound was that of a revolver's cylinder snapping closed. Francis slipped from the sheets and did not bother with his own clothes. From his belt beside the bed, however, he drew his saber and moved to stand next to the door. On the other side of the room, Kirai hastily pulled on her kimono and gripped it closed around her body. Her fear was clearly visible but she found reassurance in Francis who gestured silently for her to hide. Just as she ducked behind the wardrobe, the door burst open with a kick from the other side.

The intruder's raised revolver was the only introduction that Francis needed. His saber fell with a powerful stroke that cut deeply into the man's wrist, nearly severing it. The man screamed and stared at his gun on the floor in disbelief. He crumpled to his knees, overcome by the shock as Francis moved with fluid purpose. With the momentum of his strike, Francis crossed the doorway and spun to crouch beside the opening.

The next assailant stepped over his howling accomplice and fired a blast just over Francis' head. He had expected to see a man standing there, and the gunman had fired his weapon at chest height. Francis' lowered posture exploited this assumption, and he leapt forward with a powerful thrust, sinking his saber deep into the man's torso, expertly striking immediately below the ribcage and up into the lungs and heart with little resistance, killing him instantly. The dead man slumped against him and Francis shot a glance to where Kirai hid. "Run! Run, Kirai! Get out of here!"

Kirai gasped and peeked around the corner to witness the violence. She was stunned by the sight of it, unable to move. She knew Francis had trained at the Naval Academy, an experience he remarked upon often, but she had never thought of him as a warrior, surprised to see a man so eloquent and poetic fight at all. His skill with a saber made her suddenly question what she knew of him and the further confusion immobilized her as she sought some way to help while still trying to accept that he could defend himself better if he did not fear for her own protection.

"Shoot the whore, you idiots!" another man shouted from the hallway. Kirai saw him, and her heart sank. He was tall and thin, wearing the standard navy duster and wide brimmed hat issued to Guild Guardsmen, and the insignia upon his uniform marked him as an officer. He leveled his revolver at her, and it erupted with fire, blasting a large hole out of the wardrobe at

her side. He quickly fired again. She screamed, covering her face with tiny hands. The gunfire snapped her out of her daze and she dashed toward the balcony window, knocking the frail frame aside as she burst into the cool morning air. She hurried to the railing and glanced down at the ivy-covered lattice below as the sounds of combat continued behind her. She turned to look back at Francis. The wounded man howled in rage and pain but took up his revolver in his other hand. He leveled it at her lover but, as Francis scampered backward, the large man remaining in the hall burst into the room.

"No, you idiot!" Gideon yelled. He brought his knee up sharply against the man's head just as he pulled the trigger, the gun lurching forward with the blow. Francis cried out as the bullet, meant for his chest, dug into his shoulder. He dropped the saber as he fell back against the bed.

Kirai screamed and danced about in panic. She was trapped.

Gideon leveled the gun upon the Asian woman upon the balcony. "Time to finish this," he said.

He took his time, fearing nothing from the boy, and only momentarily reluctant. He thought of the payment he desperately needed, regretting the necessity to kill this young girl. As he pulled the trigger, Francis leapt between the gunman and the girl, taking the bullet just above his right breast. He fell dead without a word. Gideon gasped, staring in stunned disbelief at the boy, the Governor's son, now dead just paces away.

Gideon lifted his gun toward the balcony to finish the job, but the woman was gone. The instinct to chase her, to earn his contract was strong for he desperately needed to collect upon it. At his feet, however, was the body of the Governor's son. He nudged the body with his foot, turning the man onto his back. Kneeling beside him, he checked for a pulse.

The Governor's son was dead and Gideon knew that he soon would be, too.

The Three Kingdoms

When the Han Dynasty fell in the ancient Orient, chaos, conflict, and bloodshed were as common as field workers and day laborers. Invasion from northern Mongols and conquers from the west threatened what was left of one of the greatest and oldest thriving empires that stretched back as far as recorded history could measure. Now, several thousand years later, historians differ regarding the development of the Three Kingdoms union that saved its empire and culture. Most agree that the three original kingdoms was a union by the three greatest family estates, none of which could lay claim to the Empire's single throne, but all were in a position to vie for supremacy over the other. Given the destructive nature of the conflict between the three large landholdings, as well as the threat of overthrow from beyond their provinces, their fall would have been inevitable had they not put aside their provincial disputes to withstand those forces that sought to consume them.

Others believe that The Three Kingdoms is a reference to the true dynasty that formed just after this union and continues through to today. Three lords did put aside their debates to form one central empire, governed by the three warriors. It's the subsequent conquest and absorption of the former East Orient and Nippon Empires that many believe comprise The Three Empires.

Regardless of its true origins, The Three Kingdoms has evolved into a formidable world force, dominating art, music, and experimental technology. People from the Kingdoms speak an assimilation of Mandarin, Nipponese, and other historical local dialects, often interjecting keywords originally from any of them. The deep and complex rules of Three Kingdoms culture are reflected in the formality of its conversations. Hidden nuances and references are contained in even the most innocuous of exchanges. Non-native speakers often have difficulty deciphering the twisting puzzle of word choice and order that those born into the language navigate without a second thought.

After the Breach opened on the other side of the world, a great migration of Three Kingdoms people traveled to explore opportunities in the Far West, as well as through the Breach, itself, seeking an escape from the oppressive demands of their rulers. The Three Kingdoms tightened its rules governing travel outside of the empire by its citizenry. Very recently, however, The Three Kingdoms closed its borders with sudden and adamant finality. They've become silent, abruptly cutting off all trade routes and accepting no emissary from any country. Almost no one escapes its borders.

The cause of this closure remains a mystery. However, one Guild expert on The Three Kingdoms has noted that the sudden isolation oddly aligns with the Kythera event. He speculates that another Breach may have opened within the Kingdoms, but currently, no one outside of the border knows. The academic has been ordered silent on the matter pending further intelligence reports.

Smoke and Mirrors

Named in the manner of the Empire's most legendary theaters, the Star was every bit as majestic as the Rose or the Globe. Vaulted rafters ran high overhead and its namesake chandelier hung in a sparkling display, bathing the room in rich, yellow light. Crimson curtains hung along the walls, the rich velvet adding to the grandeur and allure. Intricately carved columns invoked the rapture of the heavens with dancing cherubim in murals along the walls. Regular patrons also came to notice infrequent demonic figures hidden amongst the otherwise beautiful angels. Their grotesque images sparked conversation as the audience waited for a show to begin. Finding glimpses of the demons became a game as they would appear in seemingly different locations throughout the expansive theater depending on the night. It added to the charm of the show as the shifting demons became part of the overall illusion and thrilling magic they'd witness throughout the evening.

Some people never saw any of the elusive demonic figures but certainly saw the real angels of the Star: Miss Colette DuBois and her beautiful showgirls. Though the Star was decorated with class and elegance, its bawdy shows catered to the miners returning from shifts in the foothills and settlers who'd yet to forge their way into the wilds outside of the city. The Star enjoyed a close association with the Miners and Steamfitters Union. Its skilled labor produced the enormous pipe organ that nightly accompanied the magic shows and lewd song and dance numbers the theater was known for. As the audience took their seats, a great blast of whistling steam erupted from boilers installed backstage. They never saw the operators of the steam mechanism but knew from experience what came next and quickly quieted. The traditional gaslights throughout the theater were snuffed as great exposed gears just above the great main curtain began to turn slowly. One massive brass gear was the center of attention as it spanned more than seven feet in diameter and had hundreds of needle-like teeth that spun a series of progressively smaller gears at ever increasing speeds. As the steam pressure mounted, increasing their overall speed and torque, glass bulbs slowly illuminated the stage. The bright electric lights received appreciative gasps of awe and murmurs of appreciation, regardless of how seasoned the showgoer was. One miner, relatively new to Malifaux and at the Star for the first time, leaned over to whisper to his colleague, "I swear that's worth the price of admission right there."

The veteran said, "Son, that curtain's about to open, and you'll get far more'n your money's worth, I guarantee." He winked at another who nodded in sincere agreement.

As if on cue, the organ struck up a rising crescendo and another set of visible iron gears to the upper left of the stage turned, pulling the curtains aside to reveal a line of ten beautiful women, each posed with one leg up and foot resting upon the other knee, exposing their leg far up the thigh as their pleated skirts fell aside. The men whistled with appreciation. The newcomer, Louis, thought he might cry, his emotions ran so high, and he said, "Where the hell have they been? I been up and down the streets and I never seen anything as lovely!"

His friend clapped him hard on the back. "Boy, them's just the warm-up! You better go out and douse yourself in the water trough if you're gonna get through this whole show!" He guffawed boisterously, remembering well his first time at the Star, and clapped the young miner on the back once more for good measure.

The notes of the organ came at a blistering pace, and the dancing girls kicked and spun in well practiced unison, smiling the entire time as if their frantic kicking and leaping exerted no energy at all, though many of the men in the audience were, themselves, quickly breathless.

As they performed, changing from one beautiful dress to another in a matter of seconds between acts, the patrons consumed more and more alcohol in equal pace.

Eventually, the legendary Cassandra joined the performance, and the men quieted as the lights around the stage illuminated her flaxen hair like a halo about her pale face. Their awed silence broke as she performed with the regular dancers, and everyone knew they were in the midst of one of the most incredibly beautiful and graceful women to ever live. Although billed as "The Magician's Apprentice", no one in that audience thought it anything less than tongue-in-cheek. The other performers might as well have taken a break as all eyes in the establishment were fixed to her every move. She manipulated their emotions with a slight twitch or gesture, compelling them at once to quiet and watch a slow dance that conveyed an entire story of separation and loss of a man she once loved; and then, in the next moment, her body told a rather bawdy tale met with men dancing in aisles and the stomping of booted feet throughout the hall.

As the song and dance ended, she stepped to the edge of the stage, laughing as she said, "Seems like we're all having fun tonight!" to the crowd. They exploded in agreement. "But I'm sure there are a few here for the first time, am I right?" Miners, settlers, and Guild Guardsmen all whooped and hollered and pointed out their compatriots enjoying the show for their first, and most memorable show. Those newcomers were not privy to what was to come for them as the others kept it as some unspoken secret between them, and they simply could not wait to get those new men out of their seats. Cassandra said, "Well, if this is your first time at the Star, we need you up here to meet the girls, right?"

Louis and the other new men needed very little prompting, then, to head to the stage. Others shouted, "Go easy on the lads, Cassy!" and "They have to work tomorrow, you know!"

Turned out, "Meeting the girls" meant performing with them, as the last men stepped upon the stage, the organ belted out another quick-step and the girls drew the men into the line and had them kicking as high as they could, much to the great satisfaction of the others who laughed and laughed at their ridiculous attempt to keep up. Girls unbuttoned the men's shirts, mocking them, and the audience cheered even louder. As the song reached its climax, the men on stage were exhausted and dizzy, and, on the last high note, the women stepped back and their last kick found the rear end of a man, sending him flying off stage.

The next day, each newcomer to the theater would find himself hungover and bruised throughout his body. He'd complain of the aches and pains and wished he could just sleep the whole day off. Each of them, though, would remember the night as one of the greatest of his entire life.

As the show continued, Cassandra had the stage to herself where her act involved an exotic saber and several death-defying swordplay tricks. The crowd favorite consisted of another showgirl in a box with Cassandra seeming to cut her into pieces, only to have the girl jump out unscathed.

Remarkably, Cassandra, too, was merely a warm-up magician's act, for when Colette DuBois later performed her illusions, men stared in astonishment and wonder. She awed them with acts of teleportation and remarkable pyrotechnics. As a finale, Cassandra, now just an assistant on stage, surprised the audience by pulling a Derringer pistol from her garter and fired it upon the surprised magician, Colette. The bullet struck her in the bare flesh just above the frilled top of her corset. They all saw the bullet wound and the quickly flowing blood. But, just as her body fell backward, she exploded in a booming cloud and each man in the audience jumped. At the back of the theater, Colette stood upon the bar, legs and arms stretched wide as she bellowed, "Why so glum, fellas?" There was no mark upon her perfect chest.

They cheered and cheered.

In the early morning, the theater was empty, but Miss DuBois and her girls were not idle. Colette toiled in the dim light backstage. She'd long since abandoned the silk, lace, and feathers of her costume and was instead dressed in soft leather boots, denim pants, and a man's work shirt. She loaded several large sacks into a sturdy iron cart and pushed it into the pipe organ's alcove. There, Cassandra awaited her.

"I'm so jealous that you're heading Earthside," remarked Cassandra as she sat at the organ and adjusted a few of its valves.

"It's only for a few days. I won't even make it all the way east," Colette said as she wheeled the cart next to the other woman.

"The others have already gone down, Colette," she said. "They're waiting for you to depart."

"Take us down, then."

Cassandra touched several chords on the organ's keyboards but the keystrokes produced no sound save the brief expulsion of steam from a hidden mechanism and the slow grind of gears beneath the platform. Latching bolts were released and a series of pneumatic pistons operated, lowering the organ's entire platform into the floor. A large velvet curtain drew closed around the organ's alcove from the automated gears that worked in concert with the descending mechanism. The two women chatted casually as they slowly descended. It took several minutes, but soon, the secret elevator emerged from its vertical shaft to set down in a large vault.

Although the installed water pipes and great iron and brass gears fulfilled an elaborate mechanical function, the great steam boilers and heavy mechanisms turning on the walls created a majestic image. It was a shame that so few had the opportunity to witness this clandestine place: the hub of the Arcanist Black Market. It was no accident that the Star had such a close relationship with the Miners and Steamfitters Union. Where the Union was the legitimate face of the Arcanist Organization, the Star served as its marketplace as well as the center for all of its organized smuggling operations. In the theater above, countless illicit deals were made in the exchange of Soulstone. Colette's honeyed voice served her just as well in shrewd negotiations as it did onstage. After a deal was struck, this vault executed the transport of goods. It connected to the vast Malifaux sewer system, and just a few miles away, an agent awaited them at Malifaux Station, ready to smuggle the goods onto a train bound for the Breach.

The vault was already busy with a half dozen of Colette's girls checking inventory. Soulstones weren't the only goods controlled by the Guild. This underground trade route handled weapons, magical artifacts, curios salvaged from the City itself, and even fine liquors hoping to bypass the severe Guild import taxes on luxury goods. One of the women approached to relieve Colette of her cart and rolled

it in line with two others. It was a routine trip, one made hundreds of times, but today Colette was departing to finalize a transaction Earthside with an important client Dr. Ramos would trust to no other.

"Take care of my theater, Cassandra."

"You know I will, Colette." The two hugged, and Cassandra wished she could take the other's place, not because she was truly jealous as she said, but because she knew the covert mission was fraught with innumerable dangers and Colette DuBois was as important to the freedoms the Arcanists fought for as the master magician was to her.

The group departed on Colette's order, soon leaving the stately decor of the Star's subterranean vault and entering the dark, dank passages of Malifaux's labyrinthine sewers.

It was impossible for the Guild to police these sewers, which made them ideal for smuggling. It took Arcanists months to decipher the winding maze of just a few routes they could use, and even then, smuggling teams would get lost in the confusion of

its endless passages. It stood to reason that the sewers might mirror the layout of the streets above, making it quite simple to detect and intercept people using the tunnels, but this was a false assumption. The Arcanists drilled for several days beneath the Star to reach what would eventually become the hub of its black-market operations. The chief engineer of the project reported that several other channels lay above their central vault, but none knew for certain how many. Guild attempts to uncover the passages used by the Arcanists had so far proven fruitless.

Though their destination was only a few miles away as the crow flies, the ancient sewers provided a difficult terrain to traverse. Many of its passages were broken and in several places the women were forced to ford its putrid water, holding handkerchiefs over mouth and nose to ward against the gagging stench. The Arcanists were reluctant to evoke any repairs on the passages, though they had the labor to do it, for fear that such activities might reveal their most valuable trading route. Still, in those areas that were the worst, planks of wood were stowed so they might be used to bridge the channel's flow.

As the group paused to cross one such flow, a rat toppled from overhead and landed in one of the carts. It didn't startle the woman pushing the cart, though she stopped and reached out to swat the pest away. As she reached toward the rodent, the creature hissed, turning its red eyes up at her. Before she could call to the others, a swarm of the vermin poured over her, falling from a small crack above her head as if from an open water main. The pouring stream of large rats toppled both her and her cart into the sewer's dark depths. The flow here was quick, and the cart, laden with books, spilled out to be taken up by the slimy flow and swept away; valuable, singular tomes that were lost forever. The woman, herself, was also swept away. Her companions raced alongside the channel, the screaming woman reaching out for them. When they finally hauled her out, they were five hundred yards or more from where she fell in.

Colette knelt beside the girl, the light of her gas lamp illuminating her frightened face. "Are you all right?" she asked, concern clear upon her face.

"The little bastard bit me..." The girl raised her arm into Colette's light. No blood flowed from the small wound though a sickly black ichor bubbled at the slight piercing of her skin. Her hand and arm were black as coal, as if the limb had been crushed and bruised all over. "Oh God, Miss DuBois?" The girl shook and gasped and Colette quickly covered her exposed arm.

"You'll be all right, Margaret. Hold on. Let's get you back to the Star." To reassure the girl she said, "Damned light makes it difficult to see that small bruise just right," but she was not assured, herself.

Colette's words were cut off by the girl's sudden and violent spasm. She collapsed forward, onto her hands and knees, and retched. That same black ichor poured from the girl's mouth and nose. The girl's companions watched in horror, backing away uncomfortably. The girl spasmed again and toppled over onto her back, gazing up at Colette helplessly and clutching at her stomach. The cloth of her shirt was stained black and the girl feebly clutched at her waist and stomach. Colette tore the shirt open and Margaret's belly had sunken into a black pit, her organs and flesh liquefied into black bile.

Colette leapt from the girl, her eyes scanning the corridors of the sewer as far as the lamplight revealed. "Run!" she yelled.

Colette's cry shook her girls out of their frozen horror. With their torches held before them, they ran as fast as they could, skidding around corners and leaping the channel's water in a single jump. As they approached the corner where the cart had been spilled, they saw the water had filled with a swarm of writhing rats. The putrid flow of the sewer had been consumed by a writhing stream of crawling vermin as maggots and roaches crawled endlessly over one another in an undulating mass.

Although all of her girls excelled as dancers and acrobats, none were as deft as Colette, nor as brave. She bounded toward the heart of the grotesque mass and she snatched a sack from amidst the diseased pile of rodents, shaking it in a snap to clear it of the horrible vermin, and she was back with the girls in a blink. "Let's go!" she urged. She led the way, and she spared no time for caution, but as she rounded a corner and looked back over her shoulder, she saw that one of her girls had fallen behind. The tide of rats licked at her feet and there was a look of abject horror on her face.

"Colette!" the girl called as her panic mounted.

Tearing open the bag she had salvaged, she was relieved to see that her gamble had paid off and a small cache of precious Soulstones was contained within. Colette was no mere parlor magician as everyone was led to believe. She hoisted one out and lifted it above her head. A flare of magical energy burst from her hand in a glint of light, as if reflected from a turning mirror. Like a trick in her stage show, Colette traded places with the girl, appearing in a puff of smoke where that girl had been. Looking back as the frightened girl spilled out on the wet stonework, Colette called out, again, "Run!" in a commanding voice that echoed within the twisting corridors of the sewer.

With her crew fleeing behind her, Colette faced down the tide of approaching vermin. Holding her gem out in front of her, she crushed it in her hand, the Soulstone exploding with a violent eruption of flame. The fire filled the whole of the channel and washed down the passage to consume the swarm coming at her and they hissed and popped as the fire destroyed them.

In a flash, the swarm was gone but deep in the darkness she could hear the skittering sounds of more. Looking to repeat her trick, to buy her girls more time to escape the sewer, she reached into the bag again. The stone she found was smooth and pear-shaped, not the faceted, angularity of a typical Soulstone. Drawing it out, she saw that it had the appearance of amber and deep in the heart of the stone was an insect, perhaps a spider. Despite the oddity of the stone, she felt the familiar power of magic within it.

She could hear the sound of the swarm trampling overhead and a sudden column of the creatures poured before her. She squeezed the stone, attempting to crush it and use the power within, but it would not give. Regardless, the precious energy of Soulstone fueled her. That power to contort fate flooded her body and her ring of fire came, again, to burn the swarming vermin as the flames filled the corridor.

The stone in her hand was unquenchable. Its power seemed as a well without end, a fountain of limitless strength like she had never experience before. She tapped that power and let it fill her, allowed her desperate flame to consume the plague before her.

While that power might have been limitless, her body proved insufficient to sustain it. The fire died as her body fell exhausted to the ground. On her hands and knees, she lifted her head weakly, gathering her strength as she gazed down the dark corridor. From those shadows, a sinister laugh echoed and grew.

"Feel fortunate," a man said in a strangely guttural voice. "You will be among the first to fall to this plague, a plague this world and all worlds will not soon forget." The voice was amplified by the wide diameter of the sewer channel, bouncing from the walls, slick with water.

While weak, Colette was not without her biting sense of humor. "It's typical that the villain will gloat while the heroine escapes."

"There will be no escape for you," the stranger said in that unnatural voice filled at once with grating highs and rumbling lows.

"Really?" Colette asked, a smile tugging at the corner of her lips and her voice grew strong. "There is nothing here but smoke and mirrors."

The chamber magnified a bestial roar from that man in the darkness and the tide of rats and roiling insects swelled, rushing to consume Colette DuBois, still too weak to even rise. The flood of rats crashed against a pane of glass standing in the middle of the corridor and the mirror fractured. The image of Colette in the mirror vanished in a wink.

As hundreds of shards of glass chimed on the stones below, the whole passage plunged into darkness.

New Rules

New Rules

Rule of Equivalency: When a model is killed or sacrificed, its removal from play cannot result in more Counters/effects being generated for other models than its base size allows: 1 for 30mm, 2 for 40mm and 3 for 50mm. A model's removal from play can only generate one effect that summons a model, regardless of base size. Models generate Counters/effects starting with the closest model. In case of models being an equal distance from the removed model, a friendly model has priority.

Example: McMourning kills a Bayou Gremlin. Som'er Teeth Jones and a Hog Whisperer are both within 5" the gremlin, but the Whisperer is slightly closer. McMourning gains one Body Part Counter for A Piece For Me!, and the gremlin player draws two Control Cards for Survival of the Fittest rather than four.

New Characteristics:

Nightmare: Nightmare models are not considered living models.

Object (#): Objects are not considered living models. Reduce the number of Wd suffered by an Object by #, to a minimum of 1.

Special Forces (Group Name): Up to two Special Forces models may be hired per Master. Only one Special Forces group may be hired by a Crew. Some models lift the two model hiring limit when included in a Crew, but the limit of one Special Forces group remains.

Special Forces (Doll) – In addition to the standard Special Forces rules, Zoraida may hire any number of models from this group.

Special Forces (M&SU Assets) – In addition to the standard Special Forces rules, Ramos may hire any number of models from this group.

Counters:

Because counters can be generated by other means than Graverobber and Scavenger, the following additional rules are to help clarify how models and Counters interact in Malifaux. These rules do not replace the rules in the main rulebook, instead they are included here to help clarify Counter use.

Example:
Von Schill has the Special Forces (Freikorps) characteristic as well as the Special Forces Leader (Freikorps) ability. In a Scrap, Crews containing Von Schill could not hire models from a different Special Force since Von Schill has the Special Force characteristic. However, the Crew could hire as many Friekorps models as it could afford because Von Schill has the Special Forces Leader (Freikorps) Ability.

- Counters on the table may be picked up by eligible models. A model is eligible to pick up a Counter if it has the appropriate characteristic, or possesses a Talent or Spell that uses the Counter at the time it picks the Counter up.

- Models can gain Counters if they have the applicable characteristic, or possess a Talent or Spell that uses the Counter at the time they would gain the Counter.

- Models can use Counters they carry or on the table if they have the appropriate characteristic or a Talent or Spell that requires the Counter at the time its use is indicated.

- Models drop any Counters *carried* when they are removed from play, but Counters *on* the model (such as Blight or Poison Counters) remain on the without effect while not in play.

- Models with a characteristic or Talent or Spell that allows the *use* of certain types of Counters do not drop or discard those Counters if they lose the characteristic/Talent/Spell.

- Counters may not be voluntarily dropped by a model unless a special rule allows it to do so.

- Counters may not be used when a model's action is controlled by another controller through use of an Ability or Spell.

New Counters:

Blight Counters: Whenever a model with one or more Blight Counters suffers **Wd**, it suffers 1 additional **Wd**.

Burning Counter: In the Resolve Effects Stage, a model with any number of Burning Markers removes all Burning Markers and either suffers 1 **Wd** or **Slow** (their choice).

HENCHMEN

While Masters command great power and resources in Malifaux, there are many others who have also risen in power, enough to command a Crew of their own, but not yet ready to be called Master, and as the capable lieutenants of those Masters they aspire to one day be. These individuals are collectively known as Henchmen in the Malifaux game.

The following rules apply to all models with the Henchman model type:

- All Henchmen have the **Use Soulstone** Ability.
- A Crew containing a Henchman removes the two model maximum hiring restriction on hiring models with the Henchman's Special Forces characteristic (see below).
- A Crew led by one or more Masters can hire one Henchman per Master.

Crews may hire models with the Henchman model type in one of two ways; either as a Crew's leader, or as Henchman in a Master-led Crew.

Leading a Crew

Instead of hiring a Master, you can choose to hire an eligible Henchman to lead the Crew during a Scrap. When a Henchman leads the Crew:

- The Henchman's Soulstone Cost is reduced to 0.
- Every Henchman has a Henchman Reserve, listed as Henchman # in the model's characteristics. This amount is added to the number of Soulstones the Crew has available for hiring models. **Example:** In a 25 Soulstone Scrap if you choose to hire a Henchman with a Reserve of 5 you can hire up to 30 Soulstones worth of models.
- Each Henchman has the Special Forces (Group Name) Ability. The Crew ignores the Special Forces hiring limit (see below) when the Henchman is the Crew's leader. The ability also states what models may be included in the Crew when the Henchman leads it.
- The Henchman may connect a Totem. Normal hiring restrictions for the Totem still apply. **Example:** Molly could connect the Grave Spirit Totem when leading a Crew, but could not connect the Copycat Killer.

- The Soulstone Pool for a Crew led by a Henchman is determined as normal, but each Henchman has a Soulstone Cache of 0. The maximum size of a Henchmen-led Soulstone Pool is equal to the Henchman's Reserve. **Example:** Up to 5 unspent Soulstones in the above example would form the Crew's Soulstone Pool.
- Anything that specifically affects a Master can affect the Henchman leading this Crew. Likewise, anything that cannot specifically affect a Master cannot affect the Henchman leading this Crew. **Example:** The **Obey** Spell cannot be cast on Masters. A Henchman leading a Crew cannot be affected by **Obey**.
- A Henchman leading a Crew is considered a Master for Strategy and Scheme purposes.

Henchman in a Master's Crew

Henchmen can be hired as normal in Crews led by one or more Masters. When hiring a Henchman into a Master-led Crew:

- The Henchman's Soulstone Cost must be paid as normal.
- The Henchman Reserve is ignored.
- The Henchman may connect a Totem. Normal hiring restrictions for the Totem still apply. Example: Molly could connect the Grave Spirit Totem, but could not connect the Copycat Killer.
- Each Henchman has the Special Forces (Group Name) ability. Crews containing the Henchman ignore the Special Forces hiring limit (see below). The ability may provide additional options for which models may and may not be hired by a Crew containing the Henchman.
- A Henchman hired into a Master-led Crew counts as a Henchman for Strategy and Scheme purposes.

Ragsheets

Along with contraband weapons and Soulstone cigars, the most popular items on the black market are the illegal newspapers printed at great risk by their publishers, collectively known as the Ragsheets. Borne by their shadowy creators as a badge of pride, their name stuck when the publisher of The Malifaux Record, John McKnight, denounced them as, " A collection of trash and ragsheets, not fit to diaper a tot or wipe a bum with."

Despite McKnight's claims, readership continues to grow. Knowing better than to sell them openly, the owners instead use several middle men, each taking a tiny cut of the profits, to get their messages to the populace. Most have colorful titles, With Freedom's Voice, The Breachside Tattler, and Truth's Ragsheet being the most popular. Some write their issues in direct response to the lies put forward by The Record, while others tackle their own private causes, championing crusades against the many injustices meted out by the Guild. More than one can trace its backing to the deep pockets of the Miners and Steamfitters Union, while the majority rely on what issues they sell and whatever money their publishers or backers are willing to invest personally.

Being caught with a ragsheet newspaper is a criminal offense, seen as a seditious act. Punishment ranges in severity and length for readers, usually based on the quantity of ragsheets in the reader's possession. Despite this, many people read at least one of the titles, risking harsh fines or imprisonment." The Truth is Contagious", reads Truth's Ragsheet tagline, and the increasing demand it sees with each issue proves it. While reading a ragsheet is a punishable by the Guild, those working for one or publishing a ragsheet, if caught, face long sentences in the City Gaol, or possible execution for crimes against the Guild. Most use printing presses cobbled together from scavenged parts, some hand-crafting the type letters needed to run the moveable presses. Many have set up their presses in such a way that they are easily hidden or dismantled, or even transported, if word of a Guild raid reaches them in time. Unfortunately, many have short-lived print runs, and the publishers are forced to watch as their beloved presses are axed into firewood and set alight before they are transported to the City to stand trial.

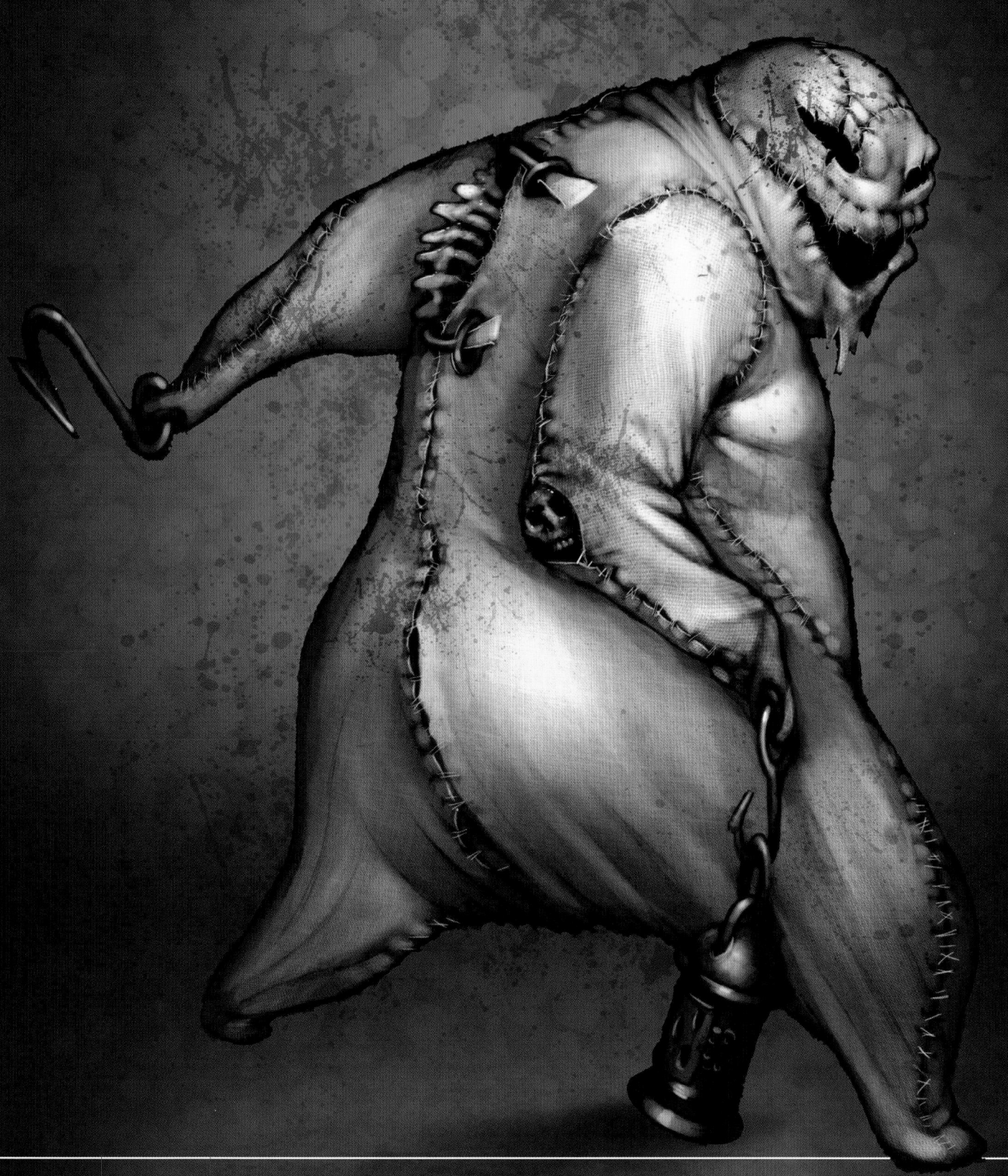

ENCOUNTERS

SETTING UP AN ENCOUNTER

When playing an Encounter of Malifaux, players follow the steps below to generate an Encounter between their Crews. Tournament or Story Encounters may change or ignore some of these steps. The goal of a Encounter of Malifaux is to have fun; players should feel free to ignore any of these steps when necessary. For example, if you do not have any terrain in your collection that would serve as a Gremlin Village, you may want to skip the random location generation step and simply play with the terrain you have.

1. Agree on Encounter Size & Number of Soulstones Available

Players begin by agreeing on the size of their Encounter. The Encounter size sets several factors in the Encounter: maximum Control Hand size, number of Masters per Crew, maximum Soulstone Pools, and so forth. Once players have agreed on the Encounter size, they choose how many Soulstones they each have for hiring their Crews.

For example, a short Encounter between two starter box Crews would be a 25 Soulstone Scrap.

Encounter Size	Scrap	Brawl
Soulstone Range	1-55	30-80
Maximum Control Hand Size per Crew	6	7
Number of Masters per Crew	1	2
Maximum Soulstone Pool Size per Crew	8	10

After deciding on an Encounter size and the number of Soulstones available to Crews, shuffle one Fate Deck and place it within easy reach of all players.

2. Choose a Faction

Once the Encounter size is determined each player must choose a Faction. They do not need to select which Master or Masters within that Faction they intend to play or hire any Minions at this time. When you are allowed to hire more than one Master by the chosen Encounter Size, the Masters hired must either belong to your chosen Faction, or be able to work with that Faction or Master.

3. Select Location for the Encounter

From abandoned Ghost Towns to the inhospitable Badlands, and the very streets of the City themselves, Encounters in Malifaux can take place in any number of unique locations. All players can either agree on a location (based on the terrain they have available), or use the following method to randomly determine a location for your Encounter.

One randomly-determined player flips two Fate Cards. The value of the first flip determines whether this is an indoor or outdoor Encounter. The value of the second flip then tells the players what location the Encounter takes place in. Additional information about these locations can be found beginning on page 47, including suggested terrain and random events or locations that may appear in the location.

Encounter Location	
Black Joker	Flipping Player Chooses Location
1-8	Outdoor Location
9-13	Indoor Location
Red Joker	Non-Flipping Player Chooses Location

Outdoor Encounter Location

Black Joker	Flipping Player Chooses Location
1	Hag's Territory
2	Gremlin Village
3	Bayou's Edge
4	Bogs
5	Downtown
6	Industrial Zone
7	Slums
8	Quarantine Zone
9	Ruins
10	Mine
11	Pioneer/Ghost Town
12	Badlands
13	Mountains
Red Joker	Non-Flipping Player Chooses Location

Indoor Encounter Location

Black Joker	Flipping Player Chooses Location
1	Theater
2	Sewers
3	Arcanist's Lab
4	Resurrectionist's Lab
5	Guild Library
6	Necropolis
7	Guild Holding Facility
8	Warehouse
9	Research Facility
10	Cave/Mine System
11	Ancient Ruins
12	Large Tavern
13	Collapsed City Block
Red Joker	Non-Flipping Player Chooses Location

Terrain Setup

Malifaux is a skirmish game where every model counts! You can't make it too easy for the enemy to draw a bead on you from halfway across the table, so be sure to stack the odds against him with smart placement of terrain.

Once the Encounter location is determined, lay out terrain. A minimum playing size of 3' by 3' (36" x 36") is required for a Encounter of Malifaux. Anything from the dining room table to a gaming board or mat will work well for players, as long as the playing surface falls into this size range.

We recommend that each square foot of the battlefield have approximately two to four pieces of terrain measuring roughly 3" X 3" each to create an engaging and entertaining battlefield. All players should agree on the placement and type of terrain used. Story and Tournament Encounters will specify terrain (and of what type) in their descriptions.

Some Strategies and Schemes or location features require additional objects be placed on the table as directed by their descriptions (under **Setup** for Strategies and Schemes, and in the description of special terrain for the location). Unless otherwise directed, these objects displace terrain already set up to locations agreed to by the players. Example: During terrain setup a wall was placed in the center of the table. If a player received the Treasure Hunt Strategy, which instructs the player to place a Treasure Counter in the center of the table, the wall would have to be moved to a mutually-agreed upon location before placing the Treasure Counter.

Game Board Example

This game board has been set up with approximately 2 pieces of terrain per square foot.

4. Choose Deployment Type

Once the terrain has been set up, players can either agree on which deployment type they would like to use or randomly determine one player who then flips a Fate Card and refers to the chart below.

The dimensions included in the diagrams below are intended for the suggested 3' X 3' table size.

Deployment Chart

Black Joker	Flipping Player Chooses from the Deployment Areas in the Deployment Chart
1-4	**Diagonal** Draw a line between two opposite table corners. Each Crew's Deployment Zone begins 12.5" from that line.
5-9	**Standard** Each Deployment Zone comprises a 6" deep section, running the entire length of the table, on opposite table edges.
10-13	**Corners** Deployment Areas are 12" x 12" squares in two opposite corners of the table.
Red Joker	Non-Flipping Player Chooses from the Deployment Areas in the Deployment Chart

DIAGONAL DEPLOYMENT

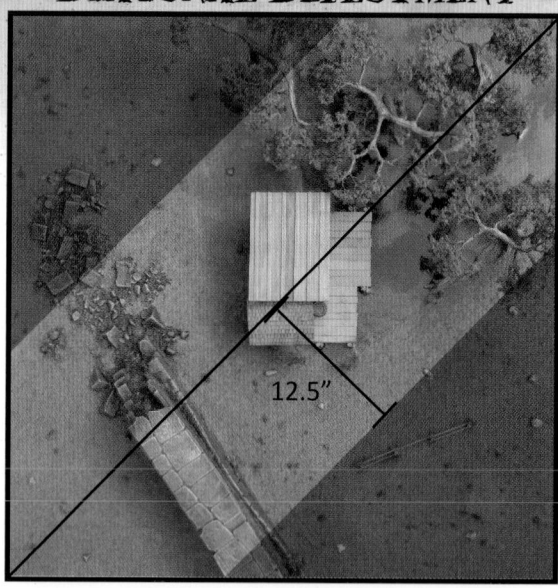

12.5"

STANDARD DEPLOYMENT

6"

CORNERS DEPLOYMENT

12"

5. Selecting a Strategy

Now that you know the Encounter size, where it is located, and where the Crews will arrive, you need something to fight over. Players agree on whether they are playing a Core or Expanded Encounter and then refer to the appropriate section below. Strategy descriptions and rules can be found in the Complete Strategies List starting on page 58.

All Strategies are public knowledge and should not be hidden from other players.

A Strategy's description lists some or all of the following:

- A name and brief fiction describing the Strategy.
- Any required objects such as terrain features or Counters or Markers under **Setup**.
- Any special rules that apply to the Strategy under **Special**.
- What victory points (VP) are available for the player or players completing the Strategy under **Victory**. When scoring a Strategy, no matter how many score lines a Crew meets the requirements for it may only claim the VP for one of those lines plus any + or - VP listed for the Strategy.

Example:

Victory
Score 4 VP If all five Dynamite Markers are armed at the end of the Encounter.
Score 2 VP If at least three Dynamite Markers are armed at the end of the Encounter.

A Crew arming all five Dynamite Markers in the **A Line in the Sand Strategy** could earn *either* 4 VP or 2 VP, but not both.

The Ten Thunders

The Ten Thunders came along with the tide of contract immigrants from the Orient. They passed through the Breach, hidden in the masses from the Far East. Slowly, they spread their influence. First, this syndicate plied its trade in opium dens, where western and eastern souls come to lose themselves in smoke-filled fugues. Smuggling and prostitution naturally followed. With the growth of Little Kingdom, the clan expanded to gambling and racketeering. Today, The Ten Thunders' interests span well beyond Little Kingdom; its criminal talons scratch at the gates of Downtown and stretch out into the wilderness, seeking purchase in the frontier boomtowns.

The Oyabun of The Ten Thunders rules from shadow. His power and influence are second to none, but he prefers to act indirectly. One thing is certain, his plans for Malifaux are grand indeed. He has turned his eyes to the dominance and oppressive hand of Guild control and the Governor General, himself. Misaki, a favored agent of the Oyabun, came to Malifaux to personally attend to business past the Breach. She has done much to solidify and expand The Ten Thunders' operations in the City.

The Ten Thunders will not stop until all of Malifaux rests at their feet.

Core Encounter

The Core Encounter Chart is designed for players who wish to play a more competitive Encounter. These Strategies represent the core causes of conflict in Malifaux, and you will find that each Faction has the tools available to accomplish them, as well as stopping your opponent from accomplishing their own Strategy. If you choose a Core Encounter, each player shuffles their Deck and flips a Fate Card to determine their Strategy for the Encounter. If both players flip the same Strategy, use the Shared version of that Strategy. (p 62)

Core Encounter Chart

Jokers	Player chooses Strategy
1-2	Treasure Hunt
3-5	Destroy the Evidence
6-8	Reconnoiter
9-11	Claim Jump
12-13	Slaughter

Expanded Encounter

The Expanded Encounter Chart was designed to give players nearly an inexhaustible supply of Strategy interactions and provides unique challenges you will not find using the Core Encounter Chart. If you choose an Expanded Encounter, randomly determine a player who shuffles their Deck and flips a Fate Card. Refer to the Expanded Encounter Chart below to determine what type of Strategy players will be using in the Encounter.

Story Encounters

You must decide if you're willing to include the option of playing the online catalog of Story Encounters, located at www.wyrd-games.net/storyencounters, before flipping on the Expanded Encounter Chart. If you agree to include Story Encounters, flips 1 and 13 on the chart direct you to flip on the Story Encounters Chart found online. Otherwise, follow the instructions for the Encounter option. Story Strategies work much like Shared Strategies, except the setup and VP awards tend to be more involved and often include special rules. As Wyrd releases additional Story Encounters, we will provide expanded Story Encounter Strategy Charts.

Expanded Encounter Chart

Jokers	Player Chooses Type of Strategy
1	Story Encounter OR Each Player Flips on the Individual Strategies Chart
2-8	Each Player Flips on the Individual Strategies Chart
9-12	One Player Flips on the Shared Strategy Chart
13	Story Encounter OR One Player Flips on the Shared Strategy Chart

(1-8) Individual Strategies Chart

If the Expanded Encounter Chart directed you to the Individual Strategies Chart, each player now flips a Card. The Strategy a player flips applies to that player only. If all players flip or choose the same Strategy, play the Shared version of it instead.

After flipping for your Individual Strategy, you may decide to decrease the number of Soulstones available to hire your Crew by one in order to re-flip. This may be done only once per player.

Individual Strategies Chart

Black Joker	Opponent's Choice
1	A Line in the Sand
2	Claim Jump
3	Contain Power
4	Deliver a Message
5	Destroy the Evidence
6	Distract
7	Escape and Survive
8	Plant Evidence
9	Reconnoiter
10	Slaughter
11	Supply Wagon
12	Treasure Hunt
13	Turf War
Red Joker	Player's Choice

(9-13) Shared Strategy Chart

If the Expanded Encounter Chart directed you to the Shared Strategy Chart, randomly determine one player to flip a Card. This Strategy applies to both players.

Shared Strategy Chart

Black Joker	Opponent's Choice
1	Shared A Line in the Sand
2	Shared Claim Jump
3	Shared Contain Power
4	Shared Deliver a Message
5	Shared Destroy the Evidence
6	Shared Distract
7	Shared Escape and Survive
8	Shared Plant Evidence
9	Shared Reconnoiter
10	Shared Slaughter
11	Shared Supply Wagon
12	Shared Treasure Hunt
13	Shared Turf War
Red Joker	Player's Choice

Story Encounter Strategies

As with Shared Strategies, you only select one Strategy for all players, and multiple players may earn VP if they accomplish the required tasks. If you have selected a Story Encounter, flip once on the Story Encounter Strategy Chart located at www.wyrd-games.net/storyencounters. You will also find a full write up for each Story Encounter at this website as well.

Little Kingdom

Nestled away in the Slum District is the quiet and colorful neighborhood nicknamed Little Kingdom. Paper lanterns illuminate brightly colored silks and banners. The smells of cherry blossoms and jasmine incense mingle with sizzling meat and exotic spices. Sounds of wind chimes and stringed instruments float on the breeze. Though built on the same cobblestone and brick as the rest of Malifaux, stepping onto the streets of Little Kingdom is like walking into another city.

Built by settlers from The Three Kingdoms, the neighborhood is a reflection of that exotic land. Here, the Guild's presence is barely felt. Residents of Little Kingdom are quiet and keep to themselves. Workers from the Far East have helped settle Malifaux since the time of the re-opening. Thousands came to work on the railroads then remained to settle in Malifaux. Most serve menial jobs, but some put their unique talents to work, carving out a better existence than the subsistence wages they might typically be paid. Exotic acupuncture and healing draws westerners from Downtown, others come to see one of the serene monasteries where monks practice the art of Zen.

Beneath the serene surface of the tranquil streets, a darker face of Little Kingdom exists. The Ten Thunders operate their criminal syndicate where their opium slowly erodes hearts and minds as sleepy souls chase the dragon. Ancient rituals and beliefs are practiced but hidden from western eyes. Also hidden within the bustling district, the Qi and Gong serves its clients a mixture of any of lustful interest he may have from one of the beautiful young women of the night to the smoky opium den and hookah lounge. The dark arts of Eastern Resurrection and demonology are practiced below, their practitioners plying their obscene crafts on human flesh. So long as they keep their practices contained within their district, Guild officials seem to ignore the trespasses against legality.

6. Hire Your Crew

Once your Strategy is set, you must now decide on the best Crew to achieve your goals.

In a Scrap, you must choose a single Master or Henchman belonging to your chosen Faction to lead your Crew. Then hire Minions with Soulstones according to the amount agreed upon in Step 1.

In a Brawl, you must choose two Masters to lead your Crew. At least one of these Masters must belong to your chosen Faction, but both must be able to work with your Faction and/or Master. Then hire Minions with Soulstones according to the amount agreed upon in Step 1.

Remember, if you decided to re-flip for your Individual Strategy, you have one less Soulstone with which to hire your Crew.

The following restrictions apply when hiring your Crew:

General

- When hiring Crew members, you may only hire models belonging to your chosen Faction, Mercenary models, or models permitted to join your Crew through a special rule. Example: If you chose Arcanists as your Faction, you could hire Marcus for your Master. You could then hire Beasts from any Faction thanks to Marcus' Beast Master Ability.
- You may hire no more than the indicated number of a Rare model in a Scrap and no more than twice the indicated number of a Rare models in a Brawl. Example: Resurrectionist Nurses are Rare 2, meaning you can hire up to two Nurses in a Scrap and up to four in a Brawl.
- Your Crew cannot contain more than one copy of any Unique model it hires.
- You can only include one version of any named Unique model in your Crew. Example: Your Crew cannot hire both Hamelin and Hamelin, the Plagued.

Masters

- Masters do not cost any Soulstones to hire.
- Your Encounter size determines the maximum number of Masters you can hire into your Crew: one for Scraps, two for Brawls . You must include at least one Master in your Crew.
- In a Brawl you must hire two Masters from the same Faction, or are eligible to be included in your Crew. When a special rule allows you to hire a Master from another Faction, you may also select that Master's Schemes when choosing Schemes (p. 70).
- In Brawls, you can 'trade in' one Master slot for additional Soulstones. If you choose this option, reduce your number of Master slots by one and increase your available Soulstones by 10.

Henchmen

- In a Scrap, you may elect to have a Henchman lead your Crew instead of a Master. If you do so, the Henchman costs 0 Soulstones to hire, just like a Master. Add the model's Henchman Resources amount to your available Soulstones for hiring models.
- When a Crew is led by one or more Masters, it can hire one Henchman per Master, deducting the Henchman's Soulstone Cost from the Crew's available Soulstones.
- Henchmen do not contribute their Henchman Resources amount to the Crew's available Soulstones when included in Crews with Masters.

Minions

- You may only hire Minions from within your chosen Faction unless a special rule allows you to hire Minions from other Factions.
- You may hire up to two models with the Mercenary characteristic from any other Factions. Mercenaries from your chosen Faction do not count toward this total.
- You may hire up to two Special Forces models from your own Faction or with the Mercenary characteristic per Master in your Crew
- Minions hired from outside your chosen Faction, regardless of whether they are Mercenaries or not, cost an additional Soulstone over their printed Soulstone Cost to hire.
- You may hire as many Minions as your Soulstones allow. Deduct the Soulstone Cost of each Minion you hire from the Crew's available Soulstones.
- Totems are manifestations of a Master's magical talents. Minions with the Totem characteristic must be connected to a Master when hired by a Crew. Each Master can only connect one Faction or Mercenary Totem. When a Master is killed or sacrificed, its Totem must be immediately sacrificed.

Starting Soulstone Pool

After you finish hiring your Crew, your remaining unspent Soulstones form your Crew's starting Soulstone Pool. Add your Masters' Soulstone Caches into the Pool. This creates your Crew's starting Soulstone Pool. The maximum number of Soulstones allowed in your Pool is determined by your Encounter size: Scraps = 8, Brawls = 10. Discard any Soulstones in excess of the maximum amount for your size Encounter.

All players must reveal the models hired for their Crew, as well as the starting size of their Soulstone Pool at this time.

7. Select your Schemes

Schemes are lesser victory objectives your Crew can attempt to achieve during the Encounter and should be kept secret from your opponents. You can select a number of Schemes based on the Encounter size. Players are not required to select Schemes if they do not want them. Scheme descriptions and rules can be found in the Master Schemes List starting on page 70.

A Scheme's description will list some or all of the following:

- A name and brief fiction describing the Scheme as well as any limitations on who can select the Scheme such as (Arcanists Only) or (Sonnia Criid Only).
- Any required objects such as terrain features or Counters or Markers under **Setup**.
- Any special rules that apply to the Scheme under **Special**.
- What victory points (VP) are available for the player completing the Scheme and whether or not it can be Announced before the Encounter begins under **Victory**. When scoring a Scheme, no matter how many score lines a Crew meets the requirements for it may only claim the VP for one of those lines plus any + or - Vp listed for the Scheme.

Encounter Size	Total # of Schemes
Scrap	0-2
Brawl	0-3

If you select less than the maximum number of Schemes, your Crew receives +2 Soulstones to their Soulstone Cache for each Scheme less than the maximum available.

When the Encounter begins, daring players can choose to announce any of their eligible Schemes to their opponents. These Schemes are worth the additional VP listed if completed.

Terrain features and models can be targeted by only one Strategy and one Scheme for each player. That is, if you choose multiple Schemes that allow you to target enemy models, you must choose a different valid target for each Scheme.

There are three types of Schemes available to players, General Schemes, Faction Specific Schemes, and Master Specific Schemes. You may take any number of General Schemes, but only one Faction Specific Scheme and one Master Specific Scheme per Master for the Encounter.

8. Deployment

After players have hired their Crews, each player flips a Fate Card. The player with the highest Card nominates a player who chooses one of the shaded deployment areas. That player then deploys his entire Crew within the area. The other player deploys his Crew in the remaining deployment area. If the flip is a tie, re-flip.

Announced Schemes can be revealed once the Crews are deployed. Starting with the player who deployed his Crew first, select the Schemes you wish to announce. These Schemes and the player's Strategy remain public knowledge throughout the Encounter.

After all Crews are deployed, all players re-shuffle their Fate Decks and start the Encounter!

Varying Encounter Length

A standard Malifaux Encounter lasts 6 turns but may take longer. At the end of turn 6, the player who activated the last model in the turn, re-shuffles his Fate Deck and flips a Fate Card. If the Card value is a 10 or higher, play another turn, but increase the value needed to continue the Encounter on next turn's flip by one. The Encounter ends when the flip is less than the value needed. Example: On turn 7 the flip's value would need to be an 11 or higher to continue the Encounter, on turn 8 it would be a 12, and so forth.

Determining a Winner

At the end of an Encounter, players reveal all secret Schemes and add up the VP they earned for completing their Strategies and Schemes. When scoring a Strategy or Scheme, no matter how many score lines a Crew meets the requirements for it may only claim the VP for one of those lines plus any + or - Vp listed for the Strategy or Scheme.

The player with the most VP is the winner. If players are tied for VP, the Encounter is a draw.

Example:

Players can score either 3 VP or 1 VP for completing the Shared Deliver a Message Strategy. 3 VP if they deliver their message during the first 4 turns of the game, or 1 VP if they deliver the message in a later turn. Each player also has the potential to score +1 VP if their opponent does not deliver their own message before the end of the Encounter.

Spirit Boards

In the well established gentlemen's clubs and ladies' lounges in New Amsterdam, games involving spirit boards are blossoming, despite their Resurrectionist undertones. Spirit board construction ranges from simple wood to ornate gold-leafed affairs inlaid with semi-precious stones. Elaborate crystal scrying lenses or simple drinking glasses serve as a means of divination. Self-styled mediums, loved ones seeking messages about their dearly departed, and the curious gather and attempt to summon spirits to the boards. Though not truly necromantic, many claim to have contacted the afterlife through this unassuming party game.

The popularity of spirit boards has spread to Malifaux. Though publicly frowned upon by the Guild, séance parties occur with increasing regularity. The boards seem to work no better or worse in Malifaux than back on Earth, save one chilling difference. Every question, every conversation, each séance with a spirit board in Malifaux ends the same regardless of the user or circumstance.

Always one final word spelled out. - "Soon."

LOCATIONS

Each location entry, whether outdoor or indoor begins with a brief description of the location, followed by a list of Suggested Terrain to populate an Encounter in that location with. Consider terrain traits to apply to common terrain features and areas and agree upon these features before play begins (Book I, page 85). For example, in a Tavern, the indoor battlefield may have multiple tables and a bar. The table might occupy a 2.5" diameter area and players agree that each table is **Ht** 1, breakable (3), covering terrain. The tavern's bar would follow all the rules of an outdoor fence: **Ht** 1, blocking, severe terrain.

During terrain setup, after a player has flipped for the Encounter location, have another player flip a Fate Card and compare its value to the chosen location's corresponding Location Feature Chart. Depending on the flip, this can result in a special terrain feature with its own special rules being placed on the table and/or a special event occurring during the Encounter that may hamper or help the Crews in their struggle. When the Black Joker is flipped, flip two more cards and apply the values. If either of those flips are duplicated, reflip one card.

Outdoor Locations

Encounters between Crews can occur just about anywhere. From the upscale streets of Downtown to the inhospitable Badlands, Malifaux provides a wide variety of settings in which Crews can settle their differences.

Hag's Territory

Because the Hag wanders the Bayou, just about any type of terrain is possible for Encounters taking place in her territory.

Suggested Terrain: sandbars (open, severe), forests, water terrain, the occasional elevated area.

Flip	Feature
Black Joker	Flip two more Cards
1-2	Dark Omens
3-4	Bog
5-7	Ancient Structure
8-9	Magic Nexus
10-11	Mysterious Effigies
12-13	Foggy
Red Joker	Player's Choice from Hag's Territory list

Gremlin Village

These crude settlements can be found scattered throughout the Bayou, home to both Gremlins and their livestock.

Suggested Terrain: animal pens (soft cover), rubble (severe), huts or other structures (blocking and breakable), soggy patches of ground (severe), forests, water effects.

Flip	Feature
Black Joker	Flip two more Cards
1-2	Disturbing Whispers
3-4	Bog
5-7	Creepy Structure
8-9	Torrential Rains
10-11	Dead Zone
12-13	Scrap Pile
Red Joker	Player's Choice from Gremlin Village list

Bayou's Edge

The area marking the border of the Bayou separates the swamp from nearby towns and hills. Often foggy and rainy, this creepy area has its abandoned buildings as well as forested wilds to hide in.

Suggested Terrain: open and severe ground, single trees and forests, tall reeds (soft cover), water effects, elevations.

Flip	Feature
Black Joker	Flip two more Cards
1-2	Forested
3-4	Creepy Structure
5-7	Torrential Rains
8-9	Graveyard
10-11	Hanging Tree
12-13	Campsite
Red Joker	Player's Choice from Bayou's Edge list

Bogs

Many of the brave souls who have dared the Bayou's dangerous bogs have never been seen again.

Suggested Terrain: large areas of severe terrain, ruins (severe and/or hard cover), hazardous terrain, single element trees and forests, tall plant and reed stands (forests), the occasional dry patch of ground (open and/or elevated).

Flip	Feature
Black Joker	Flip two more Cards
1-2	Hanging Tree
3-4	Soulstone Vein
5-7	Bog
8-9	Mysterious Effigies
10-11	Hazardous Terrain
12-13	Foggy
Red Joker	Player's Choice from Bogs list

Downtown

The downtown area, full of residences and businesses, is the Guild's shining example of what the City could be, given enough time and resources.

Suggested Terrain: walls and fences (blocking and/or covering), buildings, fountains (blocking and/or severe), bridges over dry or water terrain.

Terrain can be climbable or breakable as players see fit.

Flip	Feature
Black Joker	Flip two more Cards
1-2	Graveyard
3-4	Dead Zone
5-7	Heat Wave
8-9	Creepy Structure
10-11	Torrential Rains
12-13	Foggy
Red Joker	Player's Choice from Downtown list

Industrial Zone

The Industrial Zone is home to the majority of Malifaux's factories and industry.

Suggested Terrain: walls (soft and/or hard cover), rubble (severe and/or hard cover), hazardous terrain (blocking), climbable terrain, breakable terrain, water effects.

Flip	Feature
Black Joker	Flip two more Cards
1-2	Hazardous Terrain
3-4	Heat Wave
5-7	Scrap Pile
8-9	Rubble
10-11	Foggy
12-13	Creepy Structure
Red Joker	Player's Choice from Industrial Zone list

Slums

Those not affluent or powerful enough to live Downtown are forced to survive in the dangerous Slums, gathering in the bars, opium dens, brothels, and gambling houses and making their way through ruined buildings, cracked stone plazas, and crooked, winding streets.

Suggested Terrain: walls and fences (blocking and/or covering), ruins (severe and/or covering), fountains (blocking and/or severe), bridges over dry or water terrain

Terrain should be climbable and/or breakable as players see fit.

Flip	Feature
Black Joker	Flip two more Cards
1-2	Scrap Pile
3-4	Alone in the Dark
5-7	Rubble
8-9	Creepy Structure
10-11	Hanging Tree
12-13	Graveyard
Red Joker	Player's Choice from Slums list

Quarantine Zone

This part of the City has been given over to the rapacious forces threatening the Guild.

Suggested Terrain: rubble (severe), ruins (severe and/or hard cover), hazardous terrain, free-standing walls (blocking terrain), climbable terrain, breakable terrain.

Flip	Feature
Black Joker	Flip two more Cards
1-2	Rubble
3-4	Ancient Monument
5-7	Alone in the Dark
8-9	Magic Nexus
10-11	Foggy
12-13	Disturbing Whispers
Red Joker	Player's Choice from Quarantine Zone list

Ruins

Evidence of a civilization that predates even the City's founders is scattered across Malifaux.

Suggested Terrain: rubble (severe), ruins (severe and/or hard cover), hazardous terrain, free-standing walls (blocking terrain), climbable terrain, breakable terrain, water effects.

Flip	Feature
Black Joker	Flip two more Cards
1-2	Soulstone Vein
3-4	Disturbing Whispers
5-7	Rubble
8-9	Cruel Winds
10-11	Rockfall
12-13	Campsite
Red Joker	Player's Choice from Ruins list

Mine

Mining concerns can be found nearly anywhere in Malifaux, but are most concentrated in the Badlands.

Suggested Terrain: mining equipment (severe, blocking, and or soft/hard cover), hazardous terrain, elevations, ruins (severe and/or hard cover), climbable terrain.

Flip	Feature
Black Joker	Flip two more Cards
1-2	Alone in the Dark
3-4	Magic Nexus
5-7	Soulstone Vein
8-9	Rockfall
10-11	Dead Zone
12-13	Hazardous Terrain
Red Joker	Player's Choice from Mine list

Pioneer Town/Ghost Town

Many successful (and not so successful) expansion towns dot the Badlands.

Suggested Terrain: structures (climbable and/or breakable), walls and fences (soft and/or hard cover), ruins (severe and/or hard cover), rubble (severe), blocking terrain, water effects.

Flip	Feature
Black Joker	Flip two more Cards
1-2	Hanging Tree
3-4	Heat Wave
5-7	Mysterious Effigies
8-9	Dark Omens
10-11	Graveyard
12-13	Heavy Snows
Red Joker	Player's Choice from Pioneer/Ghost Town list

Badlands

The inhospitable Badlands stretches out from the City for hundreds of miles. Life in the Badlands is usually brutal and mercifully short.

Suggested Terrain: large areas of open terrain, cacti (single element and area terrain), hazardous terrain, boulders (hard cover), ruins (severe and/or hard cover), rubble (severe), elevations.

Flip	Feature
Black Joker	Flip two more Cards
1-2	Stampede!
3-4	Soulstone Vein
5-7	Heat Wave
8-9	Forested
10-11	Hazardous Terrain
12-13	Heavy Snows
Red Joker	Player's Choice from Badlands list

Mountains

Crews finding themselves in Malifaux's distant and mysterious mountain ranges quickly learn how unforgiving Nature can be.

Suggested Terrain: elevations, severe terrain, forests, climbable terrain, hazardous terrain, water effects.

Flip	Feature
Black Joker	Flip two more Cards
1-2	Hazardous Terrain
3-4	Ancient Monument
5-7	Rockfall
8-9	Heavy Snows
10-11	Magic Nexus
12-13	Earthquake
Red Joker	Player's Choice from Mountains list

INDOOR LOCATIONS

Malifaux battles occur in the most varied of conditions and your Masters have proven themselves necessarily adaptable to conflict in those differing conditions. Marcus has fought in city streets, Leveticus has fought at the bayou's edge, and Perdita has fought in the northern mountains. Some battles, though, are not fought in the wide open spaces, but in the tighter confines of locations like Colette's Star Theater, or narrow caves, the Qi and Gong tavern, or even Nicodem's Observatory. Fighting an Encounter at an indoor location is not significantly different from fighting at an outdoor location other than how your terrain setup looks. The most significant change to Encounter play are the walls.

Indoor Walls

- Models with **Flight** or **Float** may not pass over indoor walls.
- Walls that are less than ½" thick are breakable (unless otherwise indicated or agreed upon by players prior to Encounter play) (see breakable rules; Book I, page 84). A wall's **hardness** is determined by the players before the Encounter begins. A model attacking any segment of wall and surpassing its declared **hardness** creates a 3" hole through the wall. Mark this section as severe terrain. Each building and/or wall may have a unique hardness value assigned to it but the suggested hardness values are: wood: 3, brick: 6, stone/cobblestone: 8, metal: 10.

Example:

In an Encounter taking place in the Sewers , walls might be 1" thick (unbreakable, and follow the rules for Indoor Walls) and **Water Terrain** might cover much of the table in narrow 2"-4" wide channels. While most **Water** features have a Encounter effect of: **None**, the sewer water might be ascribed **Severe** terrain qualities, or even **Hazardous** (for example: models suffer 1 **Wd** when moving into or ending their activation in Sewer Water).

Large Theater

A chance encounter between two Crews turns this bastion of the arts into a battleground.

Suggested Terrain: Stage is **Ht** 2. severe terrain, impassable terrain (pipe organ), ½" walls to mark off a 6"x6" back room, crates and barrels (severe , covering).

Flip	Feature
Black Joker	Flip two more Cards
1-2	Bag of Soulstones
3-4	Drink Up!
5-7	Dim Lighting
8-9	Growing Fire
10-11	Pool of Aether
12-13	Hazardous Terrain
Red Joker	Player's Choice from Large Theater list

Sewers

A great labyrinth of connected water channels exists beneath the City and far beyond its borders.

Suggested Terrain: 2"-4" wide water terrain, 1"-3" unbreakable walls, severe terrain, blocking terrain, climbable terrain, varying elevations, bridges, impassable terrain.

Flip	Feature
Black Joker	Flip two more Cards
1-2	Caustic Gas
3-4	Flash Flood
5-7	Dim Lighting
8-9	Rubble
10-11	Hazardous Terrain
12-13	Disturbing Whispers
Red Joker	Player's Choice from The Sewers list

Arcanist's Lab

Arcanist labs are filled with dangerous apparatuses and mysterious equipment, some ancient and foreign.

Suggested Terrain: tables (severe, covering, breakable (3)), covering terrain, hazardous terrain, ¼" breakable walls, areas of the table divided into rooms.

Flip	Feature
Black Joker	Flip two more Cards
1-2	Bag of Soulstones
3-4	Recalibration Device
5-7	Pool of Aether
8-9	Ancient Text
10-11	Arcane Apparatus
12-13	Growing Fire
Red Joker	Player's Choice from Arcanist's Lab list

Resurrectionist's Lab

The disturbing and often macabre chambers make those Death Marshals and accompanying Guardsmen regret the discovery.

Suggested Terrain: tables (severe, covering, breakable (3)), covering terrain, hazardous terrain, ¼" breakable walls, areas of the table divided into rooms.

Flip	Feature
Black Joker	Flip two more Cards
1-2	Graveyard
3-4	Ancient Text
5-7	Dim Lighting
8-9	Alone in the Dark
10-11	Torture Chamber
12-13	Mysterious Effigies
Red Joker	Player's Choice from Resurrectionist's Lab list

Guild Library

Serving as a repository for confiscated texts and forgotten Neverborn artifacts, a Guild Library serves as a tempting target for outlaws.

Suggested Terrain: Bookshelves (**Ht** 2 walls, 1" wide, 3-4" long, covering, breakable (3)), tables (severe, covering, breakable (3)), severe terrain, covering terrain, blocking terrain, areas of the table divided into rooms.

Flip	Feature
Black Joker	Flip two more cards
1-2	Pool of Aether
3-4	Dim Lighting
5-7	Cache of Tomes
8-9	Arcane Apparatus
10-11	Disturbing Whispers
12-13	Ancient Text
Red Joker	Player's Choice from Guild Library list

Necropolis

Deep beneath the City and beyond the expansive sewer channels exists an immense system of ancient connected chambers. None who have sought to explore this network has succeeded and quickly emerge from the sewer system, covered in muck, afraid of their own shadow. Most are never heard from again.

Suggested Terrain: covering terrain, blocking terrain, climbable terrain, water terrain, the occasional climbable area, areas of the table divided into rooms, impassible terrain.

Flip	Feature
Black Joker	Flip two more Cards
1-2	Disturbing Whispers
3-4	Graveyard
5-7	Ancient Monument
8-9	Magic Nexus
10-11	Alone in the Dark
12-13	Rubble
Red Joker	Player's Choice from Necropolis list

Guild Holding Facility

Beneath the primary Guild offices are many chambers found with solid iron-shod doors. Shackles and chains dangle from secure hooks in the ceiling. The Guild, naturally, use these chambers as they were originally intended. Escape attempts are common. Success is not.

Suggested Terrain: walls to mark 5"X5" and larger rooms (unbreakable or **Hardness 8-10**), tables (severe, covering, breakable (3)), blocking terrain.

Flip	Feature
Black Joker	Flip two more Cards
1-2	Dead Zone
3-4	Torture Chamber
5-7	Rubble
8-9	Howling Voices
10-11	Dim Lighting
12-13	Alone in the Dark
Red Joker	Player's Choice from Guild Holding Facility list

Warehouse

Several large buildings are found throughout Malifaux containing great hordes of treasures. Guild confiscated items, Arcanist smuggling areas, and Resurrectionist research material are just the beginning of what can be found by a curious and resourceful Crew.

Suggested Terrain: tables (severe, covering, breakable (3)), severe terrain, blocking terrain, climbable terrain, ¼" breakable walls to create 4"x4" or larger rooms.

Flip	Feature
Black Joker	Flip two more Cards
1-2	Dim Lighting
3-4	Bag of Soulstones
5-7	Scrap Pile
8-9	Growing Fire
10-11	Ancient Text
12-13	Arcane Apparatus
Red Joker	Player's Choice from the Warehouse list

Research Facility

Many different research facilities are found throughout Malifaux. Most are conducted with the Guild's permission and support but some step beyond the line of legality, researching ancient technology and arcane lore. Though their overall purpose might be similar, the contents of these often secret places vary from the mundane to the fantastical.

Suggested Terrain: tables (severe, covering, breakable (3)), ¼" breakable walls to create 4"x4" or larger rooms, hazardous terrain, covering terrain, blocking terrain

Flip	Feature
Black Joker	Flip two more Cards
1-2	Cache of Tomes
3-4	Arcane Apparatus
5-7	Choking Smoke or Gas
8-9	Growing Fire
10-11	Hazardous Terrain
12-13	Recalibration Device
Red Joker	Player's Choice from Research Facility list

Cave/Mine System

Whether a freshly dug mine shaft or the found caves of the Northern Mountains, more and more would-be adventurers ply their trade in the excavation of Soulstone or the sometimes rewarding discoveries of spelunking. Some become so excited by the rich discoveries to be unearthed that they forget where they are: Malifaux, where the darkest tunnels are often filled with the greatest danger.

Suggested Terrain: thick walls (2"-3" thick), covering terrain, hazardous terrain, impassible terrain, climbable terrain, blocking terrain, water terrain.

Flip	Feature
Black Joker	Flip two more Cards
1-2	Rubble
3-4	Bag of Soulstones
5-7	Dim Lighting
8-9	Hazardous Terrain
10-11	Soulstone Vein
12-13	Rockfall
Red Joker	Player's Choice from Cave/Mine System list

Ancient Ruins

Lost in the overgrown wilderness of the Bayou to the east and scattered through the Northern Hills and badlands to the west, explorers and adventurers have uncovered crumbled complexes created and abandoned by a very ancient culture.

Suggested Terrain: Walls, areas divided into rooms, blocking terrain, impassible terrain, covering terrain, hazardous terrain, climbable terrain.

Flip	Feature
Black Joker	Flip two more Cards
1-2	Rockfall
3-4	Cache of Tomes
5-7	Ancient Monument
8-9	Howling Voices
10-11	Arcane Apparatus
12-13	Ancient Text
Red Joker	Player's Choice from Ancient Ruins list

Large Tavern

Within the dangerous and dirty section of the Slums, the inhabitants of Malifaux seek solace in their cups. The Qi and Gong and other taverns cater to the various lusts of settlers looking to escape the drudgery of laborious and dangerous workdays and fear of the unknown perils of the Malifaux wilderness. Fights are common, winners are not.

Suggested Terrain: Thin walls (hardness 2) separate 5"X5" rooms filled with severe, covering, or blocking terrain and tables (severe, covering, breakable (3)).

Flip	Feature
Black Joker	Flip two more Cards
1-2	Bag of Soulstones
3-4	Howling Voices
5-7	Drink Up!
8-9	Dim Lighting
10-11	Wetbar
12-13	Growing Fire
Red Joker	Player's Choice from Large Tavern list

Collapsed City Block

Within the Quarantine Zone and even within the Slums, some buildings have given in to the withering effects of time and dilapidation. Sometimes, brave and resourceful souls scavenging through the debris come out with a treasure or tale worth the risks.

Suggested Terrain: severe terrain, blocking terrain, impassible terrain, walls, hazardous terrain, climbable terrain.

Flip	Feature
Black Joker	Flip two more Cards
1-2	Ancient Text
3-4	Arcane Apparatus
5-7	Rubble
8-9	Hazardous Terrain
10-11	Rockfall
12-13	Dark Omens
Red Joker	Player's Choice from Collapsed City Zone list

LOCATION FEATURES

Special Terrain

Unless otherwise indicated in the descriptions below, a special terrain feature must be placed somewhere in the unshaded area of the table (see Deployment Areas on p 40), at least 6" from either shaded deployment area, when setting up terrain. Players should agree who will place the terrain (or flip for it). The terrain feature can be oriented in any direction on the table.

> **Reminder:**
> **(#) Interact:** The model spends the indicated number of Actions to **Interact** with the Encounter table or object in base contact. For example: Picking up a bag of Soulstones in a Story scenario is a **(1) Interact** Action.

Arcane Apparatus: Each player places a 50mm Marker. Models may **(1) Interact** with the marker once per turn to Flip a Fate Card. The model adds the suit shown on the Fate Card to its Duel totals. Flipping the Black Joker removes all suits associated with the model's statistics. Flipping the Red Joker allows the model to add any one suit to its Duel totals. The results of the flip last until the end of the model's next activation.

Ancient Monument: 50mm, **Ht** 5 blocking terrain. Models receive +1 **Ca** while within 1" of the Ancient Monument.

Ancient Text: at the beginning of the Encounter, each player places one Book Counter in base contact with a terrain feature, and at least 8" from each deployment area. A model may **(1) Interact** to pick up the Counter. A model carrying a Book Counter gains "**Arcane Reservoir:** Increase this model's Crew's Maximum Hand Size by 1 while it is in play." Before a model carrying a Book Counter leaves play, place the Book Counter in base contact with the model. Models cannot carry more than one Book Counter at any time.

Bag of Soulstones: at the beginning of the Encounter, each player places a Marker on the table, at least 10" away from their deployment area. Models with **Use Soulstone** may **(1) Interact** with a Marker to discard it and gain two Soulstones (this may exceed the maximum Soulstone Pool allowance).

Bog: For the duration of the Encounter, any portion of the table without a terrain feature receives the severe and water traits.

Cache of Tomes: Players alternate placing a total of six Book Counters on the table, following the Special Terrain setup rules. Book Counters must be placed at least 6" from one another. A model may **(1) Interact** with a Book Counter to flip a Fate Card. Apply the results of the flip to the model as follows:

Black Joker: **Paralyzed**

- ☞: The model's /// and ⌒ **Strikes** and spells receive +1 **Dg**
- ✕: The model gains **Slow to Die** and **Hard to Wound: 1**
- ♥: The model gains **Black Blood** and **(+1) Nimble**
- 📖: The model gains +1 **Ca** and **Magic Resistant +1**;

Red Joker: Flip twice and apply the effects of both cards. If the second card is the same suit as the first it has no effect.

This effect lasts until the end of the model's next activation.

Campsite: Place a 2" X 2" or larger severe terrain feature. A model may **(1) Interact** with the Campsite to discard a Control Card and then draw one Control Card.

Creepy Structure: Place a 3" X 3" or larger terrain feature. Models may **(1) Interact** with the Creepy Structure once per turn to flip a Fate Card. Apply the results of the flip to the model as follows

Joker: model is killed

1-3: model suffers 2 **Wd**

4-6: model may inflict 2 **Wd** on another model in base contact with the structure

7-9: model heals 2 **Wd**

10-11: add two Soulstones to Crew's Pool

12-13: model adds two Soulstones to Crew's Pool and heals any **Wd**.

Dead Zone: Place a 3"X3" or larger open terrain feature. Models cannot cast spells while in base contact with the Dead Zone.

Drink Up!: At the beginning of the Encounter, select one 1"x5" or larger terrain feature. Models beginning or ending their activation within 1" of the feature may **(1) Interact** with it to make a Healing Flip. The model receives **Slow** and may not make **(0)** Actions during its next activation.

Forested: For the duration of the Encounter, any portion of the table without a terrain piece receives the covering trait, and models cannot draw LoS further than 3".

Graveyard: Place a 3" x 3" or larger terrain feature. Models gain one Corpse Counter when they **(1) Interact** while their base is completely within the Graveyard. Any tombstones in the terrain feature are considered **Ht** 1, and covering.

Hanging Tree: Place a 50mm, **Ht** 6 blocking terrain feature. Tree is **Terrifying→12** against models ending their activations within 2".

Hazardous Terrain: Place a 3" X 3" or larger terrain feature. The player placing the hazardous terrain declares what type of hazard the terrain piece is and how much damage the terrain causes. Players should use one of the damage ratings from Terrain (Book I: page 85) or agree on a damage rating for the hazard.

Magic Nexus: Place a 3" X 3" terrain feature. The Casting and Resist Flips of models whose bases are completely within the area receive ⬧.

Mysterious Effigies: Each player places two 30mm Markers at least 10" outside of any Deployment Zone. At the end of the Encounter, the player with the closest model within 2" of an Effigy Marker scores 1 VP.

Pool of Aether: Place a 3"X3" or larger terrain feature. Models with **Use Soulstone** whose bases are completely within the area may spend one Soulstone per turn without deducting it from their Soulstone Pool.

Rubble: For the duration of the Encounter, any portion of the table without a terrain feature receives the severe trait.

Recalibration Device: Place a 50mm, **Ht** 4 terrain feature. Models may **(1) Interact** while in base contact with the feature to force a target non-Master Construct model in LoS of the **Recalibration Device** to make a **Wp→15** Duel or receive one of the following effects:

- **(+1) Nimble**
- **(2) Flurry**
- **Slow**
- **Dg** 1/2/4

Wetbar: Place a 3" x 3" or larger terrain feature. Models in base contact with the feature may **(2) Interact** to make two Healing Flips. The model also receives **Slow** and **Easy to Wound 1** during its next activation.

Scrap Pile: Place a 3" x 3" or larger severe terrain feature. Models gain one Scrap Counter when they **(1) Interact** while their base is completely within the Scrap Pile.

Soulstone Vein: Place a terrain feature no larger than 2" x 2". Masters gain # Soulstone when they **(#) Interact** while their bases are completely within the Soulstone Vein.

Torture Chamber: Place a 3"X3" or larger terrain feature. While a model's base is completely within the feature it adds one Soulstone to the Master's Soulstone Pool when it kills a model. A model within the feature also receives **Terrifying→12**.

SPECIAL EVENTS

Special events occur during one or more turns of the Encounter. Each event indicates when it takes place during the turn. Events that last until the end of the Encounter begin at the start of the Draw Phase in turn 1.

To determine whether a Random event happens each turn, apply the following steps at the end of the Closing Phase.

1) The last player who activated a model re-shuffles his Deck and flips a Fate Card.
2) If the card is a Joker, 10, 11, 12, or 13, the event occurs during the next turn; otherwise, no event occurs.

Alone in the Dark: Until the end of the Encounter, a model forced to fall back after a failed Morale Duel is killed instead.

Cruel Winds: At the start of the Encounter, randomly determine a table edge. During the next turn, each model is Pushed 1" toward that table edge at the end of its activation.

Caustic Gas: Until the end of the Encounter, models receive -1/-1 **Wk/Cg**. All models receive ⊟ to their ranged Attacks and ranged Casting Flips.

Dark Omens: Random. From the beginning of next turn's Draw Phase to the end of its Activation Phase, Fate Cards with a value of 1 count as value 13 and vice versa.

Dim Lighting: Until the end of the Encounter, ranged Attacks and ranged Casting Flips receive ⊟ and LoS is reduced to 8".

Disturbing Whispers: Until the end of the Encounter, all models receive -1 **Wp** when defending in a Duel.

Earthquake: Random. At the start of the next turn's Activation Phase, each player, in activation order, may Push all of their opponents' models 1" in any direction unless those models have **Flight** or **Float**.

Flash Flood: At the start of the Encounter, randomly determine a table edge. During the next turn, models cannot **Charge** and each model is Pushed 2" toward that table edge at the beginning of its activation.

Foggy: Random. During the next turn, ranged Attacks and ranged Casting Flips receive ⊟.

Growing Fire: Place a 50mm Fire Marker in base contact with terrain feature and no closer than 1" from any model. Nominate another player who then places an additional 50mm Fire Marker, touching the first Fire Marker. This Fire Marker can be placed touching or overlapping model bases.

For the remainder of the Encounter, at the end of the End Close Phase the player who activated the first model in the turn places an additional 50mm Fire Marker touching any Fire Marker already on the table. After this marker is placed, the second player in activation order also places a Fire Marker. Any of these Fire Markers can be placed touching or overlapping model bases.

These Fire Markers have the **Ht** 5, covering, obscuring, and Hazardous (2/4/7) traits.

Heat Wave: Random. During the next turn, models receive -1/-1 **Wk/Cg**.

Heavy Snows: Random. During the next turn, models cannot **Charge** and receive -2 **Cb** to ranged **Strikes**. Models with **Frozen Heart** are immune to Heavy Snows.

Howling Voices: Random. During the next turn, models cannot activate simultaneously and all models receive -2 **Ca** when targeting another model.

Rockfall: Random. At the start of the next turn's Activation Phase, any model within 1" of a terrain feature immediately suffers 1 **Wd**.

Stampede!: Random. At the start of the next turn's Activation Phase, all models within 8" of the centerline immediately suffer a number of wounds equal to their **Ht**.

Torrential Rains: Random. During the next turn, models cannot **Charge**.

COMPLETE STRATEGIES LIST

A Strategy's description lists some or all of the following:

- A name and brief fiction describing the Strategy.
- Any required objects such as terrain features or Counters or Markers under **Setup**.
- Any special rules that apply to the Strategy under **Special**.
- What victory points (VP) are available for the player or players completing the Strategy under **Victory**. When scoring a Strategy, no matter how many score lines a Crew meets the requirements for it may only claim the VP for one of those lines plus any + or - Vp listed for the Strategy.
- All markers are the size of a 30mm standard base, except when noted.

Simple Strategies

A Line in the Sand

You're tired of your opponent's models in your turf, so you're going to draw a line in the sand...with dynamite.

Setup
Place five 30mm Dynamite Markers along the centerline of the table, at least 6" apart.

Special
A model may make a **(1) Interact** Action while in base contact with a Dynamite Marker to arm it. One of your opponent's models may make an **(2) Interact** Action with a Dynamite Marker you have armed to disarm it. A model cannot take either of these Actions if they are Insignificant or engaged with an enemy model.

Victory
Score 4 VP If all five Dynamite Markers are armed at the end of the Encounter.
Score 2 VP If at least three Dynamite Markers are armed at the end of the Encounter.

Claim Jump

Time to stake your claim in someone else's territory!

Setup
Place a 30mm Claim Marker at least 8" away from the center of the table and at least 12" from your Deployment Zone.

Special
Insignificant models do not count toward the Victory condition.

Victory
Score 4 VP if you have twice as many or more models completely within 3" of the Claim Marker than your opponent at the end of the Encounter.
Score 2 VP if you have more models completely within 3" of the Claim Marker than your opponent at the end of the Encounter.

Contain Power

You have been assigned to contain the expansion of your opponent's power.

Victory
Score 4 VP if your opponent has no Masters, Henchmen and Totems in play at the end of the Encounter.
Score 2 VP if you have killed at least one of your opponent's Masters or Henchmen.

Deliver a Message

I'm just the messenger!!

Special
A model in your Crew may make a **(2) Interact** Action while within 2" of one of your opponents' Masters, or Henchmen to Deliver a Message. Insignificant models cannot take this Action.

Victory
Score 4 VP if one of your models delivered the message in the first 4 turns.
Score 2 VP if one of your models delivered the message during the Encounter.

Destroy the Evidence

The other player has set up on some key evidence left behind from a previous Encounter, and you need it destroyed!

Setup

Place one 30mm objective Marker completely inside your opponent's Deployment Zone and two 30mm objective Markers completely within 10" of your opponents Deployment Zone. Markers cannot be placed within 8" of each other.

Special

A model in your Crew in base contact with any one of these objective Markers may make a **(1) Interact** Action to remove the Marker from play. A model cannot take this Action if they are Insignificant or engaged with an enemy model.

Victory

Score 4 VP if all three of the objective Markers have been destroyed at the end of the Encounter.
Score 2 VP if two of the objective Markers have been destroyed at the end of the Encounter.

Distract

You need to get the watchful eye of your opponent off your plans.

Special

Insignificant models do not count toward the Victory condition.

Victory

Score 4 VP if your opponent does not have a Master, Henchman, or Totem completely on your half of the table at the end of the Encounter.
Score 2 VP if your opponent does not have a Master completely on your half of the table at the end of the Encounter.

Escape and Survive

You simply cannot afford any more losses right now.

Setup

At the start of the Encounter note what models your Crew hired.

Special

Insignificant models do count toward the Victory condition. Summoned models do not count toward the victory condition unless another friendly model was killed or sacrificed when summoning the model.

Victory

Score 4 VP if you have at least 75% of the number of models you started the Encounter with in play and are at least 8" from your Deployment Zone at the end of the Encounter.
Score 2 VP if you have at least 50% of the number of models you started the Encounter with in play and are at least 8" from your Deployment Zone at the end of the Encounter.

Plant Evidence

You've decided to try to turn public opinion against your opponent by framing them, but to do this you need to plant the evidence.

Special

A model in your Crew may make a **(1) Interact** Action to Plant Evidence when in base contact with a terrain feature. You may not plant evidence on the same piece of terrain more than once during the Encounter. A model cannot take this Action if they are Insignificant or engaged with an enemy model.

Victory

Score 4 VP if you Planted Evidence on at least four terrain features on your opponent's half of the table, or on at least two terrain features in their Deployment Zone during the Encounter.
Score 2 VP if you Planted Evidence on at least two terrain features on your opponent's half of the table during the Encounter.

Reconnoiter

Investigate the surrounding area.

Setup

Divide the table into equal quarters.

Special

Insignificant models and models within 3" of the center of the table do not count toward the Victory condition. A model counts as occupying a table quarter if more than half of its base is in that quarter.

Victory

Score 4 VP if, at the end of the Encounter you have as many or more models than your opponent completely within at least three of the table quarters.

Score 2 VP if, at the end of the Encounter you have as many or more models than your opponent completely within at least two of the table quarters.

Slaughter

They've gone too far. Time to wipe them out.

Special

Each time a player kills or sacrifices an enemy model during the Encounter, that player notes its Soulstone Cost. Masters are worth 10 Soulstones for the purpose of this Strategy (Multiple model Masters such as The Dreamer and Viktoria are worth 6 Soulstones per model). Models that are summoned into play and are killed will add their Soulstone costs. Models that can return to play, when killed for the first time by the opposing player count their Soulstones only the first time they are killed.

Victory

Score 4 VP if the total Soulstone Cost of enemy models you have killed or sacrificed is 1.5 times greater than the total Soulstone Cost of your models your opponent has killed or sacrificed.

Score 2 VP if the total Soulstone Cost of enemy models you have killed or sacrificed is greater than the Soulstone Cost of your models your opponent has killed or sacrificed.

Supply Wagon

You are transporting some vital supplies, and they must arrive intact!

Setup

Place a 50mm Wagon Marker in your deployment zone after you place your Crew.

Special

In the Start Closing Phase of each turn, move the Wagon Marker 6" directly towards the center of the table. A Wagon Marker has Hardness 3 and is destroyed if it is damaged 3 times. A model may not attack the Wagon Marker with ranged **Strikes** or spells or if within an enemy model's melee range. Models may not move over the Wagon Marker, and the Wagon Marker may not move over models, and stops if it comes in contact with them.

Victory

Score 4 VP if your Wagon Marker is within 3" of the center of the table and had not been damaged.

Score 2 VP if your Wagon Marker is within 3" of the center of the table and has been damaged.

Treasure Hunt

You have discovered the location of a valuable artifact and must take possession of it.

Setup

Place a 30mm Treasure Counter in the center of the table.

Special

A model in your Crew in base contact with the Counter may **(1) Interact** to pick up it up. A model can drop the Counter or pass it to another model in base contact as a **(1) Interact** Action. Models controlled by your opponent can take the Action once one of your models has picked it up at least once during the Encounter.

A model drops the Treasure Counter in base contact with itself if it changes position on the table by any effect other than the **Walk** Action or before being removed form play. A model carrying the Counter reduces its **Wk** to 4. Spirits lose the ability to move through other models and the ability ignore terrain penalties while carrying the Treasure Counter. Models lose **Fly** or **Float** while carrying the Treasure Counter. The Treasure Counter does not count as being carried if carried by an Insignificant model at the end of the Encounter.

Victory

Score 4 VP if one of your Crew's models carries the Treasure Counter and is in your Deployment Zone at the end of the Encounter.

Score 2 VP if the Treasure Counter is in your Deployment Zone but not carried by a model, or if it is currently carried by one of your models.

Turf War

You wish to claim a little of your opponent's real estate for yourself.

Special

Insignificant models do not count toward the Victory condition.

Victory

Score 4 VP if you have more models on your opponent's half of the table than they have on your half of the table and you have at least one model in their deployment zone.

Score 2 VP if you have more models on your opponent's half of the table than they have on your half of the table at the end of the Encounter.

Festival Days

The diversity of cultures flocking to Malifaux ensures an equally varied assortment of Earthside celebrations this side of the Breach. The Three Kingdom New Year is celebrated as well as Candelmas and All Hollow's Eve. Families follow the same beliefs to mark the seasons as their ancestors did before them. In addition, since passing through the Breach, Malifaux residents have added a few festival days unique to their new world.

Breach Day is the most widely celebrated of the new festival days, a day of picnics and outings. Parades sponsored by the Guild mark the day the portal was re-opened. The Guild has been known to pardon transgressors of lesser crimes and to forgive debts on Breach Day as well. On this day, it is tradition to bow one's head at the chime of every hour to remember the brave souls lost during the first crossing a century ago.

Several other Malifaux festival days are also observed throughout the year. The Day of Lanterns is celebrated in Little Kingdom and Dia De Los Fantasma honored in Promise. Conjunction Eve is celebrated on the night that Malifaux's two moons cross in the sky with the wealthy throwing elaborate masquerade balls to celebrate the event. Members of the Miners and Steamfitters Union celebrate Laborers Day, a time of rest for tradesmen. Block parties and packed saloons being the norm on that raucous holiday.

Even the Resurrectionists are rumored to celebrate their own festival. Gleaned from the knowledge and rituals of the original inhabitants of Malifaux, they are said to celebrate The Day of Flaying and Sleeper's Night. Much to the horror of Malifaux residents, these celebrations have little to do with spreading cheer. Most lock their doors when the dead wander the streets, lest they be "invited" to participate in the grisly celebrations.

Shared Strategies List

With shared Strategies, multiple players may earn VP if they accomplish the required tasks.

Shared A Line in the Sand

You're tired of your opponent's models in your turf, so you're going to draw a line in the sand... with dynamite. But your opponent isn't just going to let you do it!

Setup

After selecting this Strategy, both players flip a Card. The player with the high card decides if they would like to be the Attacker or Defender in this Strategy.

The Attacking player places five 30mm Dynamite Markers along the center line of the table, at least 6" apart. These Markers begin the Encounter Disarmed.

Special

A model in the Attacking Crew may make a **(1) Interact** Action while in base contact with a Dynamite Marker to arm it. One of the defender's models may make an **(2) Interact** Action with an armed Dynamite Marker to disarm it. Insignificant models or models engaged with an enemy model cannot take these Actions.

Victory
Attacker:
Score 2 VP If at least two Dynamite Markers are armed at the end of the Encounter.
Score +1 VP for each additional armed Dynamite Marker over three at the end of the Encounter.

Defender:
Score 2 VP If at least three Dynamite Markers are disarmed at the end of the Encounter
Score +1 VP for each additional armed Dynamite Marker over three at the end of the Encounter.

Shared Claim Jump

Time to stake your claim in someone else's territory!

Setup

Place a 30mm Claim Marker in the center of the table.

Special

Insignificant models do not count toward the Victory condition.

Victory

Score 4 VP if any of your models' bases are completely within 3" of the Claim Marker and none of your opponent's models are at the end of the Encounter.
Score 2 VP if you have more models whose bases are completely within 3" of the Claim Marker than your opponent does at the end of the Encounter.

Shared Contain Power

Both Masters have watched their opponent gain too much influence and too strong a foothold in Malifaux.

Victory

Score 3 VP if your opponent has no Masters or Henchmen in play at the end of the Encounter and you do.
Score 1 VP if you have killed at least one of your opponent's Masters or Henchmen.
Score +1 VP if you have killed all your opponent's Totems.

Shared Deliver a Message

I'm just the messenger!!

Special

A model in your Crew may take a **(2) Interact** Action while within 2" of one of your opponents' Masters, or Henchmen to Deliver a Message. Insignificant models cannot take this Action.

Victory

Score 3 VP if you are the first player to deliver the message, which must happen in the first 4 turns.
Score 1 VP if you deliver the message.
Score +1 VP if your opponent does not deliver the message during the Encounter.

Shared Destroy the Evidence

Everyone's hands are dirty; just make sure that yours appear less dirty than your opponent's.

Setup

Each player places one 30mm objective Marker completely inside your opponent's Deployment Zone and objective Markers completely within 8" of your opponent's Deployment Zone.

Special

A friendly model in base contact with an objective Marker that you placed may use a **(1) Interact** action to destroy the objective Marker and remove it from the board. This may not be done while within melee range of an opponent's model.

Victory

Score 1 VP for each objective Marker you placed that you removed from play during the Encounter.

Score +2 VP if you removed the neutral objective Marker from play during the Encounter.

Shared Distract

You need to get the watchful eye of your opponent off what you're up to.

Special

Insignificant models do not count toward the Victory condition.

Victory

Score 4 VP if your opponent does not have a Master, Henchman or Totem completely on your half of the table and you have a Master completely on their half of the table at the end of the Encounter.

Score 2 VP if your opponent does not have a Master, Henchman or Totem completely on your half of the table at the end of the Encounter.

Shared Plant Evidence

You've decided to try to turn public opinion against your opponent by framing them, but to do this you need to plant the evidence.

Special

A model may take a **(1) Interact** Action to Plant Evidence when in base contact with a terrain feature on their opponent's half of the table. You may not plant evidence on the same piece of terrain more than once during the Encounter. A model cannot take this Action if they are Insignificant or engaged with an enemy model.

Victory

Score 1 VP for each piece of evidence you plant on your opponent's half of the table.

Shared Reconnoiter

Each of you have decided to investigate the surrounding area and learn more than your opponent.

Setup

Divide the table into equal quarters.

Special

Insignificant models and models within 3" of the center of the table do not count toward the Victory condition. A model counts as occupying a table quarter if more than half of its base is in that quarter.

Victory

Score 1 VP for each quarter with more of your models than opponent's models at the end of the Encounter.

Shared Supply Wagon

You are both trying to get your supply wagon to the center of the board.

Setup

Each place a 50mm Wagon Marker in your deployment zone after you place your Crew .

Special

In the Start Closing Phase of each turn, each move the Wagon Marker 6" directly towards the center of the table, starting with the player who acted first this turn. A Wagon Marker has Hardness 3 and is destroyed if it is damaged 3 times. A model may not attack the Wagon Marker with ranged **Strikes** or spells or if within an enemy model's melee range. Models may not move over the Wagon Marker, and the Wagon Marker may not move over models, and stops if it comes in contact with them.

Victory

Score 2 VP if your Wagon Marker is within 3" of the center of the table and your opponent's is not.
Score +1 VP if you damage you're your opponent's Wagon Marker.
Score +1 VP if your Wagon Marker is undamaged at the end of the Encounter.

Shared Escape and Survive

Neither of you can afford any more loses right now.

Setup

At the start of the Encounter each player notes what models their Crew hired.

Special

Insignificant models do count toward the Victory condition. Summoned models do not count toward the victory condition unless another friendly model was killed or sacrificed when summoning the model.

Victory

Score 2 VP if you have lost fewer models than your opponent.
Score 1 VP if you have at least 50% of the number of models you started the Encounter with in play and are at least 6" from your Deployment Zone at the end of the Encounter.
Score +1 VP if you have at least 75% of the number of models you started the Encounter with in play and are at least 6" from your Deployment Zone at the end of the Encounter.

Shared Slaughter

Only one of us walks away from this...

Special

Each time a player kills or sacrifices an enemy model during the Encounter, that player notes its Soulstone Cost. Masters are worth 10 Soulstones for the purpose of this Strategy (Multiple model Masters such as The Dreamer and Viktoria are worth 6 Soulstones per model). Models that are summoned into play and are killed will add their Soulstone costs. Models that can return to play, when killed for the first time by the opposing player count their Soulstones only the first time they are killed.

Victory

Score 2 VP if the total Soulstone Cost of enemy models you have killed or sacrificed is 1.5 times greater than the total Soulstone Cost of models your opponent has killed or sacrificed of yours.
Score 1 VP if the total Soulstone Cost of enemy models you have killed or sacrificed is greater than the total Soulstone Cost of models your opponent has killed or sacrificed of yours.
Score +1 VP if your opponent has no Masters in play at the end of the Encounter.
Score +1 VP if your opponent's remaining models total Soulstone Cost is less than half the total Soulstone Cost of the Crew at the start of the Encounter.

Shared Treasure Hunt

Both you and your opponent have uncovered the location of an important Malifaux artifact, and must race to be the first to claim it.

Setup

Place one 30mm Treasure Counter in the center of the table after Crews have deployed, but before the Encounter begins.

Special

Any model in base contact with the Counter may **(2) Interact** to pick up it up. A model can drop the Counter or pass it to another model in base contact as a **(1) Interact** Action.

A model drops the Treasure Counter in base contact with itself if it changes position on the table by any effect other than the **Walk** Action or before being removed form play. A model carrying the Counter reduces its **Wk** to 4. Spirits lose the ability to move through other models and the ability ignore terrain penalties while carrying the Treasure Counter. Models lose **Fly** or **Float** while carrying the Treasure Counter. The Treasure Counter does not count as being carried if carried by an Insignificant model at the end of the Encounter.

Victory
Score 4 VP if one of your Crew's models carries the treasure and is in your Deployment Zone at the end of the Encounter.

Score 2 VP if the treasure is in your Deployment Zone but not carried by a model, or if it is currently carried by one of your models.

Shared Turf War
You each wish to claim a little of your opponent's real estate for yourself.

Special
Insignificant models do not count toward the Victory condition.

Victory
Score 3 VP if you have more models on your opponent's half of the table than they have on your half of the table and they have no models in your Deployment Zone at the end of the Encounter.

Score 1 VP if you have more models on your opponent's half of the table than they have on your half of the table. at the end of the Encounter.

Score +1 VP if you have a model in your opponent's Deployment Zone at the end of the Encounter.

The Truth

News travels slowly in Malifaux, of that there is no question. Without a more reliable means of communication outside of the City than the fastest horse, riverboat, or irregular Aethervox signal, control of what scant news that does reach the edge of civilization is critical. To that end, the Guild-run newspaper, The Malifaux Record – the only legal newspaper this side of the Breach – is the main method by which residents in boomtowns and settlements far removed from the City learn anything about what happens beyond their borders.

Overseen by its ruthless Editor-in-Chief, John McKnight, The Malifaux Record covers each fact with a half dozen misdirections, obfuscations, or outright lies. McKnight demands his reporters in the field report the entire unabashed truth in their stories, ensuring his team of editors leaves no loose ends when they bury the facts by the time the newspaper goes to press.

Recently, McKnight's newspaper has conducted several "smear campaigns" – so nicknamed for the poor quality of the newsprint ink – on rumored dissidents the Guild has targeted for a quieter removal from power than a team of Guardsmen could manage. No one is quite sure how McKnight's reporters are able to dredge up such damning secrets, or if they are even true, but more than one target has faded into the background, reputation destroyed, after a particularly revealing story ran in the paper. The most recent, "The Necrotic Dalliances of Major Sam Fitzhugh", drove the outspoken major of Havenport to take his own life, silencing his frequent speeches on the Guild's insatiable demands on his town for Soulstone shipments.

Be careful what you wish for when you want your name in the papers, that dream may just come true.

COMPLETE SCHEMES LIST

A Scheme's description will list some or all of the following:

- A name and brief fiction describing the Scheme as well as any limitations on who can select the Scheme such as (Arcanists Only) or (Sonnia Criid Only).
- Any required objects such as terrain features or Counters or Markers under **Setup**.
- Any special rules that apply to the Scheme under **Special**.
- What victory points (VP) are available for the player completing the Scheme and whether or not it can be Announced before the Encounter begins under **Victory**. When scoring a Scheme, no matter how many score lines a Crew meets the requirements for it may only claim the VP for one of those lines plus any + or - Vp listed for the Scheme.
- When announcing a Scheme, you must include all details about choices required by the special rules of the Scheme made when selecting that scheme.

General Schemes

Assassinate

Your opponent's leadership must die at all costs!

Setup
Secretly make note of one of your opponents Crew's Masters or Henchmen. This Scheme may be taken multiple times; choose a different model each time.

Victory
Score 1 VP if that model is not in play at the end of the Encounter.
Announce: +1 VP.

Bodyguard

Your Crew's leadership must be protected at all costs!

Special
Secretly note of one of your Crew's Masters or Henchmen. This Scheme may be taken multiple times; choose a different model each time.

Victory
Score 1 VP if that model is still in play at the end of the Encounter.
Score -1 VP if the model is killed or sacrificed by an enemy model before the start of turn 5.
Announce: +1 VP.

Breakthrough

Your Crew must push its way through the opposition.

Special
Insignificant models do not count toward the Victory condition.

Victory
Score 1 VP if you have more models in your opponent's Deployment Zone than they do at the end of the Encounter.
Announce: +1 VP.

Extermination

Your Crew's sights are fixed on one exterminating one threat.

Special
Select a subtype of model (i.e., Undead, Construct, Spirit, Soulless, Nightmare, Family, Nephilim, Woe, Doll, Gremlin, Pig, etc). Your opponent's Crew must contain at least three models of that subtype.

Victory
Score 1 VP if your opponent has no models of the selected subtype left in play at the end of the Encounter.
Score -1 VP if all of your opponent's models of the selected subtype are still in play at the end of the Encounter.
Announce: +1 VP.

Eye for an Eye

It's time to show the opposing Crew you can trade blow for blow when they come a'calling!

Special

Insignificant models do not count toward the Victory condition.

Victory

Score 1 VP at the end of the Encounter if the number of models you and your opponent have in play is equal or within 1 model.
Announce: +2 VP.

Frame for Murder

Never hurts to get a little blood on the hands of your rivals...well, it hurts the person providing the blood.

Special

Secretly note one model in your Crew.

Victory

Score 1 VP at the end of the Encounter if the selected model was killed by your opponent's Master .
Announce: +1 VP.

Grudge

One of your opponent's Minions rubs you the wrong way.

Special

Secretly note one of your opponent's Minions.

Victory

Score 1 VP at the end of the Encounter if the selected model was killed or sacrificed by one of your Crew's melee Strikes or melee spells.
Announce: +1 VP.

Hold Out

Stand firm against the enemy.

Special

Insignificant models do not count toward the Victory condition.

Victory

Score 1 VP if no enemy models are in your Deployment Zone at the end of the Encounter.
Announce: +1 VP.

Kill Protégée

You've heard that one your opponent's Minions is being groomed as the Master's new Henchman.

Victory

Score 1 VP at the end of the Encounter if you killed the Minion in the opposing Crew with the highest Soulstone Cost. In the case of a tie, note which Minion is the target of this Scheme.
Announce: +1 VP.

Stake a Claim

This is your territory, and you'll be damned if some other Crew is going to come in and grab it without a fight!

Special

Make note of a terrain feature on the opponent's half of the table. Insignificant models do not count toward the Victory condition.

Victory

Score 1 VP if you have a model touching the terrain feature the end of the Encounter.
Announce: +1 VP.

Steal Relic

Your opponent's Master is carrying something you really need for your plans!

Special

Your Crew's models may take a **(1) Interact** Action while engaged with your opponent's Master to conduct a **Wp → Wp** Duel with the Master. The **Interact** Action can no longer be taken after one of your models wins the Duel. Insignificant models cannot take this Action. This Scheme must be announced.

Victory

Score 1 VP at the end of the Encounter if one of your models won the Duel.
Score +2 VP if the model that succeeded in the Duel is still in play at the end of the Encounter.

Faction Specific Schemes

Round up (Guild Only)

Time to round up the little guys, and leave the big problems for later.

Victory
Score 1 VP if the only models your opponent has left in play are Masters or Henchmen at the end of the Encounter.
Announce: +1 VP.

Raid! (Guild Only)

Sometimes the Malifaux rabble needs a firm reminder who the law is this side of the Breach. Teach them a lesson.

Victory
Score 1 VP if you have more non-Totem Minions in play than your opponent does at the end of the Encounter.
Announce: +1 VP.

Army of the Dead (Resurrectionists Only)

"Raising" an army takes on an entirely different meaning for you.

Special
This Scheme must be announced.

Victory
Score 1 VP at the end of the Encounter if the number of Corpse Counters in play, either carried by your models or on the table, is greater than the number of models your opponent has left in play.
Score +1 VP at the end of the Encounter if the number of Corpse Counters carried by your models is greater than the number of models your opponent has left in play.

Death After Death (Resurrectionists Only)

Your Crew only gets larger as the battle rages on.

Special
Note the number of models in your Crew at the start of the Encounter. This Scheme must be announced.

Victory
Score 2 VP If you have more models in play at the end of the Encounter than you did at the start.
Score -1 VP if you have less than half as many models in play at the end of the Encounter as you did at the start.

Power Ritual (Arcanists Only)

You need to set up a complex ritual, get it done – fast!

Special
Your Crew's models may take a **(1) Interact** Action when they are within 8" of a corner of the table. Insignificant models cannot take this Action. This Scheme must be announced.

Victory
Score 1 VP if models in your Crew **Interacted** with all four corners of the table during the Encounter.
Score +2 VP if you complete this Scheme before the start of the 5th turn.

Sabotage (Arcanists Only)

A little sabotage causes no end of trouble for the opposition, and your Crew excels at it.

Setup
Secretly note a terrain feature on the opponent's half of the table.

Special
Models in your Crew may take a **(1) Interact** Action to Sabotage the terrain. Insignificant models cannot take this Action.

Victory
Reveal this Scheme and score 1 VP if the Sabotaging model is in play at the end of the turn it Sabotaged the terrain.
Announce: +1 VP.

Kidnap (Neverborn Only)

The residents of Malifaux tell stories about your Crew sweeping in and spiriting away its victims during the night. How right they are!

Special
Secretly note three of your opponent's Minions.

Victory
Score 1 VP if at least two of the selected models are not in play at the end of the Encounter.
Score +1 VP if all three of the selected models are not in play at the end of the Encounter.

Reclaim Malifaux (Neverborn Only)
Reclaim Malifaux for the Neverborn!

Setup
Split the table into nine equal sections,

Special
Models in your Crew within 1" of a terrain feature may take a **(1) Interact** Action with that terrain feature. Insignificant models or models engaged with an enemy model cannot take this Action. Mark the terrain feature with a Marker to indicate it has been Reclaimed. Both the terrain feature and the model's base must be in the section the model wishes to Reclaim. This Scheme must be announced.

Victory
Score 1 VP If you have Reclaimed at least six sections at the end of the Encounter.
Score +1 VP if you have Reclaimed all nine sections at the end of the Encounter.

Thwart (Outcasts Only)
Sometimes, preventing the opposition from winning is reward enough...

Special
You may not announce this Scheme.

Victory
Score 2 VP if your opponent does not earn VP for any of their announced Schemes.
Score 1 VP if your opponent does not announce any Schemes.

Gather Soulstones (Outcasts Only)
Making it out alive isn't nearly as fun as making it out rich.

Victory
Score 1 VP at the end of the Encounter if you have more Soulstones remaining in your Soulstone Pool than your opponent.
Announce: +1 VP.

Lilith's Weed

Named after the infamous Neverborn, Lilith, the unassuming stunted flower called Lilith's Weed is attributed many properties. The tale has grown that the seeds of the plant are Lilith's lust borne on the wind. If the seed lands on ground where blood has been spilled, the weed will grow. Parts of Malifaux teem with them.

Lilith's Weed has many medicinal and intoxicating properties. It's believed that a small dose of the root's extract will cause unabashed carnal desire in men and women, as well as produce euphoria. Larger doses let the mind wander into the realms of dreams and nightmares. Take too much and the mind will snap. Many simply smoke the petals for a sense of elation and expanded consciousness.

The Succubus Café is an example of a small but growing number of smoking parlors in the City. The Café is a mix of a hookah den and gentlemen's club. Smoking the flower's petals, mixed with scented tobacco, in either large water pipes or hand rolled cigarettes, patrons discuss the topics of the day. Poetry readings and musical sessions are also common on the Succubus' small stage. It's believed that the flower's leaves expand the mind's artistic consciousness.

Master Specific Schemes

Lay These Souls to Rest (Lady Justice Only)

"The souls of the innocent deserve peace. My Judge, we must lay these souls to rest."
– Lady Justice

Special

When an enemy Master or Henchman is killed, place an objective Counter in base contact with the model before it is removed from play. These Counters count as Corpse Counters, but can be picked up by anyone. Place objective Counters instead of Corpse Counters while there is a Graverobber in play. This Scheme must be announced.

Victory

Score **2 VP** if there are no enemy Masters or Henchmen in play, and Lady Justice is carrying at least half the objective Counters at the end of the Encounter.

Subjugate (Sonnia Criid Only)

"Your will is broken and your body is beyond repair. You have reaped what you have sown and now you must face the consequences. Your servitude will continue until your death." – Sonnia Criid

Victory

Score **1 VP** if you created a Witchling Stalker by casting the **Violation of Magic** spell on an enemy Master or Henchman during the Encounter.
Announce: +1 VP.

Family Justice (Perdita Ortega Only)

"It's not that I have a bullet with your name on it... it's that I have so many bullets in need of a good home" – Perdita Ortega

Victory

Score **1 VP** if you killed at least three models using **Execute** during the Encounter.
Announce: +1 VP.

Machine Spirit (C. Hoffman Only)

"I prefer machines. They wouldn't betray me."
– C. Hoffman

Victory

Score 1 VP if the only models left in play other than C. Hoffman are Constructs within 6" of C. Hoffman at the end of the Encounter.
Announce: +1 VP.

My Little Friend (Seamus, the Mad Hatter Only)

"It's not that I encourage him to be so bloodthirsty. He just wants to make me proud." – Seamus

Victory

Score **1 VP** if your Crew's Copycat Killer kills a model with a Soulstone Cost of at least 7.
Announce: +1 VP.

Precious Parts (Nicodem, the Undertaker Only)

"I do not need to animate the dead in order to subjugate my enemy. Sometimes the threat itself is enough to scatter his wits." – Nicodem

Setup

Divide the table into equal quarters.

Victory

Score **1 VP** if there are at least two Corpse Counters, not carried by or on the table within 1" of an enemy model, completely within each of at least three table quarters at the end of the Encounter.
Announce: +1 VP.

That One's a Keeper (Dr. Douglas McMourning Only)

"Everyone is not created equal. Their parts aren't either." – McMourning

Victory
Score 1 VP if McMourning gained at least five Body Part Counters from enemy Masters, Henchmen or Totems during the Encounter.
Announce: +1 VP.

Betrayed by Spirits (Kirai Ainkoku Only)

"I have no use for the bodies. It is the souls that provide the real strength." – Kirai

Victory
Score 1 VP if all enemy Masters and Henchmen were damaged at least once by a friendly Ikiryo.
Announce: +1 VP.

Do I Have To Do Everything Myself? (Ramos Only)

"Sometimes you have to get a little dirty" – Ramos

Victory
Score 1 VP if you kill at least one model with a Clockwork Fist **Strike** and one model with **Electrical Fire**.
Announce: +1 VP.

Reflections of December (Rasputina Only)

"I will bring upon them such a cold that the very air will freeze." – Rasputina

Victory
Score 1 VP at the end of the Encounter if you killed at least three models with spells cast through the **Ice Mirror** Ability.
Announce: +1 VP.

Primal Source (Marcus Only)

"We all must face the Beast Within. We are, after all, animals at heart." – Marcus

Special
This Scheme must be announced.

Victory
Score 2 VP at the end of the Encounter if at least four enemy models who gained the Beast characteristic during the Encounter died during the Encounter while they had the Beast characteristic.

Perfect Performance (Colette Du Bois Only)

"I'd say you caught me at my best dear, but I don't do off nights." –Collete

Victory
Score 1 VP if Colette's Crew has 7 or more Soulstones in its Soulstone Pool at the end of the Encounter.
Announce: +1 VP.

A Mother's Love (Lilith, Mother of Monsters Only)

"They need the blood to grow. I just like the taste." – Lilith

Victory
Score 1 VP if Lilith carries at least four Blood Counters at the end of the Encounter.
Announce: +1 VP.

Spread Sorrow (Pandora Only)

"I've seen Candy stab a man to death with those scissors and everyone knows Kade never hesitates to use that butcher's knife. But we all like my way best." – Pandora

Victory
Score 1 VP at the end of the Encounter If no enemy model was killed or sacrificed by you with a melee **Strike** or ranged **Strike**.
Announce: +1 VP.

Seeds of Betrayal (Zoraida, the Hag Only)

"My little poppets are the cutest little darlings, don't you think? Say...This one looks a bit like you." – Zoraida

Victory
Score 1 VP at the end of the Encounter if an enemy Master or Henchman was killed by an enemy model controlled by the **Obey** spell.
Announce: +1 VP.

A Bump in the Night (The Dreamer Only)

"I like to play games. Wanna play 'Hide and Seek'? You hide. I'll get'cha!" – The Dreamer

Victory
Score 1 VP at the end of the Encounter if the Dreamer's Crew killed at least two enemy models while there are no friendly Minions in play.
Announce: +1 VP.

Souless Life
(Leveticus, Steampunk Necromancer Only)

"There's a great power in death. Coming back once you know how to do it isn't the problem. It's the going that's such a bear." – Leveticus

Victory

Score 1 VP at the end of the Encounter if Leveticus has been killed or sacrificed in at least 4 turns of the Encounter.

Announce: +1 VP.

First Blood (Viktoria Only)

"I don't make money until the job gets done, so why wait to get started?" – Viktoria

Victory

Score 1 VP at the end of the Encounter if the first two models killed during the Encounter were enemy models.

Announce: +1 VP.

Pig Food (Som'er Teeth Jones Only)

"Damn pigs!" – Som'er Teeth Jones

Victory

Score 1 VP if Som'er Teeth Jones summons two Piglets with the **"Come and Get it!"** trigger when killing enemy models.

Announce: +1 VP.

Plague on Malifaux (Hamelin, the Plagued Only)

"The teeming rats and festering maggots are not harbingers of the End. Rather, they herald the beginning. " – Hamelin

Victory

Score 2 VP at the end of the Encounter if every enemy model killed was replaced by a Malifaux Rat.

Announce: +1 VP.

Badlands Fever

More and more people have been gripped by "Badlands Fever" in recent months. At first glance, the Fever seems to be nothing more than the same adventurous spirit that called out to humanity and led to the most famous discoveries and explorations Earthside and later the willingness to explore the land of Malifaux. Settlers, young and old, set out daily from the City, seeking to make a name for themselves, bitten by the Fever. Some seek to stake a claim of their own, while others search for a place to raise a roof and create a homestead. Collectively, they push out past the farthest settlements into the unknown frontier.

To date, none of these Fever-addled adventurers have been heard from again. Occasionally, trackers and scouts will come across long abandoned camps with bedrolls still rolled out and half-constructed farmhouses with no signs of struggle or evidence as to why their occupants left. Perhaps more unsettling are the personal items left behind, such as a boot or a watch, found well beyond the range of human settlement. Despite this, more and more settlers head out every day.

Some say the fever is more than a state of mind. Friends and family of the missing tell of a change that comes over their loved one. They seem more animated, or more reserved, often accompanied with new quirks in an otherwise stable personality. All were fueled by a need to head into the Badlands. Even those who successfully resist the call eventually end up glassy-eyed, mumbling to themselves. Though the rambling varies from one individual to the next, the message seems to appear again and again, "The desert must be fed."

Alone in the Dark

Racing through the narrow corridors beneath an ancient structure in the Guild Offices, the Guardsman wasted no time looking through the strange dungeons rumored to have once been used for torture by the once omnipresent Neverborn in the city. The uses by the Guild were not entirely dissimilar as these rooms had become their primary holding cells before trial and, though Guardsmen of his rank could never confirm the rumor, talk was that deeper levels of the catacombs housed other prisoners, human and otherwise. When asked, the Executioner seemed to enjoy ensuring the Guard that he certainly kept no one waiting in the basement for long.

Rounding a corner, deep beneath the offices of the Witch-Hunters, he found the Governor General and stepped quickly beyond two other Guardsmen without noticing the urgent expression each offered in warning to wait. He breathlessly exclaimed, "Sir, there is a matter that requires your attention." He realized too late that he was interrupting the Governor General's rant against Captain Gideon, bound in thick shackles beyond the reinforced open cell door. The Guardsman, regretting his transgression, bowed deeply and waited for the Governor's response.

The Witch-Hunters had the wooden doors, now dark gray with age, bewitched to withstand any force of brute strength or magical assailant that might attempt to escape. It was a dim, cold place, seemingly designed to eradicate any idea of hope or salvation. The monolithic walls and wrought iron bars communicated an atmosphere of inevitable doom, and the lengthy, winding corridors added a chorus of echoes to the Governor General's words as the Guardsman silently berated himself for speaking out of turn, though his matter required great urgency, commanded by Lady Justice, herself.

The Governor General regarded him as nothing more than an irritant, though he managed a look of disdain toward the young Guard before ignoring him completely. The Guard slowly retreated as the Governor turned back to the former Captain. "Do not think to speak to me in tones of superiority, Captain," he continued. "I am no man's subordinate, and you are in no position to make any demand."

"I fulfilled my end of the contract," Gideon responded calmly. "You agreed to-"

The Governor cut him off, barking, "Our *agreement* did not include the death of my only son, you trigger happy jackass!"

"You never mentioned the relationship he had with the girl. In all of *our* planning of the murder," he said, accentuating the Governor's involvement so that each of the Guards clearly heard, "you could have prepared me for that. Your son's death is on your head as much as it is mine."

The Governor stepped into the cell and backhanded Gideon. The blow sent the prisoner staggering back, and though Gideon desperately wished to fight, he could do nothing. "Do not think to put this upon me!" the Governor said between clenched teeth. "You'll hang with Jack Daw in the morning." The Governor spoke with a finality that allowed no argument. He beckoned to the Guard and together they left the chamber.

Gideon leapt forward as the heavy cell door closed with a resounding boom. "My wife needs that payment, General!" he bellowed through the food pass in the door. "You'll fulfill your end of this, you bastard!"

The Governor held one hand up to the Guardsman, about to speak, as he leaned toward the small slot and opened it to look eye to eye with Gideon. "What 'deal' do you speak of?" he asked.

"Don't you dare. We had an agreement. I threw away everything for you and your plan. My family needs this. You agreed."

The Governor General smiled. "Captain Gideon. Eyewitnesses report that the girl escaped from the balcony. The balcony of the room where you murdered my son."

"I killed her," Gideon said with certainty. "Afterward. I found her. I killed her."

"And her body? Where did you leave it?"

"At your mansion. At your mansion! Right in her quarters."

The Governor smiled sadistically. "I'm a fair man. I'll tell you what. You have until morning to prove that,"

"Let me out of here, and I'll be happy to."

"Hmm. That's the problem, isn't it?" the Governor said, releasing the thin metal plate of the hole.

Gideon shouted, "You owe me! I've given everything to you. I trained those men. I helped you claim this city. I am a loyal Captain of your Guard. My wife-"

"Captain?" the Governor shouted back. "You are no Captain of my Guard. You are a lowly mercenary. Desperate, pathetic. I will, of course, ship your remaining possessions Earthside to your young wife." He stood, turning to the Guard that interrupted him with calm irritation. "What?" he demanded.

"Sir," he began nervously. "The Lady, er, that is, Lady Justice, I mean, and the Death Marshals are calling for a quarantine guard on the Breach and the indefinite suspension of all rail travel out of the City," the guard explained the situation anxiously.

The Governor responded coolly, glancing sidelong at the cell door, a smile edging at the corner of his lips. "There is no issue in that," he said. "A short interruption in supply will artificially increase the market price on Soulstone. But a short interruption is all I'll tolerate. I want this plague quashed before it becomes a nuisance." More loudly, so that Gideon was sure to hear, he said, "Then, the train will not run."

"I'll see you in hell!" Gideon screamed from within as the Governor motioned for the other to leave. "You hear me? I'll be waiting for you in hell!" Gideon's curses echoed after the Governor General.

"The Lady reports that this is a disease, not the work of the Resurrectionists, though she requests you deploy Witch-Hunters to join her study of the problem," the young guard continued, visibly shaken by what he had witnessed, knowing the only good course for him was to forget the whole scene.

"Witch-Hunters? She suspects something of the arcane? Why would she suspect this?" the Governor asked.

"Sir, I apologize, but I do not have her full report as she urged me to bring this news to you with haste. I did overhear her speaking to the Judge, though, sir. Because of my, well, proximity. I had no intention of listening-"

"Yes. Go on. What did you hear?" he asked impatiently.

"That this disease is extremely strong though they could not understand how it could be passed to a person and then run its course in a matter of minutes rather than days. That's why Justice thought it might be a new Resurrectionist plot. I had trouble understanding the Judge, though, sir. He mumbles through that scarf he wears."

"His face is half rotted off," the Governor said as a matter of fact, though it startled the Guard to hear. "What do you think he said?"

"Maybe there's something new they have to find. The disease is spread through a bite of some animal, that he was certain. And any human in contact with these things, rats or some insect, he believes, gets infected. Although," the Guard hesitated, and swallowed uncomfortably, then said, "the Judge was touching that body and turning it over. He didn't seem too afraid."

The Governor smiled. "The Judge is a bit more resilient than some," he said. They ascended the worn brick steps as the Governor said, "So why the Witch-Hunters?"

"Well, there've been a number of sightings of a strange man that walks among the sick and the dead. They say he's been seen several times and doesn't show signs of the sickness. The Death Marshals have been deployed to bring him in for questioning, but Lady Justice wonders if this is something different than we've seen before, like I said. She wonders if there's something more arcane that a Witch-Hunter's expertise might shed some light on."

He led the boy to the internal offices of Sonnia Criid, head of the Witch-Hunter department, and the boy grew visibly more nervous and excited. When his day began, he could not have imagined that he would stand in proximity of the Judge and Lady Justice examining a crime scene, report directly to the Governor General, himself, and now he'd stand before the legendary Sonnia Criid as well. His eyes were wide as the Governor led him briskly past numerous scholars and deputized Hunters as they researched and studied their various assignments.

Entering her private study, though, he was disappointed that it remained dark and uninhabited, save the various clutter of artifacts and mystical apparatus on or below large books stacked haphazardly around the room.

The Governor General's fists clenched, and he growled, "Criid, Criid. Where do you think you've gone to now?" under his breath. Clearly agitated she was not at her post, he stepped to her desk, slowly turning a large sheet of parchment to examine it. The Guard leaned closer to see for himself. Upon her desk were many sheets of paper, all with numerous serpent sketches she had made.

He turned to the Guard and said, "Report to Lady Justice. This is a manhunt, and that's something we're good at. Draw up a profile and get it on the streets. Any individual that even remotely matches the description is to be shot on sight. We have a duty to get these trains back on schedule, after all." He continued to look over the manuscripts and drawings on the desk of Madame Criid. "Dismissed," he said, as he lifted another sheet of parchment, covered in images of a coiled serpent. The Guard made out the words, "Kythera," and "Tombers," in loose script

beneath overlapped drawings of the same snake image. He saw the Governor lift one sheet, in particular, and study it. It was a picture of stars with one large red star in the center. "Criid," he said to himself. "What do you think you're doing?"

For Gideon, there was no plague to fear. He had consigned himself to the gallows at the very moment he saw the Governor's son killed. Could even the unassailable Victor Ramos or the infamous Seamus stand against the fury of the Governor at the loss of his son? Even if they could, those titans would be hard pressed. He had risen through the ranks decisively and with honor. Now? Now he was nothing. He didn't have the resources or the allies necessary to escape the vengeance of Malifaux's tyrant. Ironic, then, that his life bringing law and order to the inhabitants of Malifaux – to risk his life regularly for others, would end with him on the Hanging Tree.

In these last days, alone in the bowels of Malifaux's most secure dungeon prison, Gideon discovered what isolation combined with the realization of death could do to a man. He could not sleep without the haunting gaze of the Governor's dead son and the shrieking of his lover. It was her eyes, though, that dominated his thoughts, and awoke him with a jolt. His eyes had met hers, just for a moment, before she disappeared over that balcony and into the dim morning light. In her eyes he had seen an unfathomable sadness. Though the two were merely children to him, they were more than young lovers finding a bond of the flesh. The look she conveyed was one of deepest loss - that Francis represented her only hope and her only desire. Without him, she lost not just a companion, but her very will died with the slaying of her lover. He considered his own wife Earthside and the quiet desperation she would have, awaiting news of him, her husband, and whether she would ever receive that news.

It's true that he did track the girl, rather easily, to her quarters behind the General's mansion. She had lunged at him with the long open blades of large garden shears, the only weapon she could find, though he disarmed her easily. She sobbed and struck upon his face and chest, knowing it was futile to attack a man so well seasoned and trained. He never laughed at her, though. Never mocked her. He pitied her, for he knew the anguish she felt in the finality of her separation from the man she loved. He felt it, too, for his family, which he hoped to save. But his hope withered.

"I will kill you!" she spat. She clawed at him and beat upon him. He endured those ineffectual blows. He witnessed her suffering and felt it within himself, too, because he had delivered that grief to her. She sobbed amidst screams until finally, overcome with grief and rage, the emotions and physical confrontation took hold of her and she gripped the front of the gray overcoat of Gideon's uniform. "I hate you," she sobbed over and over, pitifully crying while holding herself up against the man that had killed the only thing that gave her life any meaning.

He pulled her hands from his collar as gently as he could and she toppled back, falling beside the thatched bedding that was her mattress. Still sobbing, she picked up the garden shears again and held them open before her. Each blade was more than two feet long and as sharp as his saber. She looked at the throat of the device where the blades were linked, and he wondered if she would be able to impale herself upon them with enough force to end her life quickly. He doubted it. The dishonor of suicide would be unbearable, he thought. He had brought her to this state, and he needed the contract fulfilled, vile though he now regarded it.

"You will?" she asked him, her chest heaving. "You will kill me?"

He pulled his pistol and cocked it. She never blinked, but stared past the gun barrel at him, into his eyes. He steadied the weapon to end her, cleanly and with no pain. But he could not pull the trigger. Those eyes poured her pain and suffering into him and all he could see was his own wife, sitting there, helplessly sobbing for the loss of the man she loved. He had destroyed a part of her soul.

He regarded her for a long moment and contemplated his own life and the man he'd become. He wondered what his wife would say of him, as he was now, though she grew more desperate every day, too.

"Do it," she said, suddenly angry that he might not go through with it. She needed the release of death. She welcomed it. "Please. Please do this. End what you've begun." She could no longer tolerate living.

"I cannot," he said. "I am sorry."

She wailed in agony, hate, and desperation. She begged him to kill her.

"I'm sorry," he said again, turning to leave her. "If it means anything," he said over his shoulder, "you know I'm a dead man, too." He left his pistol, loaded and cocked at the ready, next to the entryway of her small room. She collapsed in anguish, her cries following after him. He was certain that though he could not end her life, she surely would. With his gun, it would be painless.

What chilled him, that day, facing that young girl, was the finality of her judging eyes. Rather than resolve herself to despair, for herself and the lamentation of the loss of her love, she looked upon him with unbridled loathing that he had never seen in one so young and full of grief. It was the cold certainty that the girl he found on the Governor's grounds would be the one to end him. In his cell, here, with the promise of the executioner's noose in the morning, he was still so certain that she would be the one to somehow claim his life.

Far below ground and with no torch or lamp to light the cell, Gideon contemplated his coming fate. The darkness did not comfort him, did not inspire him to sleep. Instead, his body was possessed of a great anxiety that kept his mind and his blood racing. His mind began to form shapes in the darkness, distant and indistinct. They were two orbs, side by side, and they looked down at him from overhead.

"You've come for me..." Gideon said with little more than a whisper.

Gideon knew these faintly glowing shapes were the almond eyes of that girl. They possessed that same sadness, that same detached certainty. He had seen those judging eyes a hundred times since leaving her. As he stared up at the glowing orbs, a ghostly apparition formed around them, slowly coalescing in a gossamer parody of Kirai's body. They were eyes, but the body they belonged to was twisted with grief and madness. He knew what he saw behind her eyes. He saw a spirit capable of the greatest depths of hate and malice he had never before imagined. It sprung from the great desperation of her unholy thirst for vengeance.

He said to the shadow, "You killed yourself, then? You killed yourself with my gun, Kirai Ankoku?" The shadow spirit did not respond. He couldn't tell if it even understood him.

The dim light of those eyes swelled, the ruddy glow extending to illuminate the interior of Gideon's cell, dispelling the darkness that had enveloped him. That light did not reveal cold, stone walls or thick iron bars but instead a chamber composed of visceral gore. The mortar between the bricks of the walls was slick with blood that flowed as if from deep lacerations of the flesh, and the bars high on the walls no longer absorbed the light with their dark metal surface but were the wet pink entrails of a man stretched taut, quivering slightly as if still alive. The chamber throbbed with a slow rhythmic pulse, as if it were some sort of creature, sustaining a monstrous beating heart.

Most horrifying was the chamber's floor, filled with a mass of butchered bodies, still writhing, refusing to accept their loss of life. Dismembered arms grasped blindly at the stiflingly humid air while severed legs kicked weakly at the organs twitching and quivering in the pile. A dismembered head with sinewy muscle dangling from the angular cut through the neck, sat atop the rest, its lips moving in slight gestures of speech or perhaps gasping for the breath that she once needed in life; its vacant eyes rolled slowly down from within her skull to stare at him unblinkingly. Gideon shrieked in maddened horror at the carnal images revealed to him and clawed at the fleshy walls in a desperate attempt to escape. Though the light from the apparition was dim, the heat within the cell quickly overwhelmed him, soaking his clothes with sweat. Deep in the bowels of the Witch-Hunters dungeon, no guard answered his desperate cries. No salvation came. There was no answer to his pleas for mercy.

The spirit hovered before him, smiling innocently. A faint hint of arms stretched toward him, indistinct and transparent. Like dust in sunlight, they reached out and touched his face, chilling him. As it did, he saw Kirai's thoughts and her emotions as they overwhelmed his own. It began tearing at his flesh in slow, deep lacerations. He could hardly tell, though, as the emotional pain of Kirai far surpassed the physical agony it inflicted. Still smiling innocently, as if it held

no malice toward him, it leaned closer to kiss him on his forehead with shadowy lips. Words formed in his mind as if he were speaking to himself, but it was her, the Ikiryo, he suddenly knew. "Your sin against me has earned you pain unending," it said. "The pain of the flesh is only the beginning of your suffering."

Gideon summoned the last of his self-control and courage. "It wasn't me alone," he said around the pain, and the spirit paused. Gideon said only, "The Governor General," before its ethereal claw reached out and took hold of his body, tearing him away from the wall. It picked him up and turned him, forcing him to confront that gaze, again. The spirit stared him down, those eyes piercing him to the very core of his soul. The ghost then tossed him to the floor. Blood-slick hands grasping at his body, jealously capturing him, eager for him to join the pit of their torment. It hung over him for a moment before descending to exact its final vengeance.

In the time that the Witch-Hunters had claimed the structure, none had ever escaped its prison. Even with the powerful practitioners who had been jailed there and the terrible magic they wielded, none had ever defeated its iron bars or thick brick walls. Though Gideon's howling cries of agony sounded for hours throughout the night, it wasn't until morning, when the hangman came for him, that his body was found. There was no sign of his murderer's entrance or departure, only evidence of the deed itself. Gideon's body was in a gruesome state. The bench in his cell had been broken into splinters and those splinters used to pin back the layers of his vivisected body. Gideon's mouth was frozen wide open, forever screaming, and now in silence. His frozen eyes, too, spoke of fear and pain and a longing for the anguish to end.

Upon the breadth of his forehead, carved into his flesh, was a Three Kingdoms Kanji symbol: 仇

After his retching stomach stilled, the hangman stumbled from the chamber to fetch the Officers of the Guild.

Gremlins

The remains of the gremlin shanty burned brightly and lit up the night. Hidden in the shadow of a large, mossy tree, the Ortegas made camp. As always, Perdita led the crew, her singular talents with the revolver and quick thinking made her an exemplary leader. "How these gremlins continue to survive is a mystery to me," Santiago commented as the group huddled around a stump.

"Yeah, this hunt'll be easy if they keep setting their own homes on fire." Niño was eager to add to the conversation and laughed meekly, pointing at the small shanty that finally collapsed, consumed by the blaze.

By the light of the building's dwindling flames, the group studied a map rolled out upon the stump. It showed a path through the swamp used by miners as well as the locations where gremlin raids had taken place. Gremlins had recently shown an alarming and growing interest in Soulstones. With no ability to mine the stones themselves, they took to raiding caravan routes near the swamp.

Perdita pointed to a spot on the map. "We're roughly here," she said. "Gremlins might not seem important enough for us to hunt, but things have changed. When the Governor General closed the northern caravan routes, we got reports of gremlin raiding parties that overtook them.

Santiago spat the thick brown of his chewing tobacco. "Naw," he said. "Must be those tiny Nephilim before they start growing. The lil' baby ones. Gremlins is dumber'n a sack of mierda.

"Something's changed. There's a clan leader that's been organizing them, arming them. We got plenty of reports of small raids including this big "boss" even before the Kythera incident. But now, we gotta do something about it. See for ourselves."

Francisco nodded. "The raid on the last caravan. Anything taken besides food 'n guns?"

"Si. That's the trouble. They left a lot of supplies but took all the Soulstones. There've actually been a few raids on Hollow Marsh, too."

Niño, sitting with his tio and the other fledgling recruits they brought along, and slightly apart from his cousins, suddenly piped in. "Soulstone? What's a gremlin need stones for?"

"That's what we're here to find out. The clan leader'll be in the middle of the biggest group of gremlins. We gotta find them and break them up some at the least."

"No problemo," Niño said. "What d'you say, Santiago? Five Guild scrip I can bag the big jefe gremlin before you!"

"Don't underestimate these creatures, hermano. Things can turn real ugly, real quick," Francisco warned with an exhaled breath of tobacco smoke. "Muy feo," he said in emphasis.

Just then, a quiet snort in the darkness startled them as a small boar nudged Niño's leg with its tusk. Before Niño even realized what was happening,

Perdita had drawn her revolver and shot the pig dead, with little more than a casual glance at the beast as she put it down in less time than it took Niño to recognize what it was. "Up!" she shouted and then the whole bog filled with a sudden cacophony of whoops and gunfire. However, before the others could draw their arms, a giant boar, nearly the size of a full grown bull, barreled into the camp. Its huge tusks gored into the midsection of one of the rookies and tossed him off into the darkness. Clutching desperately to the boar, a tiny, cackling gremlin held tightly to the thin row of bristles down the beast's back. In his other hand, he wielded his shotgun like a club, gripping the barrel to deliver a powerful blow to Papa Loco's head. As the heavy wooden stock of the weapon connected with the old man's skull, the weapon discharged into the gremlin's own face, blowing its head clean off its shoulders. The muzzle flash illuminated the gory event, inspiring the hysterical laughter of his fellows in the darkness. At the sound of the gun blast upon its back, the boar bucked, launching the remains of the corpse at Francisco who stepped aside from the projectile.

More gunshots sounded, and wherever there was a muzzle flash, the Ortegas answered with a round of their own. Niño's rifle had toppled into the muck at the first moment of bedlam, but Santiago had tossed him one of his pistols to keep the boy armed. Slowly, the group fell back from the ambush and into the light of the burning shanty. The towering fire penetrated the darkness into where the gremlins hid in the shadows, fire reflecting off their big eyes. More and more of their dark silhouettes could be seen just beyond the burning glow. One of the gremlins hefted an oversized bottle of alcohol and sucked on its mouth. A round from Francisco shattered the bottle and set the alcohol alight. In a

flash, the gremlin's body was consumed in fire, and he ran around madly before he tumbled into another gremlin, both falling into the bog.

"Where's Papa!?" Perdita shouted over the continuing rain of gunfire. At her side, Santiago fired his pistol with his left hand after catching a bullet in the shoulder.

"With his luck, that crazy bastard'll be the only one of us to walk out of this gunfight alive!" Santiago called out and then guffawed loudly, clearly enjoying himself. Not for the first time, Perdita wondered if he were crazier than their papa.

"We need to rout them! We're penned in, here!" she called out.

In an attempt to prove himself, Niño dove back into the darkness. The light was quickly shaded by the thick flora of the marsh, and Niño searched blindly through the water for the body of his unconscious uncle. The sounds of gunfire were slightly muffled by the swamp growth as he felt the distance grow between him and his family. In the darkness, he saw a glint of light. He squinted, trying to identify it. The distinctive sound of a shotgun being chambered quickly announced the presence of an armed gremlin in front of him.

It lifted its weapon, but before it could fire, Niño dove beneath the surface. Muffled by the water, Niño still heard the gun blast above him as it sent a shockwave through the water and rattled his bones. Lashing out, he grabbed the gremlin's legs and jerked them from underneath the beast. The two combatants waged their own private battle as the rest of the Ortegas continued to trade fire with the entrenched ambushers. They wrestled in the water until Niño finally came out on top. With a gasp for air, he leveled Santiago's revolver against the back of the gremlin's head and pulled the trigger.

The environment in Malifaux is notoriously harsh on firearms. The heavy Peacebringer revolver is prized for its reliability and its resistance against the humid, alkaline environment of this world. However, when Niño pulled the trigger of his weapon, a wet, defeated sound squished from the barrel. The gremlin turned its head, smiling a wide, toothy grin and leaped onto the boy, plunging him beneath the water's surface.

The gremlin stood above Niño, his hands around the hunter's throat, holding him struggling beneath the water. Niño kicked his legs and thrashed his arms, beating his fists against the water desperately. The pistol was still in his hand, and even as his lungs burned for air, he realized another fact about Santiago's weapons of choice. Gripping the weapon tightly, he lashed out at the gremlin's belly. The bladed grip of Santiago's pistol sliced open the gremlin's belly, and it released its hold on him. Leaping up for air, Niño was quick to capitalize on this sudden change in advantage. He pressed the attack, and with another quick slice, he slashed the creature's neck. Its body stilled, and Niño felt it sink slowly into the marsh.

"Muy bien," said the familiar voice of his uncle. "I was worried he had you, sobrino." He punctuated his words with applause. A large gash on his forehead dripped blood from the bludgeoning blow of the gremlin's attack moments earlier.

"Papa! Geeze!" Niño sloshed through the water and snatched the satchel from his uncle's shoulder before dashing away. As fast as he could, he struggled through the swamp and back to the others. Reaching the site of the burning shack, he sent the satchel sailing high over head, into the air and out toward the gremlin attackers. "'Dita!" he called out.

Perdita understood immediately. As the satchel soared though the air, she trained her pistol on it. Holding the weapon with both hands, she sighted down the barrel. She sucked in a deep breath and in that moment, the rhythm of her own heart was the only sound she heard. She counted down in time with that cadence of her pulse, waiting till the very

last instant before firing. Her bullet detonated the satchel full of dynamite, and the sound was like a hundred thunder blasts all striking at once. The sky lit up like daybreak, and the concussion threw the Ortegas to the ground. The ground shook, and the trees were cracked and bent away from the blast. Niño, himself so close to the detonation, sailed through the air to land limply in the bog. The blast served its intent, however. Gremlins not killed by the blast fled, and in the aftermath of the explosion, the roaring fire was the only sound to be heard.

When Niño woke, it was morning. The shanty had finished burning, and the camp had been moved near the blackened remains. Something was frying in pig fat over the campfire, and the smell of it roused him. Santiago was the first to notice the boy stirring and grinned widely at the sight. He clasped the boy tightly on the shoulder. "Looks like the boy'll live," he said to the others. "Get him a wedge of ham from the big one on the spit!"

Santiago's voice barely registered on Niño's still ringing ears. "You really saved the day." It was Perdita beside him. "We let our guard down and those damned swamp rats got the drop on us. If it weren't for you, they might have closed the trap."

As the group packed up camp, Niño grinned from ear to ear. It was high praise to earn a compliment from Perdita, and he was proud to finally earn her respect. She and Francisco discussed their next move while Santiago attended his wound and the gored gut of his cousin that had been tossed by the boar. They decided to travel to the second raid site and camp near the caravan trail. They'd send the others back to Malifaux with passing miners so that the kid could get bandaged up proper. Santiago refused to join them despite his own injuries.

Addressing the map, again, Perdita said, "This spot is near the area Criid wanted us to investigate," she said, pointing to the map. "We'll head there. If we encounter any gremlin shanties, we'll deal with them on the way."

Tools of the Trade

Although Colette owned the Star, Ramos showed no hesitation in stepping into the dressing rooms backstage. Showgirls in compromised states of undress covered themselves quickly, their mannequin constructs reacting to their urgency, covering their assigned showgirl as best they could, despite his seeming lack of interest in their bodies. Colette saw him enter. Although they were all still recovering from their recent attack in the sewers, she had to smile when Cassandra stood and approached him directly. She wore her stockings but little else save a sweet smile. Cassandra pushed the man more each time he "visited" them backstage, presenting more of her bare flesh each time. "He's still a man, Colette," she'd say.

Ramos was the primary shadow investor of the Star, and his involvement in its renovations was concealed in order to mask his association with the theater. The precautions he took with his finances didn't seem to carry over into actual practice.

"Unless you're part of his plan, Cassandra," Colette explained, "you might as well not exist."

"I hate to be immodest, Colette, but I'm not used to being ignored. If he thinks he can just come and go in our private rooms, I'll at least get him to acknowledge me. You'll see," she said. "Next time."

True to her word, the next time had come and she walked toward him, bare-chested, a smile on her face. Other showgirls snickered into their palms and Colette once more had reason to be thankful for her presence. All of them needed her bawdy bravado to help get over the shock and fear they'd recently experienced.

"Professor!" Cassandra said, approaching him with arms outstretched, implying that the two would embrace. "If I had known you were coming, I'd have worn something more formal." Her head lilted to the side, mocking a simplicity of mind the others knew was far from reality, and she fluttered her eyes at him seductively.

As Colette had predicted, though, he looked resolutely beyond one of Malifaux's most sought celebrities and brushed briskly past her, only fleetingly irritated that he had to shift his path.

Cassandra shrugged toward Colette, clearly shocked, though still smiling. Colette shook her head as an automated mannequin attended her, the internal clockwork gears spinning and humming as its linen-wrapped limbs draped a silk robe across the shoulders of the Master Magician.

Like the secret vault beneath the Star, very few individuals ever had an opportunity to visit this place. The treasures kept here were of a much different nature than those below. It was a room filled with gossamer curtains and silken, lacey articles of clothing strewn throughout. It smelled heavily of exotic perfumes and possessed a slightly cloudy atmosphere from the powder applied liberally to the girls' faces. An impressive array of props was stacked haphazardly - trick mirrors, boxes with false bottoms, and blunted stage swords.

Colette's mannequin worked diligently at assisting its mistress dress and apply her makeup. Once Ramos stepped within five feet of her, though, the mannequin spun to face the intruder it sensed. All mannequins were designed to discreetly function as bodyguards for the performer to which they were assigned. The graceful constructs serving

Colette and Cassandra were something a bit more threatening. Colette's mannequin spun blindingly quick and a high pitched spinning of gears within its arms and chest caused twin scythes to release from hidden chambers within the forearms. The long blades snapped forward with a clack, and the creature held them above its head like a strange and lethal praying mantis. It twirled into a crouch, looking very much like the graceful dancer it was constructed to imitate. It lifted its arm blades to strike. Colette didn't bother to rein it in as she knew Ramos could handle it easily. Indeed, he stared it in its blank linen face and motioned dismissively with his two forefingers as if batting a gnat. The Coryphée mannequin hung its head obediently, and the arm blades closed back into the hidden chambers in its forearms. Obeying Ramos, it returned to attend Colette, following his silent command without hesitation.

Colette's mechanized mannequin whirred and hummed as it returned to help her apply her make-up and fix her hair. Ramos stood behind her, his hands patiently clasped behind his back, making her uncomfortable. "I lost a girl down there, Victor," she said, mustering her courage against the formidable man. They know it's dangerous work, but none of them expected to die like Margaret did. It's shaken them up."

"It's no matter, Colette," he answered dismissively. "The Governor General has called for quarantine. Security's increased to a paranoid state at the Breach. Our operations are temporarily suspended until we see the Guild's precautions stabilize. I'm not sending anyone out there without knowing exactly what to expect at Malifaux Station. Still, it's not unreasonable for me to check after my investments."

She sighed, irritated that he missed the entire point about losing a girl as he focused only upon his plan and how to recover from a setback. She stifled it, though, as she replied, "The shipment of texts was lost, spilled into the sewer channel." Ramos winced, showing more emotion than she'd seen before. "The other two carts were abandoned. If we venture down there again, we may be able to recover them. I don't know."

Ramos lifted an eyebrow. "Was anything salvaged?"

Colette rose, tying her robe, and moved across the room to open a chest in the corner. "I was able to carry this sack of Soulstones out with me. It was a fine thing I did, too." She withdrew the sack and carried it over to her vanity. "I'm not sure we would have made it out of there without them."

Ramos opened the sack and drew out each stone, appraising them one by one. He laid them upon the vanity. Each glowed with the primal energy of magic. The other girls in the dressing room paused to gaze at the precious objects. It was clear that these stones were of a superior grade. Even those few that had laid eyes on sorcerer grade Soulstones had never seen stones of such brilliant clarity or significant size. These were the treasures of this world that the lords of Malifaux struggled so desperately to possess. One stone lacked the beauty of the others. Its glow was like a candle's flame shining through a whiskey bottle. It did not possess the sharp, faceted edges of its fellows or their crystal clarity.

"What is it?" asked Colette curiously.

Ramos lifted his hand and gestured for the room to be cleared. Several of the girls frowned at the gesture but none of them argued as they all quietly feared him. They filed out of the room without a sound, leaving Ramos and Colette alone. Though they knew Ramos intended their conversation to be private, the girls huddled around the door, pressing their ears against it in an effort to eavesdrop. Behind them, though, were the sound of heavy footfalls and a gruff man clearing his throat. His dark complexion and mohawk marked him as a native of the west, a tribe from the northwest coastal region. While many of these western natives were considered savages, their wilderness skills have allowed a number to enter the Breach and be employed as scouts. This man seemed to have bucked that stereotype, and when he adjusted his dark glasses, he asked in a suggestive tone, "Don't you ladies have something better to do?"

The girls stormed off to busy themselves with tasks backstage. "You can forget about that special dance, tonight, Joss." Joss didn't seem too concerned and didn't seem to have any issues with eavesdropping on Ramos and Colette, himself, as he took a stand against the dressing room door. They talked as tough as they could, but all had a

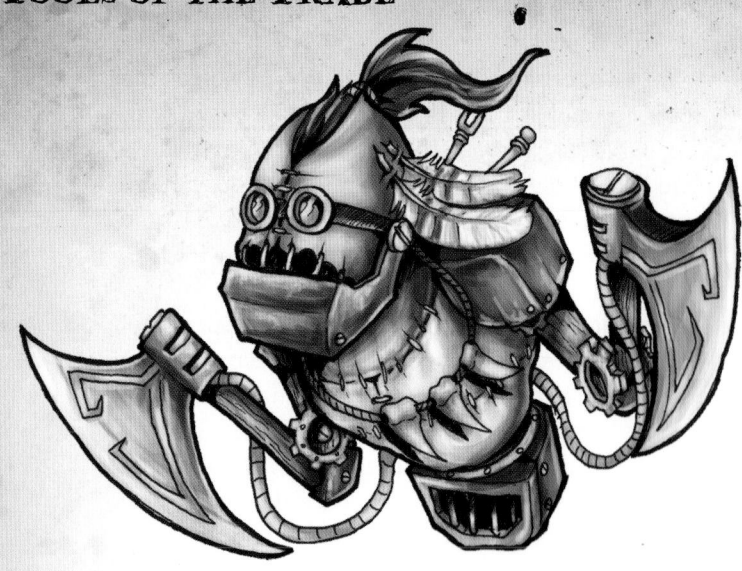

fear of the bulky tribesman. Cassandra, though, lingered behind as the others busied themselves with other backstage endeavors and took a position next to Joss against the door. He opened his mouth to chastise her, to usher her away, too, but the sharp arch of her eyebrow and the ominous sidelong glance warned him that he would be wise to let it be. He reluctantly submitted, understanding that this woman was something a bit different than the typical showgirl. He stood silent beside her, grinning rather foolishly. Like so many men, he decided he was in love with her, though he could not tell if it was more because of her beauty or her dangerous demeanor. Finally, he decided it was because she smelled like heaven.

"This is a particularly valuable gem," Ramos said within the dressing room. "It was developed at Hollow Marsh as part of an endeavor known as Project Leviathan."

"The Leviathan? It's real? I'd heard the rumors, of course, but I didn't believe them," Colette asked incredulously.

"It is real, indeed."

"If you possess such a weapon, why do you not use it to destroy the Guild, outright?"

He sighed. "Let this stone be your answer." Ramos lifted the gem in front of an electric lamp. The light glowed warm amber and made a silhouette of the spider trapped deep inside. When she looked in the stone the sewer, however, she didn't notice that the spider seemed to be perched upon a tiny web. She inspected the stone more critically, her eyes

peering into its heart. What appeared to be a web was actually a cluster of tiny fractures.

Collette asked, "It's cracked?" in a whisper.

"That's right. The process that produced this stone is very expensive and very experimental. Even after all the years that we have known Soulstone, we still do not understand the method of its form and function. This stone was an attempt to emulate a power we cannot detect, cannot perceive. Though the result was powerful, it ultimately proved insufficient to animate the Leviathan for any extended period of time. Without a stone of sufficient quality, The Leviathan is nothing more than a slumbering titan. This stone no longer possesses the motive force necessary to operate that machine. I had arranged to sell the stone to an interested party who did not know its origin, but with the Guild Quarantine as well as other lost valuables, that deal is off."

"I understand. That was the client I was intended to meet with."

"Yes," he said. "You're a clever woman, Miss DuBois, and your contribution to the Movement has not gone unnoticed," he said in reference to the growing Arcanist resistance. "I understand the loss you suffered to your staff but I have a feeling that times will be difficult for us for the foreseeable future. You may be asked to perform additional sacrifices and I can't have you doubt your place in our organization. I've worried that your mastery of arcane magic, though impressive, falls short of my typical expectations." His brutal honesty hurt, but she knew his opinion of her and others were always sharply critical. "Your control over the finer nuances of the forces of magic requires constant Soulstone fuel and I worry that supporting you as a true master in the organization would be too costly." He was silent as he regarded her, not really as a person, but as a tool to fulfill his own agenda. He eventually said, "When our trade resumes, I will send a message to our client Earthside that The Eye of the Leviathan has been lost and is no longer available. Let this stone be the compensation you are due for your loyal service."

Ramos held the stone before the light for a moment longer before handing it to her. Though it could no longer satisfy the voracious appetite of the colossal Leviathan, its deep well of power was still far from

extinguished. Colette could feel that considerable power as alluring warmth in her hand. She had felt that power coarse through her, and it was enough to burn her out if she had let it. It would be a valuable tool if such trials as Ramos described were truly on the horizon.

Colette took a moment to study the stone in her grip before meeting Ramos' gaze, "What do you mean? Sacrifices?"

With an emotionless and detached tone, Ramos responded, "No one is greater than the Movement, Miss DuBois. We will have need of you."

Colette had always known the power of Ramos' charisma and the convincing quality of his passion. She could feel its potent effect on her in this moment. Being a performer, she understood well the importance and power of presence. This immunized her to a small extent against the force of Ramos' considerable will. Where another might have been bowled over and drawn in as a loyal sycophant, that power had another effect on her. It frightened her. She could see in his eyes that he knew the power he held over her, too.

The tension broke suddenly when Joss entered the room, Cassandra behind him with arms folded, looking cross. "Boss, the theater's starting to get crowded. The girls are going to need to go on, soon."

"Yes, of course. Show them back in, Joss." Ramos said, dismissing his associate. In a lowered voice, one meant only for Colette, he said, "There is a reason I chose you for this, Miss DuBois. You will not be mastered, you will not be led. I will need strong allies such as you in the months ahead."

Before Colette could respond, her girls filed back into the room and hurried about, rushing to complete their preparations for the show, their mannequins moving as quickly as they could to keep pace. Ramos made his way to the door and turned to remark with one last comment. "Break a leg, tonight, Miss DuBois. I've been looking forward to your act." He paused at the door and said over his shoulder, "And when the show is over, I expect you'll recover my 'shipment' left in the sewers." He left without another word as the girls looked hopelessly from one to another.

Colette DuBois performed as she did every night, and none in that audience were any wiser to the clandestine activities she perpetrated in the late hours after the show ended. Her dealings with captains of industry, mercenaries, and petty crooks were far beyond the wildest imaginings of the simple miners that watched her, now. They had no concept of the true nature of the Union they supported so fervently. Their only value was in the labor they performed and the violence they could be inspired to perform.

As she demonstrated her talents for stage magic, she looked out across the crowd and saw Ramos lift his drink toward her, as isolated in the back as he could be with such a crowd of men clustering about. Even after the dramatic nature of their conversation and the grim subjects they discussed, she couldn't help but smile.

As she considered the clueless masses that filed into this theater for drink and show, she realized that she wasn't so different from that man, after all.

Finding New Purpose

"May this soul, and the souls of all the faithfully departed, through divine mercy, rest in peace," the priest said, offering the final rights to Francis, the Governor General's son.

Gathered around the grave were many officers of the Guild as well as those men and women who knew Francis in life. All were somber, and each held a candle before them.

The Governor General stepped forward and spoke in a soaring rhetoric, eulogizing his son. "We are but pioneers in a strange and forbidding new land," he said to the throng. "Pioneers that risk life for future liberties. We have come here to return magic to a world that has seen it wane," he said referring to Earth, "and we make sacrifice every day, hoping — no, knowing that our sacrifice is to better our way of life and the lives of our children. We endure great hardships. We endure the suffering brought upon us by savage creatures native to the wilds of this world. We endure the suffering brought upon us by misguided mobs bent against their own logic and manipulated against their own will to bring violence upon our own," he said in reference to the recent rebellion.

Many Union members in the audience shifted uncomfortably, but coming from the Governor as he stood over the pine casket housing his son, they somewhat reluctantly nodded in mild agreement. "My son paid a great price with his sacrifice. He came here, not in the hope to build his own empire, not to make his own mark, but to help you build a new empire in a new world! He was an artist and a poet, and I often criticized his overly romantic notions as irrelevant. I'm sorry now to realize that his purpose was to remind us of why we make those sacrifices. To remind us why we struggle. And his sacrifice was met with jealousy or rage or some two-bit attempt to strike out at me," he said, motioning toward a hastily dug grave in the cemetery where the remains of Officer Gideon, former Captain of the Guard, had been buried that same morning. Guardsmen glanced toward it nervously, aware of the unmarked grave given to him for his dishonor. No one understood just how much this eulogy twisted the story to the Governor's own political agenda as he continued. "We must bury one of our innocent today. But we must remember his sacrifice and why it was made. Not as another cheap attack upon me by the ignorant but as a reminder of how precious our time is. Let us use this as an opportunity. An opportunity to come together and build an empire that is unassailable and unshakable!"

The crowd applauded, not aware that his eulogy had shifted to a political stump-speech.

Once he ended, though, and the priest offered a final invocation over the box, the mourners felt the resounding words of the Governor General's speech echo within them as he intended. Words of "sacrifice" and "unity" struck them, and they felt the loss of the innocent. They blamed one of their own, as the Governor General intended them to. They mourned Francis more for their own guilt in thinking thoughts against the Guild and chastised themselves for their thoughts of rebellion and discontent and of forgetting the reason they had to unify rather than fragment. Even the sky over Malifaux seemed to mourn the passing of this man whose knowledge of love had tempered the heart he inherited from his father. It was a dim morning and the nebulous clouds above swirled in an uncertain wind. A dynasty that might have been redeemed was lost. They buried that hope as they slowly lowered the young man's casket.

Through the crowd pushed a tall, slender man. He walked with a cane but his movements possessed a refined grace. He wore a long, black coat, cut tightly upon his gaunt frame, and a tall hat rose on his head.

His hawk-like nose supported the polished lenses of his spectacles, opaque in the reflected sun. Behind him, a portly man wearing a round bowler hat and a trench coat, dirty at the edges, began shoveling dirt onto the casket. The tall man patted the Governor on the shoulder and gestured for him to turn away from the grave so he wouldn't need to watch the grim scene.

"My condolences, Governor," he said with a gravelly baritone. "Your son seemed a capable heir to your legacy. His loss will be a deep scar upon this City." The man's voice communicated well his cultured demeanor with a tone perfectly tuned to the situation.

"Yes, fine, Nicodem. Attend your duties." The Governor dismissed the man even as Nicodem bowed deeply and turned away from him to conference with his gathered marshals. Nicodem suffered this discourteous dismissal with the same grace that underlay everything he did. He rose slowly and turned back toward his associate, Mortimer, to leave the Governor to his private business. "Bless you, your Lordship, you and your house."

This blessing went unheard as the Governor General's attention refocused on his personal staff. Amidst the wide-brimmed hats of his Marshals, the Governor General found the thin man, Hoffman. The accent in this man's voice clearly distinguished him as a transplant from the King's Empire. He had a stern and almost perpetually humorless expression on his face and dressed sharply, as befits a man from that cultured kingdom. In a leather harness, he wore a brace to support his back, and the length of his legs were assisted by buzzing servos set in polished bronze struts. He held one of his arms across his waist in the grip of the other. The Governor addressed him, saying, "Mr. Hoffman. Have you settled into your new office?"

"Yes, sir. Thank you for inquiring. I've made good use of my time to familiarize myself with daily operational procedures as well as the impressive facilities available. In short order, I've redesigned several prototype systems, all improving upon basic system architecture-" The Governor General cut him off, clearing his throat and staring at him with a look of impatience. "Sorry, sir," Hoffman said. "Just excited. I've also begun to research the primary charge of my office."

"Unfortunately, I need you to suspend your investigations into the Arcanist ties."

The Governor looked over his shoulder, not at his son's grave, but at a series of five fresh mounds one hundred yards distant, belonging to five other men been buried there that same morning. All of them had suffered a fate similar to the mysterious murder of Captain Gideon. Each of them had been ritually slain, their bodies surgically cut open, and their hearts removed. All had been Guild officers. Several disturbing elements to the murders puzzled him and left even Lady Justice at a loss for explanation. Each Guild officer had been slain within private quarters, or, most disturbing to him, within Guild offices themselves. The Governor would quickly look into the connections each officer held within the ranks, but at least two of them he knew were assigned directly to Gideon.

He also did not like the way the murderer mocked him and his men with what the Judge called a "signature" mark. Upon the forehead of each victim, the murderer engraved a very precise Three Kingdoms script. Guild officers had begun to analyze the meaning, but so far, their Asian scholars found the interpretation somewhat difficult to comprehend.

"This new killer is your primary concern, now," the Governor said to Hoffman. "He has the ability to strike into the Guild's most secure installations. Until he is captured, no officer is safe."

"Of course, sir," Hoffman said. "But my expertise is in mechanika, not the pursuit of killers. Certainly not those practicing magic of subterfuge and obfuscation. I'm not exactly known for keeping a low profile," he said, rapping a knuckle on the metal of his assisting machinery. "Madame Criid, sir, would be better equipped-"

The Governor General cut him off. "Ms. Criid is…" he paused, searching for the right words, but his tightly clenched fists conveyed some frustration Hoffman was not privy to. He couldn't know that Sonnia Criid had recently taken herself beyond the Malifaux city lines on some quasi-official expedition according to the last notes she left. He couldn't know that the Governor found her recent independence just short of the same level of insolence the Union had been demonstrating. "Ms. Criid has other duties at the moment," he lied. "Do your best, Hoffman. You'll return to your assigned appointment shortly."

"It will be as you wish, sir." The man lifted his arm and gestured to a pile of metal squatting humbly nearby. A whir of gears sounded as the construct awoke and the machine rose from its haunches to reveal its true shape. It was a Hunter Class construct, now perched on its nimble legs. It quickly approached the side of its master. Hoffman took hold of a mechanism high up on the construct's shoulder and stepped awkwardly up onto a riveted brace near its hip. With the rig now moving in perfect unison with his crippled body, the man managed a rather stately pose as he rode aside his mechanical assistant. "I will review the case files, and I am certain I can construct a profile and bring the guilty party to swift justice."

"You are dismissed, Hoffman," the Governor said before following after the slowly departing procession. Hoffman's construct bore him away in a cloud of smoke and steam and loud clanking of metal articulation of its legs.

In short order, only the undertaker and his assistant remained on site.

Nicodem stood, leaning against his cane, and watched his assistant labor with the pile of earth. They were silent for a long time as Nicodem had no need to fill the space with needless chatter. He turned his gaze up at the churning clouds overhead as Mortimer filled the grave. The Malifaux sky was almost continuously filled with dim clouds that masked the sun of this world. Eventually he said, "The goodly Governor General requested that precautions be taken to prevent reanimation of his departed son's body. Did you see to that, Mortimer?"

The portly gravedigger stuck his shovel in the ground and turned to lean on it. He fixed Nicodem with his eyes and chomped on the butt of a half-smoked cigar before taking it out. "No suh, I did not." Mortimer scratched his sweat-soaked head in confusion.

Nicodem grinned a malevolent smile at his assistant's response. "That's a good man." Mortimer didn't understand the joke but laughed and winked all the same. Nicodem turned to leave Mortimer to finish his labor and strode a short distance to the gates of the cemetery. He took his time to complete the journey, and when he reached the entrance, he drew out a cigarette case from his coat.

The application of arcane art manifests differently in every person. Their abilities, their manipulation of those flowing energies, developed as unique as a fingerprint. Nicodem was aware of the dead bodies buried around him as he walked. It wasn't that he could see them, or even feel those corpses — he just knew they were there. With a slight press of his will, he could discern those that would most easily rise to obey him. All of those individuals adept in the Resurrectionist arts felt that oddly intangible connection with the rotting flesh of once living vessels, longing for some will to once again animate them.

Nicodem's awareness of the dead was considerable. As he walked casually from the fresh grave, the habitual probing of his mind struck something in the magical aether that was at once extremely familiar and then completely foreign. He concentrated his will against the taut fabric of magic that coursed in and around him and he grew aware of a blighting of the energies that might be used to reanimate the dead. They were the energies of death and reanimation that he had an intimate affinity with, but somehow... opposite of his understanding.

As he reminded himself, mastering the magical arts manifested differently in every person. He was seeing something strangely phenomenal; her connection to death was at least equal to his own. He could also discern from whence that feeling originated.

"You have nothing to fear from me, girl. Come on out. They've all gone," he said. Nicodem could see a girl hiding behind a nearby tree. When he spoke to her, she ducked behind it, again. "Come. I can see that you mourn. Let me accompany you to his place of rest." Kirai hesitated, afraid, but her desperation to see Francis, even at his final repose, grew far too great to ignore, despite the danger of walking in the open. She wore a modest black silk Kimono of tradition, though Nicodem saw she was clearly embarrassed that she did not have the accompanying accoutrements, probably because of her low station and meager means. Meekly, she left her hiding place and approached the side of the courteous undertaker. The man put his hand on the girl's shoulder and led her gently toward the grave. Mortimer had finished his task and beat the earth flat with the back of his shovel. As the two approached, he stepped quickly aside, knowing his presence often disturbed the grieving. Once beyond Nicodem, though, he motioned with his shovel, pointed to his head, and then to her, the smile on his toadish face revealing his hopeful expectation. Nicodem shook his head and motioned for the gravedigger to leave them.

Kirai fell to her knees beside the grave and lay prostrate over the fresh mound of earth, weeping. Even Nicodem felt the great disturbance of self-pity and saw it consume her. He knew, then, that she had little to live for. He had to be careful lest he push her too hard in the wrong direction. Yet he knew the vast depths of her grief might have been the very catalyst to allow her to manifest her connection with the dead.

She felt a touch against her arm. That contact drew her back from the pit of her despair.

"You will honor his memory in life more than in your death, child," Nicodem spoke with a soothing and warm whisper.

Kirai opened her eyes. Tears blurred her vision and her body refused to move even an inch. "I cannot live without him," she said, her breath catching. "Nothing matters."

Nicodem knelt beside the girl and shook his head. "Hmmm. Yes. It is difficult to go on, I know. Because you could not join the mass eulogizing the lad, I must assume you and he shared something private. Very personal. A secret only the two of you shared?"

She nodded though he could have said the same to any grieving loved one at a funeral, and they might have each said the same. Something about this girl, though, led him to believe the lovers shared something beyond the norm.

Despite her painful grief, Kirai could not help but be comforted by the man's presence. In the days following Francis' death, she had been alone with no one to show her any compassion. Guards searching for her had kept her from going home, and the staff of the Qi and Gong had turned her away. She gazed up at the man. In front of this stranger, she tried to compose herself, wiping her nose on her sleeve. His sympathetic gaze, though, invited her to resume her mourning, "What is the point?" she sobbed before collapsing against him, throwing her arms around his shoulders.

He held her like that for a while beside the grave of her lover. She cried until her body was exhausted from it and no more tears would come. Still he held the girl for some time after she had gone limp in his arms. In time, Nicodem's soothing tone came, again, as he said, "I have seen loss such as this. You believe you are lost as well. You have nothing left to live for?" She nodded. "You live so that you can carry on his memory, of course," he said, sweeping his arm toward the grave. "There is still more for you to do, child."

Kirai sniffled and lifted her eyes, looking up at the man's bespectacled eyes. Still so meek, her voice came in little more than a whisper, "What can I do?"

He smiled. "You have already done so much, and you do not even realize." Nicodem rose and took the girl by the hand.

A discreet distance away, Mortimer was busy leaning against a tree, examining the gnawed stump of his unlit cigar. As they approached, Nicodem said, "Mortimer. Dig up this casket," motioning to the unmarked grave, still freshly dug.

"Sir? I went an' put 'im in the ground just this mornin'," Mortimer protested. Nicodem said nothing though, and Mortimer begrudgingly complied and began digging at the mound he had just packed hours earlier.

While Mortimer labored, Kirai did nothing at all. She had detached herself from the others, certain that her very reason for living had already been buried. Nicodem, meanwhile, studied the girl and carefully considered the actions of the previous days and the alarming discovery he had made of this young woman and her link with the power of spirituality.

Finally, with a heave and grunt, Mortimer had the casket thrust back out into the open.

Nicodem slowly said, "I do not mean to alarm you child, but there is something you need to see. There is a corpse in this box. Are you prepared to see it?"

"Why?" she asked numbly. Kirai felt overwhelmed and looked longingly over her shoulder at the grave of her lover.

"You know the man in this box, and he will show you the proper way to honor your lost beau."

Nicodem had chosen his words carefully. Though this girl wanted nothing more than to expire at the side of her lover's grave, the word 'honor' held significant weight with her. The dead were meant to be honored, memories of them celebrated. They were words that tugged at her commitments to tradition. After several long moments looking back at Francis's grave, she glanced at the emerald studded ring on her finger. It seemed to her that it throbbed in time with the beating of her heart. Looking up at Nicodem, again, she nodded her head.

Even if his guess about her proved incorrect, she would be valuable to him in other capacities. The body within the pine casket would bring their journey to a new understanding. Nicodem opened the casket to reveal the ruined remains of Gideon, the killer of her lover and the first victim of this powerful new killer before him. Though the coroner had stitched much of him back together, the violence he had experienced could not be hidden. The horror he had felt was frozen in his features, an expression of terrified madness. Despite the mutilation, Kirai did recognize him. She would never be able to erase the image of him from her mind. She clasped her hand over her mouth and stood frozen looking down at the dead man.

"He is the one. And now he's dead?" Kirai's voice was soft and distant, though she could not believe that he could be dead so soon after killing Francis. "Then it is finished," she said. "There is nothing left. I thought to confront him after speaking to Francis." Her words came with difficulty and her accent thick in her exhaustion. "He left his pistol with me. So that I might kill myself. I intended to confront him and fulfill his wish." She withdrew Gideon's pistol from her Kimono. She looked upon it emotionlessly.

Nicodem placed his long fingers upon it, gently pressing it away from her. "You will not need this, young lady." Her dark eyes looked up at him, conveying her desire to end her pain the only way still available to her.

"You saw him in his cell, didn't you?" Nicodem asked with a suddenly forceful tone. "You found Captain Gideon still alive!" His urgency frightened her. Gone was the genteel man comforting her. He was strong and commanding and fierce.

Her eyes widened with fright, and she fell backward, scrambling on the ground. "No, no, that's impossible..." Nicodem grabbed hold of Gideon's torso, pulling it from the box and dropped it face down before her. Carved on his forehead was a Kanji symbol, now purple and black from the drying blood and brutality to the flesh. Her eyes widened as the memories came, memories she had hidden from herself. The blood slickened walls, the cage of entrails, the sound of Gideon's screams as his torso was cut, as his ribs were split open. Her vision faded into darkness, and she felt herself falling, tumbling into unconsciousness. In that darkness, however, she saw two ruddy orbs glowing like beacons in the mist. They approached her quickly, and their dim light revealed an indistinct form. The spirit reached for her, and as she fell, she reached out for it in return.

Her fingers met the spirit's, and at the contact, there was a sudden arc of energy that jolted her into consciousness, again. Breath surged into her burning lungs and she gasped, "I... I... it was me...I killed him?" she asked. She was suddenly aware of the truth though she didn't understand it. "I killed him," she said with finality.

Standing above her was the towering undertaker who bent over and reached out for her, "Yes, child. Come. We have much to speak of."

Ruins in the Bayou

While Perdita's crew struck into the heart of the bayou, just a few miles away and under a column of smoke was a small prospector's camp that had been forcefully commandeered by a company of hungry gremlins. One of the creatures, equipped with a roughly shaped machete, worked at quartering and butchering a horse. Nearby, a pair of wiry creatures hefted a giant earthenware cauldron into place over a campfire. As the butcher finished a cut, he tossed a hunk of horse meat into the simmering water.

"Why we eating horse again?" squawked one of scrawny gremlins. "You know I likes the piggies better!"

"We needs 'em. That's why." It wasn't the butcher to answer but a large, fleshy gremlin that towered over his companions. "We needs our piggies fer thuh fightin'." His body wasn't the only thing that was larger, the creature held a huge blunderbuss against his shoulder, his finger stroking the trigger as if he were eager for a reason to use it. Though a relic by human standards, just a museum piece at best, the gun was not only much longer than the other guns they "liberated" from the miners, but its muzzle was so big he could put a whole fist in the end of it. Bigger meant better in almost all cases, so the gun was another reminder that he was the boss. The monster lumbered into the camp and sat his lumpy body next to the fire. He stretched his legs out and the nubs of his toes wiggled in the open soles of his worn out boots.

"Ahh, Jones, I didn't mean nuthin' by it, honest I didn't," the smaller gremlin pleaded.

Jones grumbled but said nothing, and the gremlins around him went back to their former distractions. Then he thought the better of it and picked up the little gremlin by the back of the neck, kicking and flailing, frantically trying to escape the bigger one's grip. Jones tromped through the mud to a makeshift pigpen beside their camp and tossed him over the fencing. He fell amid the smaller pigs in the mud and filth.

The gremlin camp went into an uproar at the sight of one of their own amidst the piglets and adolescent boars. The boars began to charge and knock the gremlin about, and in a panic, he began jumping and weaving amongst the hungry beasts much to the delight of the onlookers. Having the attention of the entire troupe on him though caused the mud-covered gremlin to get creative in his dodging of the animals, waiting to the last moment to jump out of the way, pulling their tails, and playing up to his riveted audience. He didn't realize his folly until a near grown adolescent boar sent him sailing with a powerful charge, and that's when the panicked gremlin dashed for the fence in all haste.

He almost made it.

The gremlin onlookers thought it a marvelous show and cheered loudly.

The ruckus subsided and everyone forgot about the pigs. Jones watched in growing irritation as one of the younger gremlins hopped about pretending he was a toad. With his large lower jaw and thick jowls, he did look like a big toad. When he started to literally snap insects out of the air, though, Jones decided he'd had enough. "Cleetus!" he bellowed to summon a gremlin he couldn't find amongst the throng mingling about chaotically.

He jumped when a tiny voice piped up right next to him. "Yeah, boss?"

"Whisker on a razorspine, boy!" he cursed. "Don't sneak up on me!" though he had been the one to sit next to Cleetus. He shook his head then pointed to the little one who might have thought he really was a toad. "Lil Roscoe's done lost his mind," he said as Roscoe leapt into the air and snatched a buzzing fly in his mouth. He licked his lips as he swallowed it. He was very convincing. "Those dead miners is 'tractin' flies and skeeters. Git yer bro and drag 'em carcasses out a ways to feed the warpiggies."

"Yes, boss," Cleetus said with a salute as he ran off to fetch his brother to help in the removal of the bodies. Finding one's brother was easy when you were a gremlin because they thought they were all brothers. Many of them were. It was hard to keep track.

Despite his youth, Niño was the best hunter and scout among the remaining Ortega Hunters, so they sent him ahead to find out what he could. He watched the Gremlin interaction with strange fascination, hidden from their view on a perch just several trees away from the big Boss. Niño had the large head of the big boss, Jones, in his sights for some time, though he knew that if he took the shot, the others would scatter or stampede and the rest of the Ortegas were just beyond the makeshift pens of the deadly warpigs that housed at least three large boars that would very easily break through the feeble fencing.

Niño cautiously climbed down from the branches and rejoined the others.

Santiago stretched his wounded arm and stood as Niño approached. "What're we up against, Niño? We're ready to go."

"Give them a few minutes, and they'll be eating. We're outnumbered more'n five to one."

Santiago snorted. "So it'll be almost even! Odds are still on us, though!"

"Don't get cocky," Francisco warned.

Perdita nodded. "Si. Stay focused, Santiago. Don't underestimate these gremlin cabrónes. They might accidentally blow your head off," she said seriously.

"Give me a big Nephilim any day," Francisco agreed. "I can at least predict those things."

Perdita checked her pistol's ammunition. "Neverborn's a Neverborn," she said. "Today it's gremlins. They're disrupting mining shipments and causing all sorts of trouble."

Santiago stepped forward, saying, "Vamos. Enough talking. Let's clean 'em out!"

"Wait," Perdita said. "The clan leader? Jones? He's in this camp?"

"Si. Sits apart from the others usually. Speaks better than the others. Seems to be trying to make 'em look like normal people. Dressing them and trying to get them to act less like animals. Even has some armed with guns, but I don't think they know how to use them."

"You sure?" Perdita asked. Niño nodded, and she said, "Might be worth bringing him in. First that big female

Nephilim that attacked Criid and now this?" She thought on it for a minute. "Almost like Malifaux's fighting back? They're getting stronger. Smarter." She tossed her long hair over her shoulder and said, "We catch him if we can. If not, put him down with the others. We're going to bring the fight to them using their own tactics and turn their own weapons against them. Papa," she said to her father, absently staring at a firefly buzzing languidly nearby. "You're going to start a stampede of those big boars. We'll drive 'em right into the heart of the gremlin camp."

Santiago sneered. "'Bout time," he said.

Niño wasn't quite in place when the first dynamite explosion sounded. He cursed and scrambled higher in the tree to find a stable position and get a clearer shot through the thick growth. The high squeal of the great boars followed immediately, and his hand scraped across the rough bark of the twisted knotwood. His repeating rifle swung around, and he sighted through the scope just in time to see a gremlin leap from a tree at Francisco's blindside, far to the right flank of the stampeding boars. He fired upon the creature without aiming, yet put the bullet through the gremlin's head, sending its body spiraling before Francisco. The sound of the rifle fire caught up to him as he hesitated just a moment and gave an appreciative wave toward Niño's general location.

He scanned across the area to find Santiago on the left flank wading into the midst of the largest group, hollering challenges as he went, recklessly striding forward without an attempt to defend himself as they attacked him. His Peacebringers flashed as he strode forward and Niño quickly fired upon the gremlins as they sought to overwhelm his brash cousin. He chambered a bullet and fired, hardly having the time to aim and then chambered another, fired again. He continued to support Santiago until he felt he could handle himself.

He sought to find Perdita and swung the rifle's sight to the stampeding boars. True to her plan, she ran amongst them, charging the gremlin camp, firing her pistol with a subconscious accuracy at anything that moved before her. The boars, alarmed at the explosion and now the rapid firing pistol right in their midst, squealed in panic. Two of the giant beasts slammed together, trying to crush her, but she hit one on the back with her free hand and cart-wheeled over it, catching another gremlin in the chest with a Peacebringer strike, even firing in mid-air. She hit the ground and continued running without missing her stride, her long hair billowing behind her like a sail. Niño whistled appreciatively. He was awfully proud they were related.

The gremlins saw her coming and tried to hold their ground as there were about eleven of them. Niño fired and reloaded faster than he ever had before to clear them out, but the boars hit the group, scattering and sending several flying or trampling over them. Perdita was possibly more dangerous up close, charging them with her pistol firing, and she took them down, wide-eyed.

Niño couldn't believe it when he let loose a bullet, quickly assessing her movement against his shot, determining that as she moved in the melee it would hit her instead of his intended target. "No!" he cried, though he could do nothing and watched in terror.

At the moment the bullet should have struck her back, she stepped quickly aside, and his bullet sank into the gremlin's head directly between his eyes. Niño looked across the distance in disbelief. "How in the hell did she do that?" he asked himself.

She plunged back into the midst of the gremlins, looking for their leader. Niño scanned the area for him and saw that Santiago had broken through the line and had the fat boss on the run with Francisco double-timing to his location. A wave of gremlins poured from

the underbrush, cutting the men off from Jones. Perdita worked on routing a mob that had converged upon her, finishing them off in quick order.

"'Dita!" Niño bellowed. She spun toward him, and he fired three rapid shots on the ground near her, marking a line toward Jones. She understood and took off in a flash in the direction he indicated. Niño fired upon Jones several times to wound him, but lost the elusive gremlin in the thickness of the overgrown bayou. Although high in the tree, Niño jumped, catching a limb in his chest. He got up and ran, even with the wind knocked so violently from him. He was an Ortega, and he ran despite the pain and stars before his eyes. Stubbornly, he would catch Perdita and provide support.

He crashed through the foliage as branches lashed his flesh. The sound of her gun rang out ahead of him. As he broke through the undergrowth, he found them.

Perdita fired and hit the big gremlin in the shoulder. Instead of falling, he spun with the impact and faced her. His big gun fired, scattering the shot in a wide explosion rather than a single bullet, and the foliage all around her burst from the impact. She was thrown backward as the bulk of the explosion struck her in the chest. She landed hard. She didn't move and her dark hair spread out around her like a dark halo. Her dark skin was torn and burned about her neck and chest, steam rising from her.

Jones darted behind a dense cluster of growth for cover.

Niño dropped to his cousin's side and thankfully found her alive, blinking from the violence of the explosion. "Where is ese cabrón?" she asked, coughing and struggling to shake off the effects of the explosion. Niño nodded in the direction he had fled, seeking cover. From Perdita's revolver, however, there was no safe hiding place. She lifted her gun and peered down the sights and the world bent to accommodate her shot. Many who have witnessed Perdita performing this shot describe the bullet's trajectory bending around corners to strike its target. The truth, however, was that reality rearranged itself to provide a direct line to her target. As Perdita sighted down the length of her Peacebringer, Jones' cover rolled obligingly to the side to reveal the cowering gremlin behind. Only a nervous tick saved the gremlin from Perdita's round, the shot causing the whiskey bottle tethered to his hip to burst into shards of glass. He screamed and hopped up.

Som'er Teeth Jones, in mortal peril of Perdita's second shot, shivered in fear. Looking up, he saw that the cover he had chosen wasn't a tree or a bush or any other natural growth. A great statue towered above him. The great orange stone wound at the base and then rose straight up. The leafy vines entangling it created the illusion of scales upon a monstrous serpent rising to strike. At the sight of it, Jones called out in a shrill cry of terror, and ran, more afraid of the inanimate statue than of Perdita, which Niño found disturbing.

Perdita let him run. At the base of this serpentine statue was an emblem, one that Perdita recognized. It was a coiled serpent surrounding a shuttered eye.

"Niño," she said. "We need to contact Criid."

The Disturbing Case of Edgar Ryan

Edgar Ryan was a successful Union engineer living well in the Downtown district of Malifaux. Since coming through the Breach two years prior, he and his lovely wife Elizabeth had settled nicely in a block house that the couple had personally restored. They were also new parents of a baby boy. By all accounts, life could not be more pleasant for Edgar Ryan. Such a thing never lasts long in Malifaux.

It started simply enough. His employer had rewarded him for modifying a fitting rig to a new piping system, thereby saving the company a large expense. Ryan used the bonus scrip to buy an Aethervox, an extravagance he and his wife could never have afforded otherwise. He brought it home with glee and spent hours at night in the basement listening to various channels. Over the next few weeks, Ryan's attendance at work fell. Elizabeth did the best she could to hide the bruises and the tears, terrified by her husband's changing demeanor. She told a neighbor that he had little interest in the normal broadcasts during the evening, but he sat up until all hours of the night listening to the static that comes on after the broadcasts. Toward the end, he began having conversations with something only he could hear.

It was a warm Tuesday evening in Malifaux. Mrs. Ryan's small garden, a simple courtyard arrangement she planted when Edgar rented the place, had just come into bloom. She and their young child were out in the garden together, enjoying the weather and smell of rose blossoms. Officials believe Edgar calmly climbed the stairs from his basement to the kitchen, where he grabbed a carving knife. The reaction of the Guild's Morgue Master, Dr. McMourning, is a testament to the nature of the crime. Even he blanched at the sight despite his years of experience. There, among the trampled remains of the garden, lay the Ryan family, butchered by Edgar's own hand. After killing his wife and child, he had turned the blade on himself, repeatedly carving "Don't worry, I'm coming" until he, too, finally expired.

GUILD

THE GUILD

Hoffman fidgeted in the hard wood chair, adjusting the straps of his brass support braces, trying to keep the metal hinges from rubbing against the ribs on his back. The single kerosene lamp hanging above him cast little light, and the rest of the small room was shrouded in darkness. There was little need for light in the ascetic room with only a small table before him and the empty chair adjacent.

He was made to wait excessively long before Lucius Matheson, the Governor General's secretary, returned to the room and strode quietly past him to sit opposite. Each man was physically slight, and Lucius would be considered frail in the company of any save C. Hoffman, struggling to keep his back straight in the chair for any length of time.

"I've been instructed to change tactics with you, Mr. Hoffman," Lucius said with a slow and overly articulated inflection that Hoffman found disconcerting. From the King's Empire, he was always self-conscious of how people would look at him as a curiosity when he spoke. He had a habit of identifying the origins of speech of those around him. Lucius spoke with a unique accent he hadn't heard before. Hoffman's eyes were downcast, and sweat along his stiff collar made him more uncomfortable. "We began with the notion of interrogating you for your supposed involvement in Arcanist activities. Many witnesses identified you with wanted Arcanists at the train derailment. You and another. As you can imagine, you are a fairly identifiable man." His eyes motioned to the straps around his torso, tying him to the brass supports that ran the length of his body. "We would, of course, like to know where you've been this last week since the incident. But my employer, the Governor General, has come to believe you may not be directly tied to their seditious activities. However, we both believe you may offer insight into probable ties between recent acts of violence and rebellion and the Arcanist interests in the mines north of the city." Hoffman's head remained bowed, but his eyes lifted to stare at the small man seated opposite him beneath his narrow brow. "Would you be able to help us root out the Arcanist terrorists, Mr. Hoffman?"

The Arcanists. He wished he had never heard the word. Wished he had never agreed to cross the Breach.

Sitting on that train beside his brother Ryle as it approached the swirling eddies of aether escaping from the Breach, he had an overwhelming sense of dread.

"Relax," Ryle had said. "It's just a moment through the Breach, and we'll be on the other side, just above Malifaux!"

"Yes. Very exciting." Hoffman rolled his eyes at his older brother. "And I'm not nervous about passing through the Breach. I just cannot understand why you've decided to haul me around on your adventure. I'll be nothing but in your way," he said, motioning to the braces on his legs.

"Old chap! We're going there for you, too!"

"An excuse. Because you know I'd be lost without you. You have an opportunity. I do not want to be in your way anymore."

"You are not in the way. Ever. I'm meeting Professor Ramos, it's true. An opportunity to apprentice beside one of the greatest inventors and innovators of our time. But consider his work with clockwork constructs! Think what it'll mean to be able to walk again."

"I can walk now."

Ryle gave him a sidelong glance. "Limited. The polio's got you, and you know you cannot hide it from me. Working with Ramos, we'll have you running laps around the King's court and playing cricket in the yard!"

Ryle would focus upon creating a better mobile assistant for him, he knew. Ryle had become too obsessed with helping him defy the symptoms of the polio. Big, strong, robust, Ryle had put aside all athletics in favor of studying every minute upon biology, physiology, and engineering, looking for both cure and aid for his younger brother. Hoffman needed him, it was true, but he had hampered every opportunity for Ryle to progress, even seeing him leave Oxford in favor of this trip to Malifaux to work with Ramos. In other circumstances, it might have been a wonderful opportunity for Ryle, but he couldn't help but feel that Ryle made his choices based upon what it might offer him. Physically superior, mentally without peer, Hoffman often thought how unfair it was they were brothers. Not because he envied Ryle, though he did in every way. Because his frailty dictated his older brother's fate so drastically. He could only offer basic engineering assistance to Ryle, trying to keep up with the elder brother's flashing mind that could discern so many nuances of every science. He limited all of Ryle's opportunities due to his own glaring limitations of the flesh and mind.

"Don't worry, little brother," Ryle said with a smile. "We'll meet Ramos in just minutes, and he'll help us."

They had entered the Breach. Like all of the passengers, he was all smiles as he leaned over to see the quickly moving waves of magical aether escaping the great portal between worlds. The ride through the Breach took only a moment, and the experience was said to be filled with excitement and energy that coursed through a person. Although different for everyone, the common claim was that it would change your life.

Ryle's smile disappeared as the blue light filled their car, electricity arcing between bodies and seats. He screamed loudly, clutching his head and writhing out of his seat.

Accounts from passengers coming through the Gateway of the Breach rarely agreed upon the circumstances of the experience. The majority of travelers said the flash of blue light lasted only a brief moment with a tingling sensation in their extremities like the quick snap of static electricity. Some reported a surreal slowing of time, like they could look around the train car at the excited faces, frozen in place, the sound of the iron wheels on the rails coming in muted, distant echoes.

However, Hoffman had never heard of an account remotely similar to his experience. At first, time seemed to stretch and distort as his arms struggled to pull his feeble body over the seat, reaching for his brother in the aisle. His outstretched arm froze in place, but his mind moved frantically fast, spanning full internal conversation and thought. Ryle, too, was further disjoint in time, screaming and shaking, the spasms wracking him to and fro with sharply exaggerated movements, too fast for normal. Blue electricity crackled all around in what Hoffman might consider normal time and movement, and it centered upon Ryle, arcing to other passengers, smiling with the thrill of passing through the Breach frozen on their unmoving faces.

Then the effects of the Breach struck him in full. Howling, unintelligible voices consumed his mind, devouring the thoughts that were his own, suppressing his own will. He, too, fell back against the seat, his upper body flailing forward and back.

He could not think, but the droning of the wheels came faintly to him as if miles away, and he latched onto the sound with his mind, desperately trying to ignore the countless voices struggling for dominance of his mind. Slowly, he was able to follow a thought, but it was removed, strangely, from his consciousness, as if he tried to control a dream and think logically in that discordant realm of sleep.

The wheels continued to clack on the rails. Ryle flailed back and forth, unnaturally faster than perceivable.

The train would not go through the Breach, it seemed. His mind, ready to collapse, to succumb to the weight driving upon it, roared out the single thought, "Faster!" As if obeying him, the cars lurched, and they were through, into the open air of Malifaux.

Time resumed and pleasant gasps of excitement and various "Ooohs" and "Ahhhs" were quickly cast aside as the screaming of Ryle on the car's floor and the jerking of the brothers' bodies compelled them to panic, and they stared in wide-eyed terror at the two brothers writhing in pain. To the other passengers, only a second had passed, and they were all filled with expectant jubilation. The train bucked and the brakes ground hard, screeching madly while sparks danced at the windows. More and more of the passengers joined Ryle's screaming as the car in front of them hopped, leaving the tracks. Theirs bounced and heaved, crashing into it, sending some passengers out of their seats. They were jolted again as the car behind them struck their own.

Hoffman still couldn't think though the vast and conflicting noise within his mind slowly abated. He struggled to remain conscious, slipping in and out of that dream-state that sought to overwhelm him. "We're derailing," he said aloud. A thick gray fog enveloped his mind, and the sound around him again pulled away, lost in the darkness. "No."

The great engine at the front grabbed hold of the tracks. As if obeying his demand, all the cars bucked and would have turned end over end, killing them all. "We must stop," he thought as he slipped further into the fog.

Every remaining passenger in every car was thrown from his or her seat as each car's wheels miraculously grabbed hold of the rails. Loose luggage was thrown violently forward, too, and screaming and crying filled the car.

He couldn't think, couldn't focus on anything, save his brother in the aisle, possibly dead or dying because of a desperate adventure through the damnable Breach, to give him some hope against the paralysis and the disease that disabled him.

Time might have been moving normally, but it seemed to Hoffman that a terribly long time passed in that stunned haze.

Voices called above the din of the wounded and scared. "Ryle Hoffman!" he heard a stranger shout. "Where is Ryle Hoffman?" It was a dim and faraway voice. Hoffman could not speak. Could not call out for them to help. "Ryle Hoffman?" he heard the call again, though he knew it was moving away and he could do nothing to stop them. He raised his hand feebly with what was left of his will, then dropped as he teetered on the edge of consciousness.

"That's not Ryle," another man said, above him.

"It's the brother."

Hoffman motioned to his brother on the floor, staring vacantly at the ceiling of the car, mouth agape.

"Take him," one said. "He's not dead, and the boss may be able to fix him up."

"What about the cripple?"

"He'll slow us down. Leave him."

The passengers slowly gathered their wits, climbing back to their seats as they assessed minor injuries. Seeing the two men climb aboard their car, they naturally assumed the men were there to help the wounded, but they ignored everyone save the Hoffmans. One woman, having traveled to and from Malifaux, recognized one from wanted posters hung throughout the city. "Arcanist!" she yelled.

One of the men growled, "I knew it was a mistake to bring you, Enrique!"

Other passengers joined the call, pointing at the two. "Arcanists!" they called.

Another woman, sobbing, accused, "You did this!" as they passed her. Enrique, overwhelmed by fear and anxiety, pulled his revolver and fired upon her without thinking.

His companion grabbed him about the collar and shook him. "What have you done?" he demanded. The passengers cowered, incapable of stifling their screams as panic mounted.

"They think we did this!" Enrique yelled.

"Now the Guards will come straight for this car," the other said. "Grab that one, too, you fool," he said, pointing to Hoffman, who had succumbed to unconsciousness. "Guild Guards are coming now because of this damned accident. Of all days for the thing to derail!"

Hoffman slipped in and out of consciousness as the men fled, once hearing gunshots and cursing next to him before slipping out again. One said, "Enough of this! Let's dump them with Ramos and be done with it!"

As his mind cleared and he reluctantly fought back into a normal state of thought, he looked about a room with great and wondrous science apparatus and metal bits from great machines. Articulated legs, bigger than a man, hung along walls, and dark oiled gears were scattered throughout the room.

On a worktable in the center of the room, lit from above, remarkably, by electrical lights, glowing fiercely, was his brother Ryle. A slight man, older, hovered over Ryle, working with an acetylene torch and dark goggles protecting his eyes from the bright flashes and sparks.

Hoffman struggled to sit upright on the small cot against the wall, but he swooned from the effort. "What...what are you doing?" he murmured.

Viktor Ramos looked up from his work, staring at Hoffman through the welding goggles. "Saving his life," he said as the younger Hoffman passed out again.

When he awoke again, he had no concept of time, of how long he might have been unconscious. His head, still splitting with pain, had a lingering thought of voices at the back of his mind, indistinct and quiet. "Ramos?" he said to the man now sitting beside him. The smell of oil and the acrid smell of solder and burnt metal permeated the room.

"Yes. Welcome back. It's good you are awake. We have much to discuss." Ramos, clearly, was a man that wasted little time.

"Ryle?"

Ramos hesitated, though he had expected the need to discuss what had befallen his older brother. "Alive. But the Breach nearly consumed him. It happens infrequently. Only when a person has great potential in the arcane."

"Can I see him? Speak to him?"

"Not yet. He's recovering. He was nearly lost. He'll... he'll need time to recover. As will you. Unfortunately, we do not have much time to spare. You'll soon be apprehended. The Guild saw you and your brother and some Arcanist agents."

"Yes," Hoffman said angrily. "They did this!"

"Excuse me?" Ramos asked, genuinely surprised.

"It was an attack. Why would they do this?" Ramos was puzzled and nearly chastised the man before his quick thinking mind put the pieces together that the younger brother of Ryle Hoffman did not know why they were coming to Malifaux, who they were to meet there. If not for the conflict at Kythera keeping him from the arrival at the train station, he would have been there to meet the new protégé, Ryle, so many of his old colleagues Earthside spoke so highly of. Ramos proceeded cautiously.

"The Arcanists may not have had anything to do with the train derailment," he said thoughtfully. If Hoffman truly believed there was no connection between his brother, Ramos, and the Arcanist movement, there would be nothing to learn in interrogating him.

Hoffman leaned back upon his pillow, closing his eyes to diminish the pain in his head. "They were there. Looking for Ryle. I thought they might be there to help. But I think they wanted to kill us."

Ramos said nothing, but thought quietly to himself about what Hoffman said. "I'm not sure of that. Regardless, the Arcanists demand the freedom to practice the magic they believe is their birthright. Malifaux, and the Breach, sometimes awakens a power in an individual he may not have known was even there. Take you, for example."

"Me? What about me?"

"While Earthside – did you ever know the power you possessed?"

"What power?"

Ramos smiled from his chair, evaluating the accidental gift he might have discovered in the form of this frail man, crippled since childhood. "Do you see these constructs about us?" Hoffman opened his eyes looking at the various machines, each vaguely reminiscent of an animal he might recognize from home. Spidery machines, no bigger than a small dog scampered about near his bed and one much larger, feline-like construct faced him from near the center of the room, its eyes glowing red within the sockets of its plated head.

"Yes. But my brother said you were a master engineer. Inventor without peer."

"Thank you."

"He revered your ability to revolutionize mining and your work with electricity generation, storage, and usage is studied at University, Earthside. These are your work, no doubt?"

"They are my work."

"What does that have to do with me, then?"

"They have no operational cortex. They're shells. On the scrap heap."

"But they move. They function."

"When you were brought here, they came alive. Without a mechanika cortex. They've been tending you. Bringing you water when you were thirsty, though you never spoke aloud. They put a wet cloth on your forehead when you ran fever. They retrieved me when you stirred, just moments ago."

"I...I have no such ability, sir."

"You do now, Mr. Hoffman. We have not much time to speak. I must be very brief, and what I will tell you may shock you. I fear it will disturb you greatly, and I apologize. I intend to help you understand this new gift. This new ability. I suspect we will need it to help your brother Ryle. The Breach nearly destroyed him, and he is very wounded in the body and mind." Ramos spoke with increasing urgency, the words coming faster. "In order to save him, I had to integrate very innovative new technology with his body and brain. He was comatose and his organs failing. The legality of this work is questionable at best. I had no choice."

"What? I don't–" Hoffman's breathing came as quickly as Ramos' words, and he was on the edge of hyper-ventilation.

"Listen!" Ramos barked. "He's still lost, his body rejecting much of the mechanika. You can save him!"

"Me? How?"

"The Guild officials will come and take you for questioning. Too many witnesses at the derailment. Too many things said that should not have been spoken." Ramos said the last through gnashing teeth. "If they link you or your brother to Arcanists, they will lock you away. Your brother will be lost. Forever."

"Why did they do this?" he asked, his head pounding through the resurgent fever burning through him.

"No time for that," Ramos said. "We must get you to a safe-house. You cannot be seen here. Not with me. Not yet."

Within minutes, he was dressed and carried from the laboratory of Viktor Ramos by constructs the professor said had no functioning cortex. He was found the next day, burning with fever, hidden in a small room along the edge of the slum district of Malifaux.

A vision of his brother on Ramos' lab table haunted him. He was tormented by the thought of a man, gifted with brawn, an acclaimed academic scholar, now inches from death because of a personal mission to save him, his younger brother. Now, to save his life, he had construct technology grafted to his flesh, and his mind was broken. Hoffman had the sinking feeling that Ryle was attempting to meet some covert Arcanist, all, no doubt, to help him. 'Fortunately,' he thought, 'They were scared. Pursued. They brought us to Ramos, instead.'

"Would you be able to help us root out the Arcanist terrorists, Mr. Hoffman?" Hoffman didn't respond but his eyes turned away from Lucius, again.

"So, Mr. Hoffman. We understand that you've discovered a latent power, having been awakened through the Breach. It's a common indication of a potential master of the art." Hoffman said nothing, his head bowed, sweating with fever. "You've demonstrated an affinity with constructs?" Hoffman said nothing, remaining motionless, eyes downcast. Lucius sighed. "Mr. Hoffman, you'll either be able to help us or we'll be forced to pursue the investigation into possible connections you might have with the Arcanists."

At the word, his eyes lifted and he stared at Lucius angrily. "The 'ties' I have to the Arcanists will drive me until my death," he said.

"Then you will help us?"

"You will help me," he said. "I will find the Arcanists. They will pay for what they've done to me." He was careful not to mention his brother lest they trace him to the Arcanists before he could uncover the connections his brother had made. "I need access to a lab. Material."

"Of course, Mr. Hoffman. All you need. Construct technology. After all, that's the office you will be heading up."

"How's that, again?"

"Construct-human grafting. It should lead us to the parties we seek. The technology is unique to Malifaux and is highly illegal. Many enemies to the Guild, excuse me, to all peaceful settlers here..." He continued to speak, but Hoffman could no longer follow the words.

Ramos fit the description of those the Guild hoped to implicate for Arcanist ties, as Ramos feared. His brother, Ryle, quickly integrated with technological construct equipment fit the description of those the Guild would soon be hunting, too.

The Arcanists did this. With the full might of the Guild backing him, he would doggedly pursue those that took his brother.

C. HOFFMAN - MASTER

C. Hoffman will likely never know that he passed through the Great Breach on the same day that many of the most powerful and influential people in Malifaux fought for dominion at Kythera. These two events have nothing in common other than Fate chose Hoffman and the individuals at Kythera to embroil in lives of unwanted adventure. For Hoffman, he was dragged reluctantly by his older brother on a quest to meet a man rumored to possess the technology and scientific wherewithal to help free him from the effects of polio, achieving an independence and strength denied him since early childhood.

As the more gifted of the two brothers, Ryle always cast a long and deep shadow over his frail sibling. Ryle was commanding and strong. He had few academic peers. Socially, he fit in with the highest lords of state as well as fraternized with laborers in pubs after a long workday. There was nothing Ryle could not accomplish. Hoffman, however, struggled in everything.

Confined to his wheelchair or hobbling about in braces with heavy machinery strapped to his back, he studied, trying to keep pace with Ryle in just a few disciplines. Without the elder Hoffman to be compared to, the younger would have been considered a skilled engineer and mechanical scientist. As it was, he never had the chance to prove it Earthside.

Going through the Breach changed his destiny.

Ryle nearly succumbed to the overwhelming energy within the Breach during his transition between Earth and Malifaux. His mind snapped, and his body shut down. C. Hoffman, too, underwent a transformation. The energy that enveloped them unlocked the dormant potential within him. His awakened mind reached out to the silent machines around him, bringing them to life to obey his will, as if extensions of his otherwise frail body.

Arriving in Malifaux to meet with Ramos, the circumstances were far different than the brothers expected. Ramos saved Ryle's life, albeit with a few modifications, thrusting the once weaker brother into a position where he must look after his elder brother. Ramos' knowledge wasn't enough, though. Hoffman needed additional resources, possessed only by the Guild, to prolong his brother's life.

The Guild was looking for a way to infiltrate the ranks of the Arcanists and willingly took in both Hoffmans to aid those battles. C. Hoffman now heads a new division, dubbed the "Flesh-Construct Grafting Illegality Charter", hunting those that illegally merge the flesh with the mechanical. With his newfound affinity with machinery, awakening some kind of ghost-within-the-machine spirit, he might be perfect to apprehend those that illegally use Construct technology. His brother, however, is a perfect example of exactly the type of creature he is charged with apprehending.

CONSTRUCT, M&SU MEMBER, MASTER, SCAVENGER

WK/CG	HT	WP	CA	DF	WD
3/-	2	6	5🪝	3	10

SOULSTONE TORCH

RG	🗲 1
CB	4🪝
DG	3/4/6

TALENTS:

Abilities

Arcanist Ties: Crews containing this model may hire Arcanist Constructs that do not have **Frozen Heart** or **Smoldering Heart**.

Dampening: No 🏆 may be placed, and no 🕸 or (🕱) effects may originate, within 3" of this model, except during this model's activation.

Drawn to Metal: If a friendly Construct of Ht 2 or more announces a move Action while in base contact with this model, you may Push this model into base contact with the Construct after the move.

Empowered: This model receives +1 **Ca** up to a maximum of +5 for each other friendly Construct within 4".

Feedback: This model heals 1 **Wd** when a friendly Construct in base contact is healed, and suffers 1 **Wd** when a friendly Construct in base contact is killed or sacrificed.

Maintain Machines: Other friendly Constructs within 6" may choose to ignore any of their listed Abilities.

Perfect Machine: This model may choose to ignore any effect that targets only Constructs.

Protected by Machines: Nominate a friendly Construct within 3" when this model suffers damage. This model gains **Armor** equal to the nominated Construct's when applying the damage. This **Armor** does not stack with any other **Armor**.

Weapon

Soulstone Torch: This Weapon's damage ignores **Armor**.

Actions

(+1) Instinctual

(0) Assimilate: This model gains one Talent or Spell possessed by a target Construct within 6". Effects that reference a model by name cannot be **Assimilated**.

(0) Linked In: One friendly Construct within 6" of C. Hoffman activates after this model's activation ends.

(0) Tap Power: Target friendly Construct within 6" receives **Slow**. This model receives **Fast**.

(1) Detonate Scrap: Target up to three Scrap Counters within 5". These Counters may be on the table or carried. Each Counter inflicts a (🕱)2, **Dg** 1. The (🕱) originates from a model carrying a Counter or the Counter itself if on the table.

(1) Machine Puppet: Target Construct within 4" makes a **Strike** with one of its basic Weapons. The Construct uses **Cb** 6🪝 instead of the Weapon's **Cb** for the **Strike**. The Construct gains "Cb(🪝) **Critical Strike [Weapon Used]**" during the **Strike**.

Triggers

Cb (🪝🪝) Exploit Design Flaw [Soulstone Torch]: Target Construct damaged by this Weapon is killed unless its Controller discards two Control Cards.

SPELLS:

(1) Combat Mechanic
(CC: 15🪝📖 / Rst: - / Rg: 6) Sacrifice target Scrap Counter, or kill target friendly Construct. This model or friendly Construct within 6" makes a Healing Flip.

(1) Open Circuit
(CC: 13🪝 / Rst: Df / Rg: (🕱)3) Non-Constructs suffer **Dg** 2, as well as +1 **Dg** per Construct in base contact with this model.

(2) Override Edict
(CC: 15🪝🐄 / Rst: Wp / Rg: 4) Activate target Construct after this model's activation ends, regardless of whether target has activated or not this turn. This model's Controller controls the target during this activation. After this activation target cannot activate again this turn.

MECHANICAL ATTENDANT - TOTEM

Specifically created by C. Hoffman to aid him, this little machine lacks built in programming or power sources and exists completely as an extension of Hoffmann's will. Its multiple arms include every manner of tool to assist in design work.

No one need look further than C. Hoffman's Mechanical Attendant to see the man's genius. The diminutive Construct is almost a constant fixture by Hoffman's side, serving as both aide and bodyguard. Equipped with a small workshop's worth of tools, the mechanical attendant is able to fine tune other Constructs to keep them running for spans of time, bypassing deficiencies in their construction that prevent them from functioning efficiently.

Ever mindful of the dangers of Malifaux, Hoffman also equipped his attendant with a Mauser 9 pistol, a semi-automatic weapon deadly in its mechanical employ. Hoffman finds the personal use of firearms reprehensible but has no qualms about equipping his Constructs with them if they are used to defend humans from the predations of the City's inhuman inhabitants.

One mystery does surround the Mechanical Attendant's Construction - its mode of power. The Construct does not possess an access panel for replacing a worn-out Soulstone, nor does it have a power plant of any kind – from a steam engine, to something more esoteric, such as a giant windup key. Instead, Hoffman installed an aetheric receiver into his workhorse assistant. A device of his own design, the receiver absorbs a small portion of the ambient energy coursing through Malifaux, converting it to power the Attendant. Hoffman has yet to share this secret with anyone, especially his Guild employers, instead keeping his assistant close by lest the keys to his greatest invention fall into the wrong hands. Besides, this creation, like much of his latest work, is so intuitive that he has no way to document and blueprint the revolutionary device.

30MM BASE

SOULSTONE COST: 3

CONSTRUCT, SCAVENGER, TOTEM (C. HOFFMAN)

WK/CG	HT	WP	CA	DF	WD
4/6	1	5	5🌀	4	5

MAUSER 9

RG	⌐8
CB	4🌀
DG	1/2/3

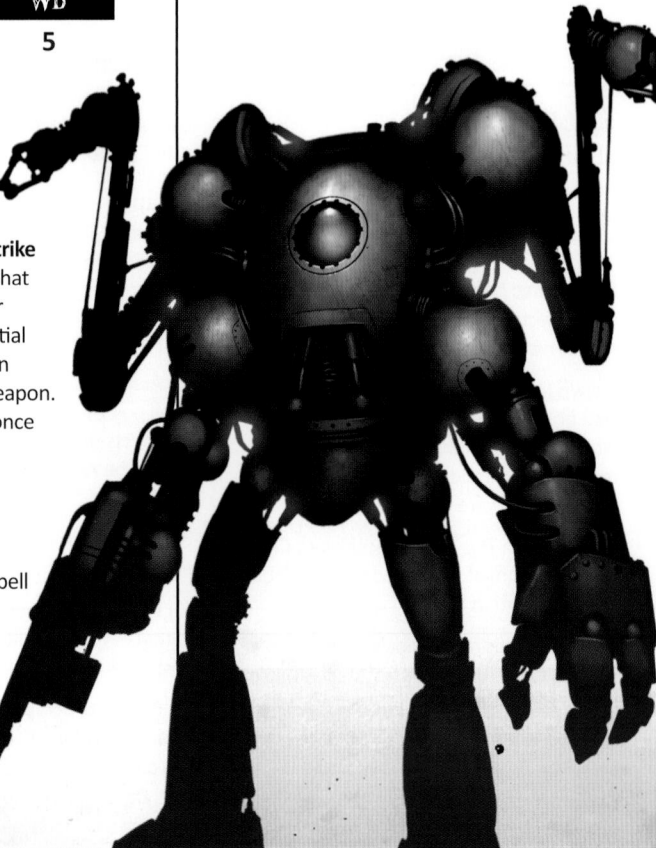

TALENTS:

Abilities

Armor +1

Clockwork Tools: This model may gain one Scrap Counter when a Construct within 3" and LoS is sacrificed. This model suffers 1 **Wd** for each Scrap Counter gained this way.

Companion (C. Hoffman)

Maintain Machines: Other friendly Constructs within 6" may choose to ignore any of their listed Abilities.

Weapon

Mauser 9: After causing Severe damage with this Weapon, defender suffers a **Dg** 1/2/3 Flip which may not be Cheated.

Actions

(2) Automatic Fire [Mauser 9]: Discard one Control Card. Target a model within range and LoS. This model makes a **Strike** with this Weapon against that model and up to two other models within 2" of the initial target which are also within range and LoS with this Weapon. This Action may be taken once per turn.

SPELLS:

(1) Magical Extension (CC: * /Rst: * /Rg: *) This Spell may be cast only once per activation. Cast one of the connected Master's **(1)** Spells. During this casting, this model may use a Soulstone to change its starting total.

DRILL SERGEANT - TOTEM

AWRIGHT, MAGGOT!

YA GOT THROUGH BASIC TRAINING AND THINK YER NIGHTMARES ARE OVER? THINK AGAIN.

I. AM. YER. NEW. NIGHTMARE.

I AM ONE OF THOSE BAD DREAMS YA WISH ON YER ENEMIES.

I WILL NOT GO AWAY. I DO NOT SLEEP. I WILL STICK TO YOU LIKE HONEY ON A BEAR'S SNOUT FOR AS LONG AS IT TAKES. TAKES WHAT? TO WHIP YOU INTO SHAPE, MAGGOT! LOOK AT YOU. SINVELING, WEAK, A POOR EXCUSE FOR A GUILDSMAN IF THAT'S WHAT YOU'RE TRYING TO BE. AND THAT'S 'TAKES WHAT, SERGEANT?' I CAN'T HEAR YOOOOU! THAT'S BETTER.

SACK UP AND WIPE THOSE TEARS. WE HAVE WORK TO DO. I'M HERE TO SHOW YOU HOW TO USE YOUR WEAPON AND FACE CERTAIN DEATH IN THE EYE AND SPIT IN THAT EYE. THOSE ARE MY ORDERS AND YOU. WILL. NOT. DISAPPOINT. ME!

NOW, YOU MAY BE ASKING YOURSELF, 'WHAT DID I DO TO BE BLESSED WITH SUCH A KIND AND BENEVOLENT DRILL SERGEANT?' I AM ASKING MYSELF THE SAME QUESTION

RIGHT NOW....BUT THE POWERS THAT BE (lord help them) HAVE DECIDED THAT MY TRAINING YOU AND KEEPING YOU ON YER FEET IS CHEAPER THAN HAVING TO RETRAIN YOUR REPLACEMENT WHEN THE 'BORN EAT YOUR FACE. DOES THAT ANSWER YER QUESTION?

I CAN'T HEAR YOOOOOU!

30MM BASE   SOULSTONE COST: 3

GUARDSMAN, INSIGNIFICANT, TOTEM

WK/CG	HT	WP	CA	DF	WD
4/6	2	6	3	3	4

BATON	
RG	1
CB	4
DG	1/3/4

TALENTS:

Abilities

Companion (Master)

Extra Training: Melee Attack Flips made by a friendly non-Master model linked to this model receive ⊕.

Actions

(0) Link: This model and target model in base contact with it are **Linked**. After the model this model is **Linked** to completes a **Walk** Action or ends its activation, Push this model into base contact with the **Linked** model. A model can be **Linked** to only one model at a time. **Link** ends if the two models are not in base contact at the Start Closing Phase.

(2) Shooting Range: ⬤4. Ranged Attack Flips made by friendly Guardsmen receive ⊕.

SPELLS:

(1) "Attennn-Hut!"
(CC: 9 /Rst: - /Rg: 12) End **Slow** on target model. Target model is immune to **Slow** until the End Closing Phase.

(1) Magical Extension
(CC: * /Rst: * /Rg: *) This Spell may be cast only once per activation. Cast one of the connected Master's **(1)** Spells. During this casting, this model may use a Soulstone to change its starting total.

(1) On Yer Feet!
(CC: 12/Rst: - /Rg: 6) End **Paralyzed** on target model. Target model is immune to **Paralyzed** until the End Closing Phase.

LUCIUS, GOVERNOR'S SECRETARY - HENCHMAN

Few know the true power Lucius Mattheson wields in Malifaux.

• To most, he is the Governor General's Secretary, an unassuming but powerful functionary of the most powerful man in Malifaux. Guild representatives follow his orders as if they came from the Governor General himself. With a snap of his fingers, Lucius can summon forth the might of the Guild Guard, using their legitimate authority to enforce order on behalf of his employer. He does this sparingly, instead relying on the weight of his own office to remove difficulties from his path by intimidation alone.

A select group follows his orders with unquestioned loyalty, well aware that Lucius also has an ear in, or holds the reins of,

many of the Guild's clandestine operations in the City and beyond. Lucius demands only two things from these men and women - their unwavering loyalty to both himself and the Governor General and results. Those unable to do either vanish and are never heard from again.

Lucius has his share of enemies and surrounds himself with bodyguards when he must leave the Governor's Mansion on Guild business. Anyone seeking to harm the Secretary finds it not an easy task. If an assailant were to somehow make it through his protective cordon, he would never heard from again; Lucius is capable of protecting himself and leaves no one to tell how.

30MM BASE **SOULSTONE COST: 10**

HENCHMAN 4, SPECIAL FORCES (ELITE DIVISION)

WK/CG	HT	WP	CA	DF	WD
5/7	2	6	6⚑	4	9

SWORD-CANE

RG	⚔ 1
CB	6⚑
DG	2/3/4

TALENTS:

Abilities

Advanced Planning: If a Crew containing this model used a Soulstone to reflip for Strategy when selecting a Strategy, it gains one Soulstone to its Soulstone Cache.

Special Forces Leader (Elite Division): Crews led by this model may only hire Elite Division, Guardsmen, or Totems.

Highest Authority: Strikes or Casts targeting this model receive ⊟ to Attack and Casting flips.

Secret Service: This model receives +2 **Df** while one or more friendly Elite Division or Guardsmen are within 2".

Slow to Die

Terrifying → 12

Actions

(+1) Casting Expert

(0) Advanced Training: ⚫8. friendly Elite Division or Guardsman gain +2 **Cb** until the end of this model's activation.

(0) Ruthless Leadership: Sacrifice a friendly Elite Division or Guardsman model within 2". This model receives **Reactivate**. This Action may be taken once per turn.

Triggers

Cb (⚑⚑) Governor's Authority [Sword-Cane]: After successfully striking defender, the defender may not target this model with any attacks.

SPELLS:

(0) Reinforcements
(CC: 13⚑ /Rst: - /Rg: 18) Place a friendly model in its Controller's Deployment Zone within 4" of this model.

(1) Guild Intelligence
(CC: 12⚑ /Rst: - /Rg: C) Draw one Control Card then discard one Control Card.

(1) Hidden Sniper
(CC: 11⚑⚑ /Rst: Df /Rg: 16) **Dg** 1/2/4. This Spell may target a model in LoS of any friendly Elite Division, but must be in range of this model.

(1) Issue Command
(CC: 14⚑ /Rst: - /Rg: 12) Target friendly Elite Division or Guardsman model immediately makes a melee or ranged **Strike** or takes the **Walk** Action.

ABUELA ORTEGA - MINION

Nobody knows exactly how old Abuela Ortega really is. If asked, her curt reply of "old enough," followed by a swat with a wooden spoon, is enough deterrent to keep it from being asked a second time. Abuela's mind remains honed to a knife's edge, despite her aged appearance. She brooks no excuses from the young'uns, and everyone who thinks they have the pepper to stand up to her has fled her presence in tears.

Ornery as a Razorspine Rattler with a toothache, Abuela Ortega sees to the day to day running of the family's sprawling compound, known as Latigo. As the family's matriarch, she oversees the chores and defenses, often making sound strategic suggestions to her grandchildren that surprise even the veterans among them. She takes a turn at watch for Neverborn along Latigo's walls, often taunting those within earshot with blistering insults against their lineage, sex, and reproductive preferences. Neverborn foolish enough to respond to her with force find the shotgun leaning casually against Latigo's wall is not just there for show. Despite its kick, Abuela refuses to give up her favorite weapon in favor of something lighter and easier to manage.

Latigo's kitchen is where Abuela's crusty demeanor softens. She insists on doing most of the cooking for the family herself, rushing around from bubbling pot to hot plate while constantly wiping the sweat from her brow with the hem of her ever-present apron. The joke is that the Neverborn swarm near Latigo near suppertime, drawn there by the smells of Abuela Ortega's cooking. There might be more truth to it than one might think.

30MM BASE

FAMILY, UNIQUE

WK/CG	HT	WP	CA	DF	WD
4/-	2	7	6⚡	4⚡	6

SAWED-OFF SHOTGUN

RG	⟡7
CB	5⚡
DG	2/3🌳/4🌳🌳

TALENTS:

Abilities

Companion (Family)

Gunfighter [Sawed-off Shotgun]

Harmless

Immune to Influence

Matriarch: After resolving an enemy **Strike** or Spell that targeted this model, friendly Family models within 12" and LoS of this model may Push up to their **Wk** toward the attacking model.

Weapon

Sawed-off Shotgun: After this model **Strikes** with this weapon, Push it 1" directly away from the target.

Actions

(0) Shotgun Wedding: Target non-Unique friendly living model within 8" gains Family and **Companion (Family)** until the end of the Encounter. This Action may be taken once per Encounter.

SPELLS:

(0) Shrug Off
(CC: 10 /Rst: - /Rg: C) Discard one Counter or end one effect on this model +1 effect or Counter per ⚡ in the casting total. Wounds on the model or Counters carried by the model cannot be discarded.

(1) Matriarch's Care
(CC: 17⚡ /Rst: - /Rg: (ᗢ)3) This model makes a Healing Flip. Friendly Family models within range also heal the same number of **Wd**.

(1) Obey
(CC: 14♥ /Rst: Wp /Rg: 12) Target non-Master model immediately takes a **(1)** Action or a **Charge** controlled by this model's Controller. The action selected may not cause the model to be killed or sacrificed as a part of the action. This Spell may be cast once per activation.

(1) "Play Nice!"
(CC: 12♥ /Rst: - /Rg: ●6) Enemy models declaring a **Strike**, **Focus**, **Cast**, or **Channel** Action must win a **WP → 13** Duel, or the Action ends.

(1) "Wash Your Mouth Out"
(CC: 12♥ /Rst: Wp /Rg: 10) Nominate one of target model's Spells. Target may not cast that Spell.

GUARDIAN - MINION

It's difficult for anyone involved in the Guardian Project to believe its earliest contribution to the Guild's Construct resources would become obsolete after only four years of service. But, even with the creation of so many newer and more efficient Constructs, none of the Project members would argue that its days as a workhorse are numbered.

Standing taller than a man, the Guardian was developed to provide defensive support for Guardsmen exploring the Quarantine Zone. Because the conditions of the Quarantine Zone vary from block to block, a bipedal humanoid form was envisioned. Due to the demands operating in the Quarantine Zone would put on the Guardian, the Project's prevailing belief was a sturdy combination of offensive and defensive melee weapons would be more reliable than attempting a ranged support offering in the Zone's debris fields.

The first edict inserted into a Guardian's Logic Engine is *protect*. Its durable iron chassis and massive shield have saved the lives of many a Guardsman, allowing it to withstand tremendous punishment while its charges escape. The second edict inserted is *survive*, giving the Guardian a sense of self-preservation. Once it has successfully achieved its first edict, a Guardian will brutally

enforce its second, employing its weapons to defeat the threat to itself and those it is assigned to protect.

Some of the earliest Guardsmen have called the plan to take these loyal Constructs off the front lines a mistake, citing dozens of examples where they have stepped beyond their simple programming to rescue Guardsmen or civilians. Unfortunately, their erratic behavior suggests a breakdown of the early Logic Engines, accelerating the decommission process rather than forestalling it.

40MM BASE — SOULSTONE COST: 7

CONSTRUCT, RARE 2

WK/CG	HT	WP	CA	DF	WD
4/6	2	6	4	3👁	9

SWORD	
RG	⚔ 2
CB	5👁
DG	2/4/4

SHIELD	
RG	⚔ 1
CB	3👁
DG	1/2/3

TALENTS:

Abilities

Armor +2

Borrowed Technology: Crews containing Ramos may hire this model.

Immune to Influence

Overprotective: If this model is not in base contact with a friendly model during the End Closing Phase, it Pushes into base contact with a friendly model within 6".

Weapon

Shield: After this model misses with this Weapon, inflict a Damage Flip which receives ⊟⊟ on the target of the **Strike**.

Actions

(0) Disrupt Magic: ⚫6. Enemy models' Casting Flips receive ⊟.

(0) Stalwart: Friendly models within 2" of the Guardian gain **Armor +2**. This model suffers 1 **Wd** each time affected models suffer damage.

Triggers

Df (👁📖) Shielded: After resolving a Duel with an enemy model, but before applying the Duel's effects, this model gains the effects as though it had successfully cast **Shield Wall**.

SPELLS:

(all) Shield Wall
(CC: 13 /Rst: - /Rg: C) This model gains **Armor +2**. Friendly models in base contact with this model gain **Armor +4**. **Shield Wall** ends either the next time this model moves or attacks, or in the Resolve Effects Step as normal.

(0) Self Repair
(CC: 12👁 /Rst: - /Rg: C) This model makes a Healing Flip.

(1) Protect
(CC: 14 /Rst: - /Rg: 3) When target model suffers **Wds** while within 3" of this model, this model may suffer those **Wds** instead. This Spell ends when this model or the target is removed from play or this Spell is cast on another target.

GUILD HOUND - MINION

Imported from the finest breeds of tracking dogs Earth has to offer, Guild hounds provide crucial support to the Guild's peacekeeping efforts. Convict escapes are an inevitability in Malifaux. Guild hounds lend their keen sense of smell and sight to the pursuit of escapees, able to track a quarry over hundreds of miles once the trail is detected. Generations of breeding have ensured a pure bloodline in these canines, with each generation's olfactory talents more acute than the last.

Recent events have the Guild's kennel masters questioning the reliability of their breeding programs. Many instances of heightened aggression in the animals have been reported. Fewer pups are surviving to adulthood, having fought their littermates for dominance until only one remains whole. Even more unsettling is that this aggression manifests itself before the pups have finished weaning from their mother.

Separating the pups soon after whelping seems to lessen their aggression toward one another but increases it toward humans, leading kennel masters to suspect that the hounds will fixate on and challenge whatever they perceive as an immediate threat. Lest the hand that feeds them be devoured, the program has been put on hiatus until answers to these questions can be found. In the meantime, the older, less aggressive hounds are being called upon more often than ever before, and in return, they are treated by their masters as if they are worth their weight in gold.

30MM BASE

SOULSTONE COST: 3

BEAST, INSIGNIFICANT, GUARDSMAN

WK/CG	HT	WP	CA	DF	WD
6/9	1	4	3	5	5

TEETH	
RG	⚔ 1
CB	5
DG	1/3/4

TALENTS:

Abilities

Companion (Guild Hound)

Companion (Master)

Evasive 2

Guild Kennels: Guild Crews receive one additional Soulstone in their Soulstone Pool at the start of the Encounter for every two Guild Hounds hired. The Soulstone Pool's maximum number of Soulstones remains unchanged.

Pack Mentality: This model loses Insignificant while another friendly Guild Hound is within 3".

Trained in Pairs: This model cannot take Actions other than **Move** and **Strike**, and may not use Triggers unless it activates within 4" of a friendly Master or another friendly Guild Hound.

Actions

(+1) On the Trail: This model receives an additional **Walk** Action if it activates within 3" of another friendly Guild Hound.

(1) Bloodscent: This model **Charges** target model carrying at least one Corpse, Blood, Body Parts, or Eye Counter.

(1) Bury: (ꙮ)3. Discard all Corpse, Scrap, Blood, and Body Part Counters not carried by other models.

Triggers

Cb (🐾) Source of Blood [Teeth]: After damaging defender with this Weapon, the defender must discard one Corpse, Blood, Eye, or Body Part Counter if it is carrying any.

GUILD GUARD CAPTAIN - MINION

When the Guard is deployed in large numbers to support a Guild special department's activities, they are typically accompanied by a ranking offer, usually a Captain. The Captain ensures the chain of command is followed during an operation and that the operation itself runs smoothly.

In addition to the typical Guard work of protecting the City, Guard Captains often spend time in the field working with the Guild's various special departments. This cross-training provides the Captain with additional skills specific to each department. The training is lengthy, allowing the Captain to learn how to match his men's talents to the special department's expectations and unique emphases. When completed, the Captain better understands what the department's operatives need and is able to relay that information to his men, who scramble to follow them.

Captains demand loyalty from their men and receive it. They command their men from the thick of the fight, standing side by side against whatever threat Malifaux throws their way. Shouting orders, the Captain's presence and force of will steels the spine and inspires bravery. He brooks no interference from the operatives that he and his men are assigned to, demanding they answer only to him. They are his responsibility, and he is damned sure that if someone is going to put them in harm's way, it will only be on his say-so. Once the plan is set, he is the first in a charge, fixing his eyes on the target and firing his Mauser pistol with unerring accuracy, proud with the knowledge that his Guardsmen are at his side.

30MM BASE

SOULSTONE COST: 7

GUARDSMAN, RARE 2, SPECIAL FORCES (ELITE DIVISION)

WK/CG	HT	WP	CA	DF	WD
3/5	2	5	5	4	10

AXE			MAUSER 9		
RG	⚔ 1		RG	↗8	
CB	5 🌀		CB	6 🌀	
DG	2/3/4		DG	1/2/3	

TALENTS:

Abilities

Armor +1

Companion (Master)

Duty: This model's Controller cannot be changed.

Hard to Wound 1

Officer of the Guild: This model receives +3 Ca when casting **Menace**. Increase **Menace's Rg** to 10.

Weapon

Mauser 9: After causing Severe damage with this Weapon, defender suffers a **Dg** 1/2/3 Flip which may not be Cheated.

Actions

(0) Captain: One friendly Guardsman within 6" of Guild Guard Captain activates after this model's activation ends.

(0) Frightening Authority: ☠6. Friendly Guild models receive 🎴 to starting Flips in a Morale Duel.

(2) Automatic Fire [Mauser 9]: Discard one Control Card. Target a model within range and LoS. This model makes a **Strike** with this Weapon against that model and up to two other models within 2" of the initial target which are also within range and LoS with this Weapon. This Action may be taken once per turn.

Triggers

Cb (🌀) Critical Strike [Axe]

SPELLS:

(1) "Attennn-Hut!"
(CC: 9 /Rst: - /Rg: 12) End **Slow** on target model. Target model is immune to **Slow** until the End Closing Phase.

(1) Menace
(CC: 10 /Rst: Wp /Rg: 6) Move this model up to 4" toward target model. Target may not take move Actions.

HUNTER - MINION

Despite its obvious uses in crowd control and as heavy support, the Peacekeeper's size and cost limit its deployment flexibility, namely in the arena of convict recovery. To address this deficiency, the Guild has begrudgingly worked with the Miners and Steamfitters Union, developing a smaller and more cost-effective law-enforcement Construct. The resulting design, the Hunter, stands much smaller than the Peacekeeper but packs much of the same armament and punch at a smaller price tag.

The Hunter's main role is convict retrieval. Programmed to hunt and apprehend escapees from the Quarantine Zone, a Hunter's Logic Engine is focused on little other than pursuit and arrest. Equipped with advanced instruments, the Hunter can use the lay of the land to its advantage and is capable of almost silent movement, which it uses to stalk its target. Because the

Hunter is smaller and lightly armored compared to its larger cousin, it was designed to use the geography around its target to its advantage, taking the escapee by surprise whenever possible.

The Hunter can reliably face off against Neverborn and Undead threats as well as more mundane human criminals. The Guild has been quite pleased with the results of this Construct in the short time it has seen service but expects to utilize variants of its chassis for other tasks in the future.

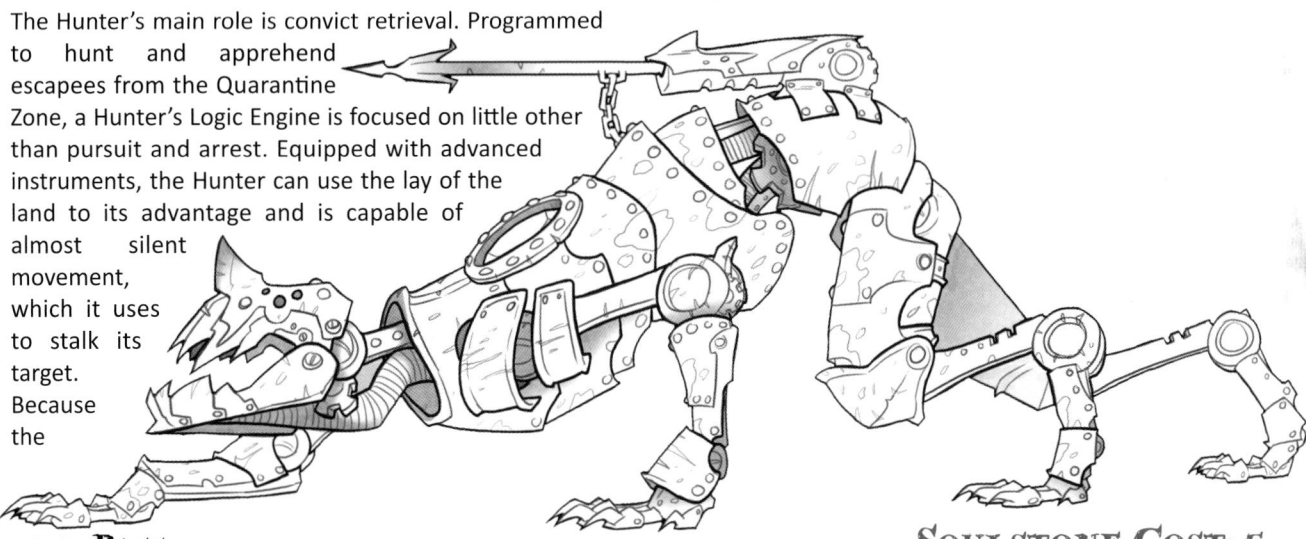

4OMM BASE

SOULSTONE COST: 6

CONSTRUCT, RARE 2

WK/CG	HT	WP	CA	DF	WD
5/7	2	5	3	5	6

MECHANICAL CLAWS	
RG	/// 1
CB	5 🌀
DG	2/3/4

CHAIN SPEAR	
RG	⌐8
CB	4 🌀
DG	1/2/4

TALENTS:

Abilities

Ambush: This model's Attack and Damage Flips receive ♦ against models that have not yet activated this turn.

Armor +1

Borrowed Technology: Crews containing Ramos may hire this model.

Immune to Influence

Weapon

Chain Spear: Models wounded by this Weapon receive **Slow.**

Actions

(2) Flurry [Mechanical Claws]

(0) Shadow: Target an enemy model in LoS. Each time the target takes a **Walk** or **Charge** Action while in this model's LoS, this model may move up to its **Wk** toward that model after it completes the Action. **Shadow** lasts until this model takes this Action again.

Triggers

Cb (🌀) Drag [Chain Spear]: After damaging defender, Push defender 4" directly toward this model.

SPELLS:

(1) Arrest
(CC: 10 ✗ /Rst: Wp /Rg: 12) Target model must discard one Control Card when declaring a **Walk** or **Charge** Action for the rest of the Encounter. If target model discards two Control Cards instead of one, **Arrest** is cancelled.

LAWYER, SECRETARY'S AIDE - MINION

Stalking the corridors of the City's Courthouse, seeking unsuspecting citizens to litigate, capable of shredding an unprepared defendant's brief in the blink of an eye, these fiendish creatures defend the Guild's interests when guns and swords have little effect. Despite its veneer of civility, the courtroom is no less bloodthirsty or lethal than the Badlands. The Lawyer wields Guild law like a weapon, artfully twisting and manipulating the meaning to suit its foul purposes. Few can withstand its blistering cross examination, and many a fortune has been brought to ruin by a well-placed objection or last-minute witness disclosed. The Guild demands convictions of its criminal prosecutors, men and women who would never allow such a thing as the truth to get in the way of making their monthly quota of guilty verdicts.

Filing motions, arguing cases, prosecuting criminals are what the Lawyer relishes. Wielding the Guild's legal codes like a mandate from the heavens, Guild Lawyers weave the law around them like a protective shield. When forced to defend themselves from an angry client or convict released from the Gaol after being wrongly convicted, they are able to use their litigious talents to argue their attacker to a standstill and are capable of bringing even the charge of a Nephilim to a halt with a well-placed objection. Rumors suggest each Lawyer is required to sign a binding contract when taking their oath of office, but none will admit with whom that contract is signed.

30MM BASE   **SOULSTONE COST: 7**

BEAST, RARE 2, SPECIAL FORCES (ELITE DIVISION)

WK/CG	HT	WP	CA	DF	WD
3/5	2	7	7	3	6

TALENTS:

Abilities

Red Tape: Strikes or Casts targeting this model receive ⊟ to Attack, Casting and Damage Flips. **Focus** or **Channel** Actions receive an additional 🃏 to the Attack and Casting Flips.

Slow to Die

Actions
(2) Furious Casting

Triggers
Ca(✗) Confuse: Reduce target's resist total by 1.

SPELLS:

(2) Closing Argument
(CC: 17✗ /Rst: Wp /Rg: 1) Target model receives **Paralyzed**. This model receives 🃏 to its Cast, Defense and Resist Flips and the target receives ⊟ ⊟ to its Defense and Resist Flips until the end of this models next activation.

(1) Censure
(CC: 14 /Rst: Wp /Rg: 8) This model chooses one of the following Actions: **Walk, Charge, Strike, Cast**. Target enemy model cannot take the chosen Action during its next activation unless it discards two Control Cards. Multiple **Censures** are cumulative but a different Action must be chosen each time.

(1) Cross Examination
(CC: 14✗ /Rst: Wp /Rg: 8) Resisting this Spell is considered a Morale Duel.

(1) Defense
(CC: 14 /Rst: - /Rg: 12) Target model gains **Hard to Wound 2**.

(1) Prosecute
(CC: 16 /Rst: Wp /Rg: 12) Target non-Master model is not considered a friendly model by its Crew for the purpose of selecting a target for Talents or Spells for the remainder of the Encounter.

RYLE GUILD PAWN - MINION

Ryle Hoffman began his journey to Malifaux as a hopeful apprentice; strong in both body and spirit, he was anxious to answer an invitation to work with Ramos. His controversial work in Construct theory and Difference Engine integration into existing Logic Engine operating systems had drawn the attention of the brilliant inventor, and they had begun a correspondence with one another while Ryle attended Oxford. Soon, Ryle was sending Ramos concepts and suggestions on how to improve designs. Ryle was stunned by his own audacity, but when Ramos replied with an invitation for him to come and train under his tutelage, Ryle could not believe his good fortune.

He indicated his interest to Ramos, but explained that much of his theory was centered around helping his brother, who was afflicted with polio. Ryle informed Ramos that he would not rest until he devised a means to counteract his brother's crippling paralysis. Ramos told him that with M&SU resources along with the infinite possibilities Malifaux offered, the two of them would find a way to help his brother together.

Ryle abandoned his studies at Oxford mid-semester and dragged C. Hoffman along with him on the train ride that would change his life, but not in the way he had expected. While travelling through the Breach, Ryle and his brother were bombarded with raw aether, the energy drawn to their magical potential. Both collapsed under the assault; but where C. Hoffman's talents were unlocked by the experience, Ryle's body and mind were nearly destroyed. His organs were unable to withstand the punishment wrought by the Breach, and they shut down, one after the other. Even his mind was torn apart by the experience. He exited the Breach broken and comatose.

While Ryle lay dying, Ramos worked feverishly to save his life. He stripped away the flesh and organs laid waste by the aether, replacing them with life-sustaining mechanical parts. For his damaged mind, Ramos constructed a very specific Logic Engine, designed to maintain whatever remained of the once hopeful apprentice until such a time as he the damage could be more thoroughly repaired.

Ryle and his brother are both in the Guild's employ now. C. Hoffman works feverishly to find some way to unlock his brother's mind and body from their mechanical prison while Ryle serves the Guild as an enforcer, his new body further augmented and armed by the Guild. Some of Ryle's magical potential remains, and hopefully, in addition to this magic, some other essence of Ryle remains hidden within the half-machine, half-man monstrosity Ramos created.

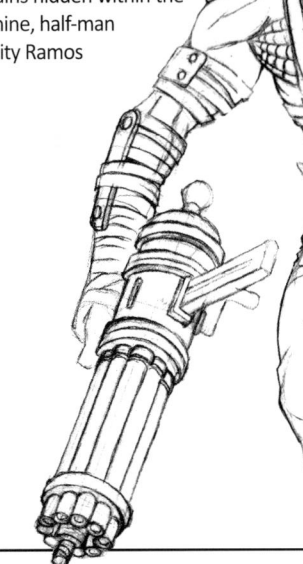

40MM BASE **SOULSTONE COST: 8**

CONSTRUCT, SPECIAL FORCES (ELITE DIVISION), UNIQUE

Wk/Cg	Ht	Wp	Ca	Df	Wd
4/6	3	5	2	3	10

HYDRAULIC FIST	
Rg	⚡ 2
Cb	5 🌀
Dg	2/4/6

GATLING GUN	
Rg	↗ 12
Cb	5 🌀
Dg	1/3/4

TALENTS:

Abilities

Armor +1

Breach Psychosis: This model is immune to other model's Talents and Spells that require it to make a **Wp** Duel.

Can't Connect: This model is never considered a friendly model to its Crew for the purpose of selecting a target for Talents or Spells.

Destructive Impulse: Until this model kills another model, it receives -3 **Wp** and has the Insignificant characteristic.

Hulking: Ht 1 or Ht 2 models cannot perform a Parting **Strike** against this model when it disengages.

Mechanized: This model is both a Construct and a living model. When killed, it produces three Scrap Counters.

Weapon

Gatling Gun: After causing Severe damage with this Weapon, target suffers a **Dg** 1/2/4 Flip which may not be Cheated.

Actions
(+1) Ranged Expert

(0) Socially Repressed: Push this model 4" directly away from the closest living model.

(2) Automatic Fire [Gatling Gun]: Discard one Control Card. Target a model within range and LoS. This model makes a **Strike** with this Weapon against that model and up to two other models within 2" of the initial target which are also within range and LoS with this Weapon. This Action may be taken once per turn.

Triggers
Cb (🌀) Critical Strike [Hydraulic Fist]

Cb (🌀🌀) Fully Automatic [Gatling Gun]: After inflicting damage, make a **Dg** 1/2/4 Flip against the same target.

Cb (🌀🌀) Lack of Empathy [Hydraulic Fist, Gatling Gun]: Cancel any activated Triggers. No other Triggers may be activated during this Action.

WATCHER - MINION

The Watcher is a remarkable Construct providing Guild surveillance and reconnaissance support in a small, maneuverable package. A magnificent achievement, the Watcher is borne aloft by steam jets and leather wings, making it the first Guild Construct capable of sustained flight.

These "eyes in the sky" operate as scouts, functioning on specific edicts installed by the Guild. Because of the small size of its Logic Engine, a Watcher is permitted little deviation from its programming. Far too much of the processing power is devoted to controlling the Construct's complex flight mechanisms. When ordered to survey a location, the Watcher is typically given the edicts *seek*, *record*, and *survive*. Once dispatched, it locates the designated site or individual, takes several photographs of the target, and returns to deliver the information gathered.

Some Watchers are set to follow a target from a distance, keeping it in view and relaying that location to Guild operatives in the area via a sophisticated heliograph mounted on the spherical frame. Watchers are notoriously unreliable after sunset, effectively blind without the sun's illumination to maneuver by. Although their small searchlight does provide some assistance during nocturnal missions, much of their ability depends on the sun's illumination to function. This drawback to the Watcher's use is exploited by those who are aware of it, allowing them to operate at night and avoid the Construct's merciless gaze.

30MM BASE

SOULSTONE COST: 3

CONSTRUCT

Wk/Cg	Ht	Wp	Ca	Df	Wd
7/-	1	5	4	5	4

SKY EYE	
Rg	⌐16
Cb	6🌀
Dg	0/1/1

TALENTS:

Abilities

Always Watching: Friendly models ignore cover modifiers when targeting a model within 4" of this model.

Battlefield Knowledge: Enemy models cannot be deployed outside their Crew's Deployment Zone during deployment.

Flight

Fly High: This model ignores friendly models when determining LoS. This model cannot be targeted with Parting **Strikes**.

Immune to Influence

Preprogrammed: This model ignores **Harmless**, and **Pitiful**.

Slow to Die

Weapon

Sky Eye: Until the End Closing Phase, friendly models ignore cover modifiers when targeting a model hit by this Weapon.

Actions

(1) Forward Observer: This model's Controller looks at the top card of their Fate Deck and then places it back on either the top or the bottom of the Deck.

(2) Forewarned: This model's Controller looks at the top two cards of their Fate Deck and then places each back on either the top or the bottom of the Deck in any order.

Triggers

Cb (🌀) Light Target [Sky Eye]: Defender loses **Terrifying** when hit by this Weapon.

Cb (🌀) Mark Target [Sky Eye]: End **Harmless** or **Pitiful** on defender hit by this Weapon.

RESURRECTIONISTS

RESURRECTIONISTS

As the morning sun drew high, Kirai Ankoku's strength withered until she collapsed in the gutter, deep within the slum district, but she had no idea where. She was too weak to continue crying, but the thin trickle of water from her weeping stained her face with smeared makeup bleeding down her dark cheek.

She lost not just the will and strength to keep moving, but the very will to live. How could she awaken to the most beautiful day of her life, filled with more joy and comfort than she had every hoped she might have found when she left her family in the Three Kingdoms, only to have it dashed away in moments?

Rainwater mixed with the waste of inhabitants of the slums washed into her eye from the drainage trough beside the cobblestone road and into her gaping mouth. She no longer cared. She was vulnerable, prostrate, in this dark section of the City. Now, with the memory of those moments running through her head over and over again, she wished she had never run at all, but simply let the man have his way. She drew her hand to her face and stared at the green serpent ring, the circumference too big for her dainty fingers. It was all that mattered to her now; the only possession of any value, more even than her life. If she died, she would take it to her grave, she vowed. If anyone would bother to have her buried. It was more likely that someone would take it, there in that nearly lawless district, and let her live.

Mustering what little strength she retained, she rolled onto her back and removed the thin chain from around her neck. Her vision blurred, and her arms were heavy as she shook aside the worthless charm dangling from it and slipped her ring upon the links. Clasping it again, she tucked the serpentine ring within her pale kimono, stained with dirt from the street and filth from the gutter as well as her own sweat and tears.

Her mind faltered and slipped deeper into unconsciousness and, as she passed out, her last thought was that she hoped she might never awaken again. The ring at her neck beat as if a heart throbbed within the metal and emerald form.

Although still alive, her spirit rose from her body. Its gossamer form billowed in the wind like thin vapor lingering above an extinguished candle. It regarded the girl lying below it in the street, eyes of strangers dismissing her from open windows. No one came to help her. Some might cause harm to the body, but the detached soul knew it no longer mattered. Only one thing mattered to her now, and that was vengeance for what had been done to her. The Ikiryo spirit of Kirai Ankoku flew high above Malifaux and began its search for those that committed such atrocities.

It reached into the aether separating the tangible worlds known to man, the source of her power, and the home of immeasurable spirits. It was a simple gesture of her great will to pull forth several of the weakest spirits, old, and with little thought and understanding remaining to them of their lives and the world of the living. The Ikiryo gave five of them form, locked them to the physical world, yet their bodies longed to dissipate back into the comfort of the spirit aether where they belonged, their substance rolling away like fog in the noonday sun. But she held them in place and commanded them to seek out the men that were responsible for what they had done to her – to Kirai.

The Seishin spirits meandered reluctantly through the narrow alleys of the City, following their charge, invisibly seeking out an end to their mission so that they might be released and once more forgotten.

The first they discovered were two ex-Guardsmen, returning from the morning's encounter at the Qi and Gong. Albert McDonnell cradled his bloody arm while the other laughed at his misfortune, jangling the coins in the small pouch strapped to his belt.

"He almost cut off my hand," McDonnell complained as they rounded Cascylle Boulevard.

"Ah. You'll heal. Stop yer bellyachin' and appreciate the work you got. Botched the job and still got some coin for the trouble. Not bad."

"Need more. And need true Guild scrip, not a few clinkers of change. Getting too hard to make ends meet and you know it. Muscle for hire's getting to be a common enough racket that ev'ry blamed fool with a gun-"

He never finished his statement. Never said another word. Before the two men stood a beautiful woman, judging by her thin body and the rigid posture of a lady expected to present herself to a high station. Her arms stretched out, and the wide open sleeves of the white kimono fell beyond her waist. She wore a thick alabaster mask, devoid of any human features save the narrow almond-shaped eyeholes of the Orient. She appeared transparent, and as she took form before the two men, the gaseous lower part of her body developed into multiple layers of kimono with a loose outer robe, blowing in a wind that was not there.

The Onryo solidified before them, and they merely looked upon it, mouths agape and eyes growing wide.

A howl erupted from its throat, and its arms lashed forward. Despite a breadth of four yards separating them, McDonnell was thrown backward by the sheer malevolence made tangible, the breath struck from his body and his hat rolled away, caught up in the eddy of the spiritual gust. She pounced, and the second mercenary jumped away, trying to escape, screaming in terror. The Onryo descended upon him, raking its razor-like nails across his back, driving him to the ground. It fell upon him, mauling his flesh, screaming in hatred as it tore into him. As his body stilled, the pool of blood growing beneath it, its masked face lifted to regard McDonnell, scampering away. Its claws gleamed in the light falling between buildings, and its chest heaved in a mockery of growling and breath from the exertion, though it did not breathe.

McDonnell screamed and covered his face with his arms as it covered the distance between them in the span of a heartbeat.

The Ikiryo was there, then, and stopped the Onryo from fulfilling its purpose. It held the wrist of the Onryo, flailing and screaming madly to be allowed to destroy the man, its rage immense and unbridled. But the Ikiryo was strong and held its hand effortlessly from slicing into the guilty. The Ikiryo's other hand found the man's throat and held him to the ground, and he beat upon it ineffectually. It wrapped its fingers about the hand of the Onryo, extending its index finger and holding it like a quill pen. Screaming through the ordeal, the Ikiryo used the extended finger to carve an elaborate Kanji symbol across his forehead.

He continued screaming wildly as it used the Onryo finger as a scalpel, cutting his vest and shirt aside and then the flesh of his torso. It cut layer upon layer aside until it exposed his heart. It wouldn't let him die. Finally, the Ikiryo released the Onryo whose mask was pulled aside to reveal a face twisted in the anguish of a damnation of denied revenge for something McDonnell had nothing to do with. It didn't care. It ripped his beating heart from the cavity of his chest, severing the arteries and vessels and freeing it from his body.

Hours later, Nicodem the Undertaker looked upon the two bodies, hiding his interest as a Death Marshal and two Witch Hunters poked and prodded a the remains. He would not reveal the curiosity that flashed thrillingly through his mind as they recounted the several eyewitness accounts they had procured.

Likely, no one would have come to aid the dark men during an attack in that section of the City, or any other section. Yet, each account of this dual murder proved more sinister as each witness agreed that the men were attacked by invisible apparitions. If not for the gore and visceral remains, no one would have thought the victims were anything other than insane, flailing against the air, from their perspective.

The Guild Officers debated about the possibility of an arcane assassin.

Nicodem scoffed silently at their simple minded efforts at understanding what was so clear to him.

They waited for a scholar to arrive to decipher the marks on both men's heads, now that the coagulated blood had been cleaned away and the flesh put into place. The first bore a mark that read 罰. The second said 罪.

The Seishin found a third man that had first informed the assailants of Kirai's whereabouts and reported his location to the Ikiryo. It descended upon the building where he worked, oblivious to the crimes to which he was a part. In fact, he believed himself to be a bastion of lawfulness in a world filled with anarchy and criminality, dutifully carrying out his work without complaint or question. He had no idea who "Kirai Ankoku" was until the request came before him to locate her whereabouts, and he quickly had Deputy Reynolds, another Guardsmen, assigned to track her down, reporting to his superior the findings of that tracker.

Here he worked, just a clerk going about his business. The Ikiryo passed through the Guild offices unseen and silent. It waited until he was alone in a back room, filing paper and returning arcane tomes to their proper place when the Ikiryo held shut the door.

The room was within the deepest interior of the building and had no windows to let in the light of day. The candles illuminating his work flickered in a wind though no breeze could infiltrate the closed room. He looked up from his paperwork, confused, but without concern as he worked within the heart of the greatest Guild building in Malifaux, likely the safest place in the entire world.

The air grew stifling and sweat beaded on his forehead and upper lip, and he felt it so thick that he could hardly breathe; he knew something was wrong. He held the candle before him with a hand shielding it as he walked so as not to extinguish the flame.

As he neared the door, anxious to the leave the oppressive room, a dark figure loomed before him as the candlelight fell upon it. She was a tall woman, old and bent with long features and eyes hidden behind a thick fold of cloth. She smiled, exposing a row of pointed teeth, each dark and stained. She raised a large lantern, wrapped in rice paper, and as she did, it began to glow, illuminating them both.

"You've been a bad man," the Datsue-Ba said. "I've come to weigh your sins against your character."

He staggered backward and fell, crawling away from the sinister woman that had somehow infiltrated the inner-most chambers of the Guild offices. She raised a slender carving knife before her smiling face.

He whimpered, "I have no sins. I'm a good man."

She cackled a low, dry laugh. "Oh, that's what they all say. You won't have much to fear then, I suppose."

She took her time slicing away his clothes to expose him, naked and struggling, but she didn't mind the effort to hold him down. The blows against her to ward off the attack were easily ignored, and she hummed quietly as she worked. She cut away a thin layer of flesh, and his screams took on a higher pitch. Surgically, she peeled away more and more layers until his screaming tore the lining in his throat. Later, there would be no way to know it, but he died choking on his own blood.

Guardsmen and officers beat upon the door to aid him, but it withstood all of their efforts. As a final blow struck the wood, it burst into the room, torn easily from its iron hinges as if nothing ever resisted its opening.

The sounds of the clerk's screaming had ceased minutes earlier, and none dared enter the darkness of the room. When they were each armed with a gaslight and ready weapon, they entered to find the man, naked and flayed, his blood spilled beneath him. His chest was open and it took no time to discern his heart had been removed.

The mark upon his head was an elaborate carving of the Kanji symbol: 裁.

There was no egress from the room save the one thick door they had broken down. No signs of any other person could be found in the room.

Nicodem was summoned to deal with the remains, and he found it amusing that each death, just as peculiar and mysterious and clearly the work of something supernatural, elicited only one step of elevation for the Guild investigators. No Lady Justice. No Madame Criid. They brought in higher ranking officers to scratch their heads and debate the significance of the Kanji symbol they didn't recognize. Having chosen the Nipponese warrior as his preferred animated soldier, he knew this symbol upon the man's head.

It meant, "Judgment."

The fourth man the Ikiryo wanted was Reynolds, the man that had followed her that night to the Qi and Gong and reported her whereabouts to the one that wanted her dead.

It was now late in the day, and he was finishing his duties, thinking nothing at all of the work he had done regarding the tracking of a mere girl, a prostitute, and how it might be linked to the growing rumors surrounding these mysterious deaths. He had a curiosity about such things, and anxiety, too, but living in Malifaux had a desensitizing effect about those kinds of issues.

As he walked to the Guild stables at the back of the Guild offices, two Shikome spirits, great bat-like beasts with long teeth, descended upon him from the darkening sky. One moment, he was whistling absently, and the next, he was shrieking wildly as the two carried him aloft, fighting for pieces of his flesh, tearing his body away from one another to covet his flesh as their own. They struggled over him, and the Ikiryo remained close, holding his soul within him, refusing to let him die.

When he could take no more, the Ikiryo dismissed the two beasts, and his body, unnaturally held alive, fell back to the ground. His bones shattered and tore through what flesh remained.

The Ikiryo hovered above him. He could not feel his limbs, of course, as they were shattered and most of the flesh torn away and devoured. He didn't even breathe, though he knew something was wrong when he tried to scream and not even a gasp escaped him. His eyes darted back and forth in fear and anguish. Her claws tore open his

chest and removed his heart while he watched it lifted before his eyes. She let him die as his mind, like the remains of his body, was truly broken.

They found him soon thereafter and would have thought him attacked and killed by something much more carnal than the typical surgical cutting they had found on the other bodies that day. Little remained of him save a picked over skeleton and greasy smear beneath it that even the bugs around didn't seem interested in. The precisely carved Kanji symbol on his forehead, however, marked him as the fourth of the day's victims.

被

The sun rested on the edge of the horizon as Kirai stirred, awakening in the gutter where she had fallen unconscious. Remarkably, she was unmolested, even having spent the entire day in the street, her kimono barely fastened about her otherwise naked body.

The thought of the Ikiryo was nothing but a quickly fading dream. She believed that's all it was — just the wish for revenge that she was impotent to enact.

It saw her, though, and knew she had no desire to go on living. Vengeance for one so small and frail seemed beyond her capability. Her Ikiryo spirit, however, had plans for two more men responsible for the depths of her suffering. If Kirai lived through the day, her spirit vowed she would visit the Captain, herself, and drag him to hell.

The final victim would be most difficult to reach for he was powerful and ever surrounded by other potent practitioners of the arcane arts. Still, she would mete out vengeance for the crimes committed against the young girl that rose from the cobblestone pavement and dragged herself reluctantly to the servant's shack behind the Governor General's mansion.

KIRAI ANKOKU - MASTER

[kee-rah-ee ahn-koh-koo]

Kirai Ankoku immigrated to Malifaux, desperate to change her fate. Although very young, she left the Three Kingdoms, determined to forge a life for herself and help her family members remaining behind. Making her way around the globe, penniless and alone, then procuring passage through the Breach, stands as a testament to her perseverance.

Stepping off the train, she looked upon the faces of other settlers, each one a mixture of nervousness and hope at the prospect of forging a new life in a new world. Each settler thought they had found a

way to defy the destiny that fate had written for them.

Sadly, Kirai found that fate is not easily defied.

She struggled, the need to survive overcoming her pride when she took work as one of the "upper parlor girls" at the Qi and Gong. She quickly became known to high ranking Guild officials who pulled strings and helped her find employment as a groundskeeper for the Governor General.

30MM BASE

SOULSTONE CACHE: 3

MASTER

WK/CG	HT	WP	CA	DF	WD
4/4	2	5	6✗	2	8

BLOODY SHEARS

RG	⚔ 1
CB	4
DG	2/3/4

TALENTS:

Abilities

Detached: Crews containing this model may hire Spirits from any Faction at no additional cost during Scraps or Brawls. During Scraps, any non-Spirit model gains Rare 1 when hired by this Crew.

Immediate Revenge 2: Models inflicting damage on this model with ranged attacks suffer 2 **Wd** after resolving the damage.

Pitiful: Until this model activates each turn, models targeting this model must win a Wp→Wp Duel or the Action immediately ends.

Spirit Anchor: When a living, Spirit, or Undead model is killed within 8", Place one Seishin in base contact with this model.

Actions

(+1) Instinctual

(0) Seishin Beacon: 🐾2. When a friendly Seishin is killed, this model may suffer 1 **Wd** to allow that Seishin to ignore its **Fragile Connection** Ability.

(0) Soothe Spirit: Target friendly Spirit within 8" makes a Healing Flip.

(0) Spirit Food: Target an enemy living or Undead model within 12". If the target is killed this turn, summon one Gaki into base contact with the model before it is removed from play.

(0) Uncontrolled Crying: This model is affected by **Pitiful** as if it had not yet activated this turn.

(1) Absorb Spirit: Sacrifice a friendly Spirit within 6". Draw two Control Cards. This model heals 2 **Wd** and receives **Fast**.

(1) Swirling Spirits: Switch two friendly Spirits within 12" of this model.

Triggers

Ca (✗ ✗) Don't Blink [Evolve Spirit, Summon Ikiryo]: This model suffers 1 **Wd**. Place summoned Spirit within 12".

Wp (✗) Twisted Mind: After winning a Duel, the opposing model in the Duel suffers 2 **Wd**.

SPELLS:

(0) In the Spirit World
(CC: 13 ✗ 🐾 /Rst: - /Rg: C) Place this model in base contact with target friendly Spirit within 18". This model gains Spirit.

(1) Chill of Death
(CC: 12 ✗ /Rst: Wp /Rg: 8) Target's **Strike**, **Cast**, **Wp**, and **Df** Flips in Duels involving a Spirit receive ⊟.

(1) Evolve Spirit
(CC: 17 ✗ /Rst: - /Rg: C) After successfully casting this Spell, choose one of the following effects:
- Sacrifice a friendly Spirit within 6", suffer 1 **Wd**, Summon one Gaki.
- Sacrifice a friendly Spirit within 6", suffer 2 **Wd**, Summon one Onryo.
- Sacrifice two friendly Spirits within 6", suffer 3 **Wd**, Summon one Shikome.

(1) Summon Ikiryo
(CC: 11 ✗ ✗ /Rst: - /Rg: C) Suffer 4 **Wd** . Summon Ikiryo.

(2) Spiritual Combination
(CC: 14 ✗ ✗ /Rst: - /Rg: 8) Sacrifice a friendly Spirit within 6". Target Spirit receives **Reactivate**.

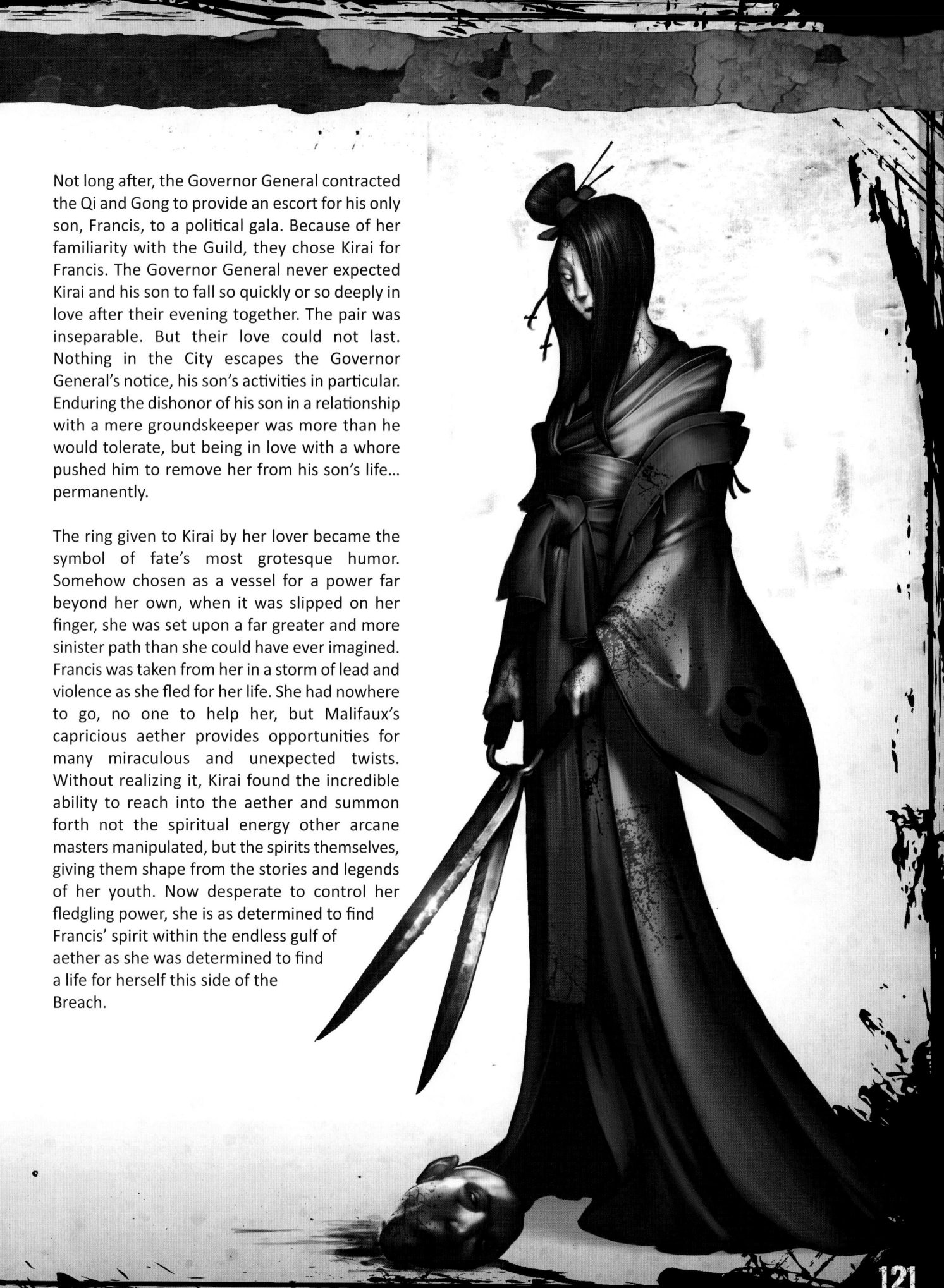

Not long after, the Governor General contracted the Qi and Gong to provide an escort for his only son, Francis, to a political gala. Because of her familiarity with the Guild, they chose Kirai for Francis. The Governor General never expected Kirai and his son to fall so quickly or so deeply in love after their evening together. The pair was inseparable. But their love could not last. Nothing in the City escapes the Governor General's notice, his son's activities in particular. Enduring the dishonor of his son in a relationship with a mere groundskeeper was more than he would tolerate, but being in love with a whore pushed him to remove her from his son's life... permanently.

The ring given to Kirai by her lover became the symbol of fate's most grotesque humor. Somehow chosen as a vessel for a power far beyond her own, when it was slipped on her finger, she was set upon a far greater and more sinister path than she could have ever imagined. Francis was taken from her in a storm of lead and violence as she fled for her life. She had nowhere to go, no one to help her, but Malifaux's capricious aether provides opportunities for many miraculous and unexpected twists. Without realizing it, Kirai found the incredible ability to reach into the aether and summon forth not the spiritual energy other arcane masters manipulated, but the spirits themselves, giving them shape from the stories and legends of her youth. Now desperate to control her fledgling power, she is as determined to find Francis' spirit within the endless gulf of aether as she was determined to find a life for herself this side of the Breach.

IKIRYO - MINION
[ee-kee-ryoh]

The Ikiryo is a spiritual anomaly. In almost all cases, spiritual manifestation results as residual soul energy cannot find its way to join the vast maelstrom in the aether regions beyond Malifaux and Earth. The Ikiryo is still very attached to the world of the living because it is the living soul of Kirai Ankoku.

It may never be understood how Kirai developed the ability to call forth her spirit in the physical world. Nicodem studies her, hoping she may infuse his risen corpses with better, autonomous spirits that have thoughts and wills of their own, to make them more fearsome warriors to contend with. His view of the Ikiryo is that it was first called upon to carry out the vengeance that Kirai desperately wanted but could never fulfill.

He was mostly correct - the Ikiryo is a powerful embodiment of anger and revenge that cannot be sated until it has found vengeance for the atrocities done to Kirai. However, unknown to him, and even to Kirai, is a deeper mystery to its origin and purpose. Linked somehow to the ancient Gorgon spirit, the Ikiryo is an unknowing harbinger of a coming conflict involving great beings, long forgotten, that will embroil the young Kirai Ankoku in ways she could never imagine.

Time will tell if the Ikiryo remains until it has completed its task of vengeance or if its purpose is tied to some greater task.

30MM BASE — SOULSTONE COST: SUMMONED

SPIRIT, UNIQUE

WK/CG	HT	WP	CA	DF	WD
5/7	3	6	4✗	5	5

RAZOR SHARP FINGERNAILS		VENGEFUL WAIL	
RG	⚔1	RG	➹10
CB	6✗	CB	5
DG	2/3/5	DG	2/2♧/3♧

TALENTS:

Abilities

Kirai's Soul: This model may not be controlled by any crew other than the one it was summoned into. If this model is killed or sacrificed, its Controller discards two Control Cards.

Moment of Clarity: Heal friendly Kirai 2 **Wd** if this model is sacrificed.

Spirit Touch: Melee attacks made by this model ignore **Armor**.

Vengeance Attained: When this model kills an enemy model, a friendly Kirai in play makes a Healing Flip.

Weapons

Razor Sharp Fingernails: This Weapon's Attack Duels use either the target's **Df** or **Wp**. Declare the statistic used when declaring the attack.

Actions

(+1) Melee Expert

(0) Call Spirits: (⚅)18. This model's Controller may Push friendly Spirits within range up to 4" toward this model.

Triggers

Cb (✗ ✗) Maul [Razor Sharp Fingernails]: This Weapon's Damage Flip receives ➕ ➕ .

Lost Love - Totem

Francis died.

As his lifeblood pumped onto the dingy hotel room floor that day, Francis watched the love of his life, the woman he swore himself to eternally, escape thanks to his sacrifice. After that, he knew nothing save the aching loss of his final separation from Kirai.

For a time, his spirit drifted, caught in aetheric currents and eddies, mingling with other spiritual energies. He could sense some were new to the aether, as he was, while others had drifted along for centuries. All seemed to be losing themselves to the aether, their forms slowly unraveling and dissipating to mingle with other spirits similarly unraveled.

Francis watched these dissolutions closely. When would he start to unravel as they were? Had he already? What memories would be the first to fade, and would he even realize there were gaps? How could he hold onto his memories of his *qing ren*? He focused on her face, her scent, the color of her eyes, and he realized how he could fight the tides seeking to wash him away. He had to fight! Those spirits fading around him had given up; they were letting the aether claim them bit by bit. Only by staying focused on what he loved most could he remain himself,

maybe he could stay afloat long enough to find Kirai...if not, he mused sadly, he may be able to hold on until she came to join him.

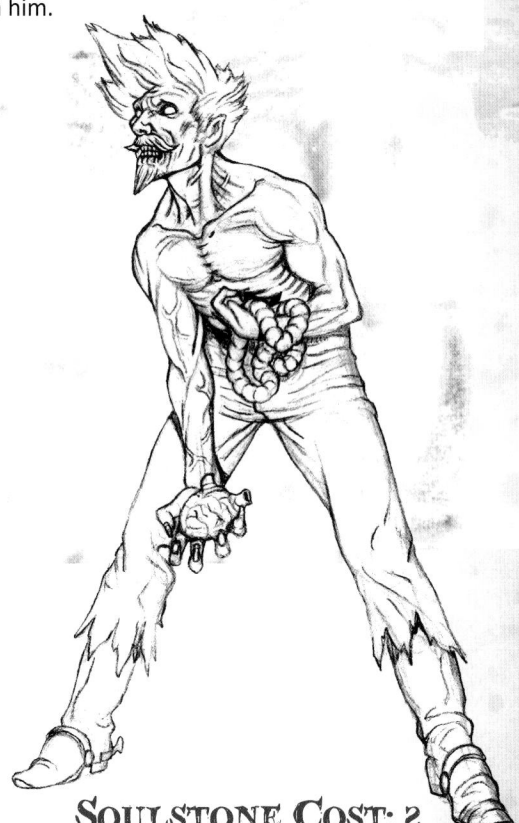

SOULSTONE COST: 2

30MM BASE

SPIRIT, TOTEM (KIRAI)

WK/CG	HT	WP	CA	DF	WD
5/-	2	5	3✗	4	3

COLD EMBRACE

RG	⫽ 1
CB	4
DG	1/2/4

TALENTS:

Abilities

Companion (Kirai)

For Love: When a friendly Kirai would be killed or sacrificed, sacrifice this model instead. The friendly Kirai remains in play with 4 **Wd** remaining and gains Spirit until the end of the Encounter.

Kirai's Soul: This model may not be controlled by any crew other than the one it was summoned into. If this model is killed or sacrificed, its Controller discards two Control Cards.

Actions

(0) I Will Never Leave You: Push this model into base contact with a friendly Kirai within 12".

SPELLS:

(1) Magical Extension
(CC: * /Rst: * /Rg: *) This Spell may be cast only once per activation. Cast one of the connected Master's (1) Spells. During this casting, this model may use a Soulstone to change its starting total.

(1) Pass Beyond
(CC: 14✗ ✗ /Rst: - /Rg: 2) Target friendly non-Master model suffers half of its remaining **Wd**. That model receives Spirit until the end of the Encounter.

(1) Soothe Spirit
(CC: 11🕊 /Rst: - /Rg: 8) Target Spirit makes a Healing Flip.

NECROTIC MACHINE – TOTEM

Where most Constructs are powered by draining Soulstones of their concentrated charge, many of the devices created during the days of Old Malifaux relied on drawing the ambient spirit energy present in the aether to power them.

The Necrotic Machine is a remnant of this old technology, created using a blend of necromantic and scientific techniques. Its original purpose is lost to the ages, but it is capable of focusing necromantic power, temporarily imbuing an individual with the energy of the dead. The Construct is also equipped with a wicked syringe that has an inexaustible supply of a deadly toxin.

After Old Malifaux fell, the machine lay dormant and forgotten for centuries until Seamus and Molly stumbled across it. The machine sensed the power Molly had absorbed from the Gorgon's Tear and activated, drawn to what it sensed as a kindred contradiction of animated form and necromantic power. This mysterious blending of animating energy intrigues the machine, and it continues to follow Molly in an attempt to reconcile its senses.

The events at Kythera released a potent form of necromantic energy into Malifaux. This energy revitalized the machine, providing power to some of its higher functions. It has regained some sense of a once slumbering awareness. Its consciousness stirs, and it plans and schemes once more. Sensing Molly has the means to aid its quest to restore Old Malifaux, the machine has begun telling her about the empire's wonders in the hope of enlisting her aid when the time comes.

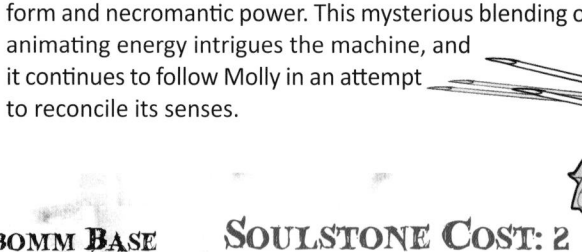

30MM BASE — SOULSTONE COST: 2

CONSTRUCT, INSIGNIFICANT, TOTEM, UNDEAD, UNIQUE

WK/CG	HT	WP	CA	DF	WD
5/-	1	5	4✗	3	4

NECROTIC INJECTION

RG	⚔ 1
CB	4✗
DG	2/2/4

TALENTS:

Abilities

Companion (Master)

Hard to Wound 1

Molly's Toy: When this model is connected to Molly Squidpiddge, that model gains the following Action until the end of the Encounter: "**(0) Fix Toy:** Friendly Necrotic Machine within 4" makes a Healing Flip."

Undead Construct: When this model is killed, it generates one Corpse Counter.

Actions

(0) Create Undeath: Target non-Master, living model within 2" gains Undead.

Triggers

Cb (✗✗) Undead Infection: Poison 3.

SPELLS:

(1) Magical Extension
(CC: * /Rst: * /Rg: *) This Spell may be cast only once per activation. Cast one of the connected Master's **(1)** Spells. During this casting, this model may use a Soulstone to change its starting total.

MOLLY SQUIDPIDDGE – HENCHMAN

Bound, body and soul, to the man who killed her, Molly Squidpiddge is a walking contradiction. Molly's devotion to and revulsion of Seamus are constantly conflicting emotions, threatening to overwhelm her when her Master demands her to act.

Through the increasingly hazy memories Molly has of being alive, she can vaguely recall her murder at his hands, followed soon after by the cold embrace of the grave. Seamus' summoning her back from the afterlife the first time was anything but gentle; she remembers her bouts of bloody coughing, testament to a resurrection gone horribly wrong. Molly's second resurrection was gentler, having been facilitated by the Gorgon's Tear, then in Seamus' possession. He knew she had some connection to the mysterious gem and swore to get his money's worth from her the second time around.

Most of the time Molly serves as little more than a glorified porter, bearing the raving head of Phillip Tombers in the event it may yield some nugget of information Seamus requires. She also bears Seamus' verbal haranguing with a fragile poise, frequently breaking into uncontrollable tears. Seamus often reminds her she is an awful mess, far different from how beautiful she had been when they first met. For her part, Molly suffers his jabs, unable to run away, wondering how long before she goes completely mad. Recently, Molly has been exhibiting a strange affinity for the more bizarre Undead she comes across. Oddities, such as the horrifying creatures McMourning keeps locked in his laboratories, willingly follow her orders, as if some unspoken bond between them exists. While Seamus tries to use Molly's *gift* to his advantage, she has found a degree of freedom she thought she would never have again and intends on using it to its fullest, perhaps even escaping the macabre purgatory Seamus has consigned her to.

30MM BASE

SOULSTONE COST: 9

BELLE, GRAVEROBBER, HENCHMAN 5, SPECIAL FORCES (HORROR), UNDEAD

WK/CG	HT	WP	CA	DF	WD
4/6	2	5	7✗	4✗	10

TALENTS:

Abilities

Extraordinary Dead: ⚫4. Friendly Belles and Horrors receive +2 **Wk** to **Walk** Actions they initiate.

Hard to Wound 1

Necrotic Spray: Living models within 1" of this model suffer 1 **Wd** when it suffers damage from a melee attack.

Pitiful: Until this model activates each turn, models targeting this model must win a **Wp→Wp** Duel or the Action immediately ends.

Slow to Die

Special Forces Leader (Horror): A Crew led by this model may only hire Horrors, Belles and Totems.

Superior Dead: This model is immune to effects that specifically target Undead.

Actions

(+1) Instinctual

(0) Impossible Knowledge: ⚫6. Friendly Undead models gain **Necrotic Spray**.

(0) The Gorgon's Tear: This model gains **Terrifying → 14.**

(0) Uncontrolled Crying: This model is affected by **Pitiful** as if it had not yet activated this turn.

(1) Reveal Philip: (✗)4. Living models must immediately make a **Wp → 12** Morale Duel.

Triggers

Df (✗ ✗) Masterful Dead: When this model suffers damage, its Controller may discard two Control Cards. This model suffers no **Wd** from the damage.

Wp (✗) Twisted Mind: After this model wins the Duel, the opposing model suffers 2 **Wd**.

SPELLS:

(0) Undead Construction
(CC: 15✗ ✗ /Rst: - /Rg: C) Discard two Corpse Counters. Summon one Belle, or one Horror with a base size no larger than 30mm, or a Necrotic Machine

(0) Whispered Secret
(CC: 12✗ ✗ /Rst: Wp /Rg: 12) Gain one of target's **(1)** Spells. This spell lasts until this model casts the nominated Spell, or casts this Spell again. You may not copy spells which reference a specific model by name.

(1) Imbue Vigor
(CC: 14❤ /Rst: - /Rg: 18) Target model gains +3 **Wk**.

(1) The Philosophy of Uncertainty
(CC: 15✗ ✗ /Rst: Wp /Rg: 4) Sacrifice this model. Kill target model.

(1) The Shocking Truth
(CC: 12✗ /Rst: Wp /Rg: 3)
Dg 2/3+Slow/3+Paralyzed.

(1) Terrible Secret
(CC: 14✗ /Rst: Wp /Rg: 12) Target model receives ⊟ ⊟ on all Attack and Defense Flips.

DATSUE-BA - MINION
[dah-tsoo-eh-bah]

Appearing as a bony elderly woman bearing a knife and lantern, the Datsue-Ba visits sinners to judge their lives, ready to weigh the character and souls of the righteous and the wicked. She watches over the gateway between life and death, measuring everyone she meets along the way to determine who can move on and who is to be denied, sent back to atone for their crimes.

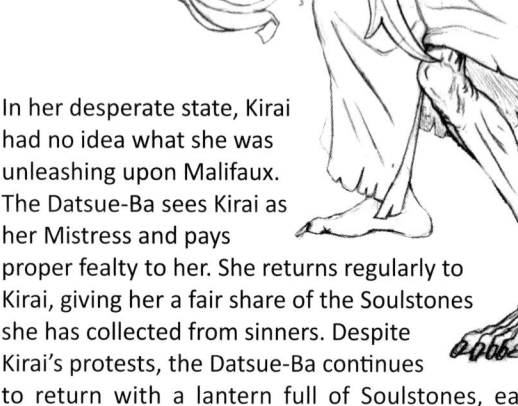

Corrupted by Malifaux's power, the spirit that once kindly waited for the dead to pass by now seeks out the living, wishing to hasten their journey to judgment in the afterlife. Her attacks seek to evaluate a man's bravery, his will against her terrifying visage. She strips the clothing and skin off those she slays, weighing each to determine the value of their soul. Those she finds lacking, she banishes to the Soulstones powering her lantern. Souls she deems worthy, she releases, their energy dissipating and mingling with the ever present aether.

The Datsue-Ba hunts other spirits as well. In her damaged state, she imagines each of these spirits is attempting to escape her judgment, and she desperately wants to appropriately judge them before they can get away. Spirits caught by Datsue-Ba are weighed harshly, most being trapped, fueling the glow of her lantern.

In her desperate state, Kirai had no idea what she was unleashing upon Malifaux. The Datsue-Ba sees Kirai as her Mistress and pays proper fealty to her. She returns regularly to Kirai, giving her a fair share of the Soulstones she has collected from sinners. Despite Kirai's protests, the Datsue-Ba continues to return with a lantern full of Soulstones, each one representing a life she has taken, thanks to Kirai.

30MM BASE

SOULSTONE COST: 7

SPIRIT, UNIQUE

WK/CG	HT	WP	CA	DF	WD
5/8	2	5	6✗	4	8

SKINNING KNIFE

RG	⫻ 1
CB	6✗
DG	2/3/4

TALENTS:

Abilities

Spirit Touch: Melee attacks made by this model ignore **Armor**.

Terrifying → 12

Weapons

Skinning Knife: This Weapon's Attack Duels uses either the target's **Df** or **Wp**. Declare the statistic used when declaring the attack.

Actions

(1) Face Your Sins: (ϒ)3. Non-Spirit models must immediately make a **Wp → 11** Duel. Models losing the Duel receive **Slow**.

(2) Harvest Sinners [Skinning Knife]: Discard a Control Card. This model immediately makes a **Strike** with this Weapon against every non-Spirit model within 2".

Triggers

Ca (✗ ✗) Wrongfully Judged [Weigh Sins]: Summon an Onryo instead of a Gaki if the target model is killed by this Spell.

Cb (✗ ✗) Skinned Alive [Skinning Knife]: After resolving this attack's Damage Flip, this model casts **Weigh Sins** on the same target.

SPELLS:

(0) Denial of Sanzu
(CC: 13✗ /Rst: Wp /Rg: 8) Target model cannot take movement Actions.

(0) Guide Spirits
(CC: 11♥ /Rst: - /Rg: 8) Target friendly Spirit takes a **Walk** Action.

(1) No Escaping
(CC: 13♥ /Rst: Wp /Rg: 12) Push this model into base contact with target model.

(1) Soothe Spirit
(CC: 11♠ /Rst: - /Rg: 8) Target Spirit makes a Healing Flip.

(1) Weigh Sins
(CC: 14✗ /Rst: Wp /Rg: 6) Target non-Spirit model suffers **Dg** 1/2/6. If the model is killed by this damage, summon a Gaki into base contact with the model before it is removed from play.

DEAD RIDER – MINION

No one knows the origins of the fearsome Dead Rider.

The first recorded sighting of this fell monstrosity occurred about four months ago, out near Granite Springs. A detail of Guardsmen escorting a wagonload of Soulstones was set upon by what the survivors could only describe as Death itself, come to claim them all.

The Construct rode into the caravan, cutting down Guardsmen too slow to escape the reach of its deadly scythe. As the Dead Rider circled for another pass, the Guardsmen recovered their wits and formed a ragged defensive line by putting their backs to the wagon and blades and pistols toward the Rider. Pistols barked, slamming bullets into the Rider and its mount, with no appreciable effect. Another swing of its scythe, and two more Guardsmen died as it rode by their line.

On its third pass, the Guardsmen broke and fled in all directions, scattering into underbrush. The Rider paid them little heed, instead gathering up as many Soulstones as it could carry and slinging the bodies of two Guardsmen over its saddle before galloping off.

Since that time, teams transporting Soulstone have been ambushed by the Dead Rider in three separate instances. Each time, it menaces the men guarding the shipment before cutting its way to their cargo. The details of its appearance vary from telling to telling, but the Dead Rider appears to be part Undead and part Construct, using the bodies of its victims to patch and replace the parts of its body damaged as a result of the attacks. Whatever its true purpose, just the threat of it has the Guild doubling the guard on shipments returning from badland mines to the City.

50MM BASE

SOULSTONE COST: 10

CONSTRUCT, UNDEAD, UNIQUE

WK/CG	HT	WP	CA	DF	WD
6/10	3	6	5	5	9

SCYTHE	
RG	⚡ 3
CB	6 ✗
DG	3/4/5

TALENTS:

Abilities

Hard to Wound 2

Immune to Influence

Regeneration 1

Undead Construct: When killed, this model generates one Corpse Counter and one Scrap Counter.

Unnatural Purpose: Depending on how many **Wd** this model has remaining at the start of its activation, it gains the benefits of one of the three Purposes below. This model benefits from only one of the three Purposes at any time.

Purpose: Seek (8-9 Wd): While this model has 8-9 **Wd** remaining it gains:
  Pass Through
  Scout

Purpose: Engage (5-7 Wd): While this model has 5-7 **Wd** remaining it gains:
  (+1) Fast
  Terrifying → 13

Purpose: Destroy (1-4 Wd): While this model has 1-4 **Wd** remaining it gains:
  (+1) Melee Expert
  Hard to Kill
  Scythe: Poison 2

Actions

(2) Flurry [Scythe]

(2) Mounted Combat: Push this model up to its **Cg**. This model may interrupt the Push to make one Scythe **Strike** which receives ⚡ to the Damage Flip. Continue the Push after resolving the **Strike**.

Triggers

Cb (✗) Drag Along [Scythe]: After damaging target with a Scythe **Strike** made while using the **Mounted Combat** Action, Push target into base contact with this model after finishing the **Mounted Combat** Action.

SPELLS:

(0) Adjust Purpose
(CC: 9 /Rst: - /Rg: C) This Spell must be cast before taking any other Action. This model suffers or heals up to 2 **Wd** and gains the appropriate Purpose under **Unnatural Purpose** for its new **Wd** total. The model loses any other Purpose it had gained.

GAKI - MINION

[gah-kee]

Afflicted with an insatiable jealousy or greed in life, the Gaki carry on in the afterlife as hungry spirits, incapable of finding enough sustenance to slake their ravenous appetites. Appearing most commonly as small humanoids with oversized tooth-filled maws, Gaki are most often encountered in the badlands, beyond the edge of what passes for civilization in Malifaux.

They occasionally range into Guild territory, attacking and devouring livestock or the lonely traveler between towns. Gaki usually hunt in packs to better fell large animals or when they expect they'll encounter humans. Despite their spiritual nature, Gaki are susceptible to man-made weapons, and after a day spent gorging on a farmer's herd, a laden Gaki makes for an easy target.

The Gaki's only weapon is its massive mouth, which it can expand to three times the normal size. Gaki can consume massive amounts of food, sometimes in quantities exceeding their body weight, which repulsively distend their stomachs.

Gaki are not picky eaters. As long as their meal crawls, slithers, or flies, they are willing to try it. When times are desperate enough, Gaki find one another appetizing and set upon each other with a frenzied intensity that would put any human off food for a week if they chanced upon it. That is, assuming the human escaped the Gaki and lived to tell the tale.

30MM BASE   **SOULSTONE COST: 3**

GRAVEROBBER, SPIRIT

Wk/Cg	Ht	Wp	Ca	Df	Wd
5/8	2	3	3✗	4	4

GORGE

Rg	〜 1	
Cb	4✗	
Dg	2/2/4	

TALENTS:

Abilities

Insatiable Hunger: If there is a living model in LoS in the Start Closing Phase, this model may **Walk** directly toward the living model.

Slow to Die

Spirit Scent: This model's melee attacks inflict +1 **Dg** while within 6" of a friendly Kirai.

Unstoppable Eaters: If there are two Gaki within 6" of this model, it may target **Ht** 2 models with **Devour Anything**.

Actions

(0) Eat your Fill: This model may use this Action after it kills another model with a melee **Strike**. Heal all **Wd** suffered by this model and immediately end its activation.

(1) Snack: Discard a Corpse Counter within 6". Make a Healing Flip. End this model's activation.

Triggers

Cb (✗ ✗) Feeding Frenzy [Gorge]: After damaging defender, nominate another friendly Gaki with the defender in its melee range. That model makes a Gorge **Strike** against the defender.

SPELLS:

(1) Absorb
(CC: 10✗ ✗ /Rst: Df /Rg: 〜 2) Sacrifice target model with 3 **Wd** or less. This model receives **Fast**. The second time this model is affected by **Absorb** in a turn it receives **Reactivate** instead.

(1) Devour Anything
(CC: 11✗ ✗ /Rst: Df /Rg: 〜 2) Sacrifice target **Ht** 1 model.

Guild Autopsy - Minion

Something is amiss in the City's Morgue.

Bodies continue to disappear, despite the efforts of Dr. McMourning and his capable assistant, Sebastian, to keep them where they belong. Corpses vanish from locked rooms, are discovered missing from gurneys in the Morgue's secure hallways, some have even disappeared before being handed over to the good doctor's care. Investigators are baffled by the disappearances, but suspicion has fallen firmly on Dr. McMourning's shoulders, sullying his years of dedicated service to the Guild. His superiors hope the culprit is apprehended soon and the entire business can be put behind them. Unfortunately for the Guild, Dr. McMourning is the exact reason for this spate of disappearances.

Unable to resist the lure of necromantic power, McMourning has been experimenting with a number of the bodies under his charge, reanimating the occasional corpse on company time. Many of these Undead monstrosities are the corpses of Guardsmen slain in the line of duty and shipped to his offices for autopsy.

To confuse the investigation, McMourning is falsifying paperwork pertaining to the bodies' deliveries, claiming he never took possession of them. His feigned anger at the incompetence of others within the Guild has served him well, for now. He knows his next task is to select a scapegoat upon which to pin the disappearances before his ruse is discovered. To that end, he is trying to decide which of the investigators one of his autopsies should visit for a spell...about the time the Guild receives an anonymous tip...

30MM BASE

SOULSTONE COST: 3

UNDEAD

WK/CG	HT	WP	CA	DF	WD
3/5	2	4	4	3	6

SWORD	
RG	〰 1
CB	4✗
DG	2/3/4

GUARD PISTOL	
RG	⌐10
CB	4
DG	2/3/4

TALENTS:

Abilities

Easy to Wound 1

Guild Uniform: Guardsmen may only target this model after winning a **Wp → 12** Duel.

Too Far Gone: This model does not generate Corpse Counters and cannot be used to create Body Part Counters.

Surgeon's Creation: Models casting the **Monstrous Creation** Spell may summon this model by spending three Body Part Counters.

Weapons

Guard Pistol: This Weapon's Damage Flips receive ⬛. This Weapon's **Cb** cannot be raised by Abilities or Spells.

Actions

(all) Confront Mortality: Sacrifice this model. Target living model within 4" must make a **WP → 13** Morale Duel. If the target fails the Duel, it suffers an unmodified **Dg** 1/3/6 Flip in addition to falling back.

Triggers

Cb (✗ ✗) Rot [Sword]

SPELLS:

(0) Surprise!
(CC: 12✗ /Rst: - /Rg: (✗)2) Living models make a **Wp → 10** Morale Duel.

129

NIGHT TERROR – MINION

Night Terrors are the spirits of creatures that once lived in Old Malifaux. These spirits became trapped between life and death during Old Malifaux's fall, and they now haunt the night, borne aloft on spectral wings. Wreathed in an unnatural darkness of their own creation, Night Terrors hunt just as they did so long ago, but instead of seeking sustenance from the flesh and blood of their prey, they drain its vitality, inhaling it through the mouths which replaced their eyes.

Because the Night Terror kills without doing harm to the body, Resurrectionists adept in spirit lore hunt down and bind the spirits to their will. To a Resurrectionist, an unmolested body is worth its weight in scrip. They use Night Terrors to help them hunt down and incapacitate fresh material for their necromantic practices.

30MM BASE   SOULSTONE COST: 3

BEAST, NIGHTMARE, SPIRIT

WK/CG	HT	WP	CA	DF	WD
6/9	1	5	4	5	4

CLAWS	
RG	⚔ 1
CB	3✗
DG	1/2/3

TALENTS:

Abilities

Attracted to Noise: When an enemy model within 8" makes a ranged **Strike** or casts a Spell, this model's Controller may Push it up to 3" directly toward that model.

Flight

Hard to Kill

Actions

(0) Flock Together: (✗)6. Push all friendly Night Terror models into base contact with this model.

Triggers

Ca (✗) Cold Darkness [Night Falls]: Models within range receive -2 **Wp**.

Cb (✗ 🦇) Blind [Claws]: If target suffers damage from this **Strike**, it cannot make ranged attacks.

SPELLS:

(1) Night Falls
(CC: 12 /Rist: - /Rg: ⊕6) Models receive -4 **Rg** to their ranged attacks.

ONRYO - MINION
[ohn-ryoh]

Silent specters, the Onryo wander Malifaux's nights in search of release from their pain. Hidden behind perfect alabaster masks, their faces writhe in unending torment, betrayal and loss forever gnawing at their souls. Each Onryo is trapped in its own personal hell. Their anger was such at the time of their death that they were forever bound to the mortal plane, doomed to eternally wander in search of a peace they can never attain.

Kirai's connection to the spirit world has forced several Onryo to manifest. These spirits were trapped in the aether without form until she unwittingly called them to her through her singular talent, demanding they bring violence down on the men who wronged her. Needing little more encouragement than that, the Onryo traveled the conduit through which they could take shape, answering her unspoken plea.

To come across an Onryo is to find death. Their only succor from eternal suffering is the infliction of that same suffering on others. No joy is to be gained from what they do to the living. It simply serves as a distraction, allowing them a few minutes respite before the horrible events which led to their damnation fill their minds once again.

30MM BASE

SOULSTONE COST: 5

SPIRIT

WK/CG	HT	WP	CA	DF	WD
4/6	2	5	5✗	3	6

RAZOR SHARP FINGERNAILS

Rg	⫸	1
Cb		5✗
Dg		2/3/5

TALENTS:

Abilities

Haunt: When this model is killed or sacrificed, target model within 6" performs a **Wp → Wp** Duel before this model is removed from play. If target model loses the Duel, it receives **Slow** until the end of the Encounter.

Immediate Revenge 1: Models inflicting damage on this model with ranged attacks suffer 1 **Wd** after resolving the damage.

Spirit Touch: Melee attacks made by this model ignore **Armor**.

Terrifying → 10

Weapons

Razor Sharp Fingernails: This Weapon's Attack Duels use either the target's **Df** or **Wp**. Declare the statistic used when declaring the attack.

Actions

(0) Vengeful Whisper: Target friendly Spirit model within 6" gains **Immediate Revenge 1**.

Triggers

Ca (✗ ▦) Vindictive [Malevolence]: This Spell receives 🎴🎴 to the Damage Flip.

Cb (✗ ✗) Maul [Razor Sharp Fingernails]: This Weapon receives 🎴🎴 to the Damage Flip.

SPELLS:

(1) Blind to Spirits
(CC: 12 ✗ ▤ /Rst: Wp /Rg: 8) Target model cannot target Spirits with **Charges**, Spells, or ranged attacks.

(1) Malevolence
(CC: 12 ✗ /Rst: Wp /Rg: ⟋10) Inflict **Dg** 2/3/5 on target non-Spirit.

(1) Mark of Jigoku
(CC: 12 ✗ /Rst: Ca /Rg: 12) Target model loses any immunity to **Wp** Duels. Target loses any effects giving it a bonus to its **Wp** in Duels.

131

SEISHIN - MINION

These semi-sentient wisps of spiritual energy are drawn to Kirai. Her spiritual awakening shone like a beacon in the aether, pulling any spirit which witnessed it. Seishin that drifted too close were snared by her power, unable to escape its grasp. Some fought against this, their individual flames extinguished in the blink of an eye, while other Seishin accepted their fate.

As Kirai learned to command the forces at her disposal, she found Seishin to be useful allies. She could draw upon them to bolster her power as well as the power of other spirits around them. She quickly learned that pushing a Seishin too hard was akin to poking a soap bubble, too much pressure and the bubble would pop. As she honed her talents, she found she could gently coax a Seishin to follow her commands without expending all of its energy or having it collapse under the withering force of her psyche.

Kirai also uses Seishin as spiritual messengers. The messages they carry are short, but she has had some success with ordering them to deliver information across Malifaux. Their deliveries are in constant jeopardy from malevolent spirits, prompting her to tie a bit of her own spiritual energy to each when they leave. Although Kirai cannot aid them directly, her energy helps insulate the Seishin from assault as well as informs her when they are consumed by another spirit, or worse.

30MM BASE

SOULSTONE COST: 2

INSIGNIFICANT, RARE 5, SPIRIT

WK/CG	HT	WP	CA	DF	WD
4/-	1	3	2	4	2

TALENTS:

Abilities

Enslaved by Kirai: If this model is not in base contact with a friendly Kirai at the end of any model's activation, this model's Controller may move it into base contact with a friendly Kirai.

Fragile Connection: When killed, this model counts as sacrificed.

Secret Spirit: Only Crews containing Kirai may hire this model.

Spirit Sheath: While this model is in base contact with a friendly Kirai, its Controller may apply the affects of a successful attack against Kirai to this model instead of Kirai.

Spirit Sacrifice: This model's Controller may sacrifice this model at the start of any model's activation to make all friendly Seishin and Kirai within 3" immune to damage from ♠, (𝕏), and ◐ until the end of the current model's activation.

Actions

(0) Cure Spirit: Friendly Spirit within 3" makes a Healing Flip. Sacrifice this model.

(2) Spiritually Empower: Friendly Spirit within 3" receives +2 Cb to its melee attacks.

SHIKOME – MINION

Unleashed upon Malifaux to punish the wicked, the Shikome range its skies in search of deserving prey.

Three Kingdoms legends are filled with tales of these spirits of retribution, telling of how they seek revenge on those who have wronged their summoner. Once a Shikome has avenged its master, it remains manifest, continuing to wreak vengeance on anyone associated with the master's target, whether guilty or not.

Shikome can smell their prey from miles away, hunting them as a hawk might hunt field mice. They are tenacious in their hunting and will not give up the pursuit until either their prey or they themselves are slain. When the prey is within reach, their approach is almost silent, their fang-filled mouths moving in silent fury as they swoop down to bury their talons into the prey's back.

These vicious hunters rarely work alone, relying on another of their kind or some other carnivorous creature to bring down targets from the ground. When working in tandem with another Shikome, the spirits close in to ensure no escape is possible from their trap. Prey surviving their initial attack finds the Shikome a fearsome opponent, quickly torn apart in a frenzy of talons and fangs.

Many try to escape the wrath of a Shikome, hoping to hide until the creature forgets its mission or grows weary of the hunt. These unfortunate souls do not realize it is not by choice they are hunted, it is their fate.

30MM BASE

SOULSTONE COST: 8

BEAST, RARE 2, SPIRIT

WK/CG	HT	WP	CA	DF	WD
5/8	2	6	6✗	5	7

TALONS

RG	〰 1
CB	6✗
DG	2/3/5

TALENTS:

Abilities

Hunter

Flight

Relentless: This model's **Wk/Cg** cannot be reduced by Talent or Spell effects. This model is never affected by **Slow** or **Paralyzed**.

Single Minded: Before the Initiative Flip on turn 1, this model's controller must nominate an enemy model in play as this model's Prey. This model may not attack another model while its Prey is in play. While within 4" of its Prey, this model receives **Fast**, and ⊕ to its Attack and Damage Flips. If the Prey is removed from play, **Single Minded** ends.

Terrifying → 12

Wicked: This model's **Strikes** against disengaging models deal damage in addition to ending the Action.

Weapons

Talons: This Weapon's Attack Duels use either the target's **Df** or **Wp**. Declare the statistic used when declaring the attack.

Actions

(+1) Nimble

(0) Hunting Partner: Target a friendly Beast within 12". Target Beast may not attack another model while this model's Prey is in play. While target Beast is within 4" of this model's Prey, it receives **Fast**, and ⊕ to its Attack and Damage Flips.

(All) New Prey: This model regains **Single Minded** and must nominate a new model as its Prey.

Triggers

Cb (✗ ✗) Maul [Talons]: When damaging defender, this Weapon receives ⊕⊕ to the Damage Flip.

Cb (✗ 📖) Poisonous [Talons]: Poison 2.

SPELLS:

(0) Denial of Sanzu
(CC: 13✗ /Rst: Wp /Rg: 8) Target model may not take any movement Actions.

(1) Guarantee Fate
(CC: 14✗ ✗ /Rst: Wp /Rg: 16) Target model suffers 2 **Wd** if it is not within 6" of this model at the start of the Start Closing Phase.

(1) Stalk Prey
(CC: 12✗ / Rst: - /Rg: C) This model may **Walk** after its Prey takes a movement Action.

ROGUE NECROMANCY - MINION

Hidden deep within the Quarantine Zone, Dr. McMourning's personal laboratories contain much more than the results of his experiments with the materials he has gathered from the Guild Morgue. His earliest obsession with the power over life and death led him to experiment first with raising animals from the dead, successfully animating dogs and cows before moving on to humans.

After mastering the art of raising whole bodies from the dead, McMourning began to experiment with animating dead flesh assembled from a number of sources. For each successful splicing McMourning performed, there were a dozen or more failures, many of which lumber about the workshop ignored by their creator.

His most successful creation, one he has been unable to duplicate, is a disturbing collection of pieces sutured together from multiple creatures into an unspeakable creation. The beast possesses the strengths of each as well as the frightening ability to spit a caustic fluid from its Razorspine maw. The horrible creation's appearance confuses other living beasts, giving them a moment's pause before it pounces, hungrily tearing into their hide.

Only on rare occasion is the pieced together beast ever released from its cage. McMourning sometimes runs out of failed experiments to feed the creature and allows it to roam the Quarantine Zone near the laboratory in search of prey. It possesses some base loyalty to McMourning, and for some reason, it returns to the workshop after hunting, dutifully bringing any leftovers back to its creator to use in his ghastly experiments. McMourning is fascinated by its desire to please him. The only thing it enjoys more is killing. Fortunately, killing is the most common command McMourning gives it.

50MM BASE　　**SOULSTONE COST: 10**

BEAST, RARE 1, SPECIAL FORCES (HORROR), UNDEAD

WK/CG	HT	WP	CA	DF	WD
5/9	3	5	5✗	4	10

CLAWS	
RG	⚔ 2
CB	7
DG	3/4/5

FANGS	
RG	⚔ 1
CB	5✗
DG	2/5/7

TALENTS:

Abilities

Difficult to Construct: Models casting the **Reanimator** Spell may sacrifice four Corpse Counters to summon this model. Models casting the **Monstrous Creation** Spell may discard eight Body Part Counters to summon this model. This model may not be summoned by any other means.

Hard to Wound 1

Stalker: If this model receives cover from all enemy models at the start of the End Closing Phase, Push it up to 6". This model must be in cover from all enemy models after the Push.

Superior Dead: This model is immune to effects that specifically target Undead.

Terrifying → 13

Weapons
Claws: Paired.

Fangs: Poison 2.

Actions
(+2) Three Headed: This model receives two additional melee **Strikes** during its activation while it has over half its **Wd** remaining.

(0) Smell Fear: When a model loses a Morale Duel within 6" of this model, but before the model falls back, this model may immediately **Charge** the model. **Smell Fear** ends when this model **Charges** this turn or at the Start Closing Phase.

(0) Scent of Death: Beasts declaring a melee **Strike** targeting this model must first win a **Wp → 12** or the Action immediately ends.

Triggers
Cb (✗ ✗) Rot [Fangs, Claws]

SPELLS:

(1) Acid Breath
(CC: 9 /Rst: Df /Rg: 12) Dg 3/3♣/4♣. This Spell may only be used once per activation.

(2) True Form
(CC: 15✗ /Rst: Wp /Rg: (↕)6) Living and Undead models failing to resist this Spell fall back.

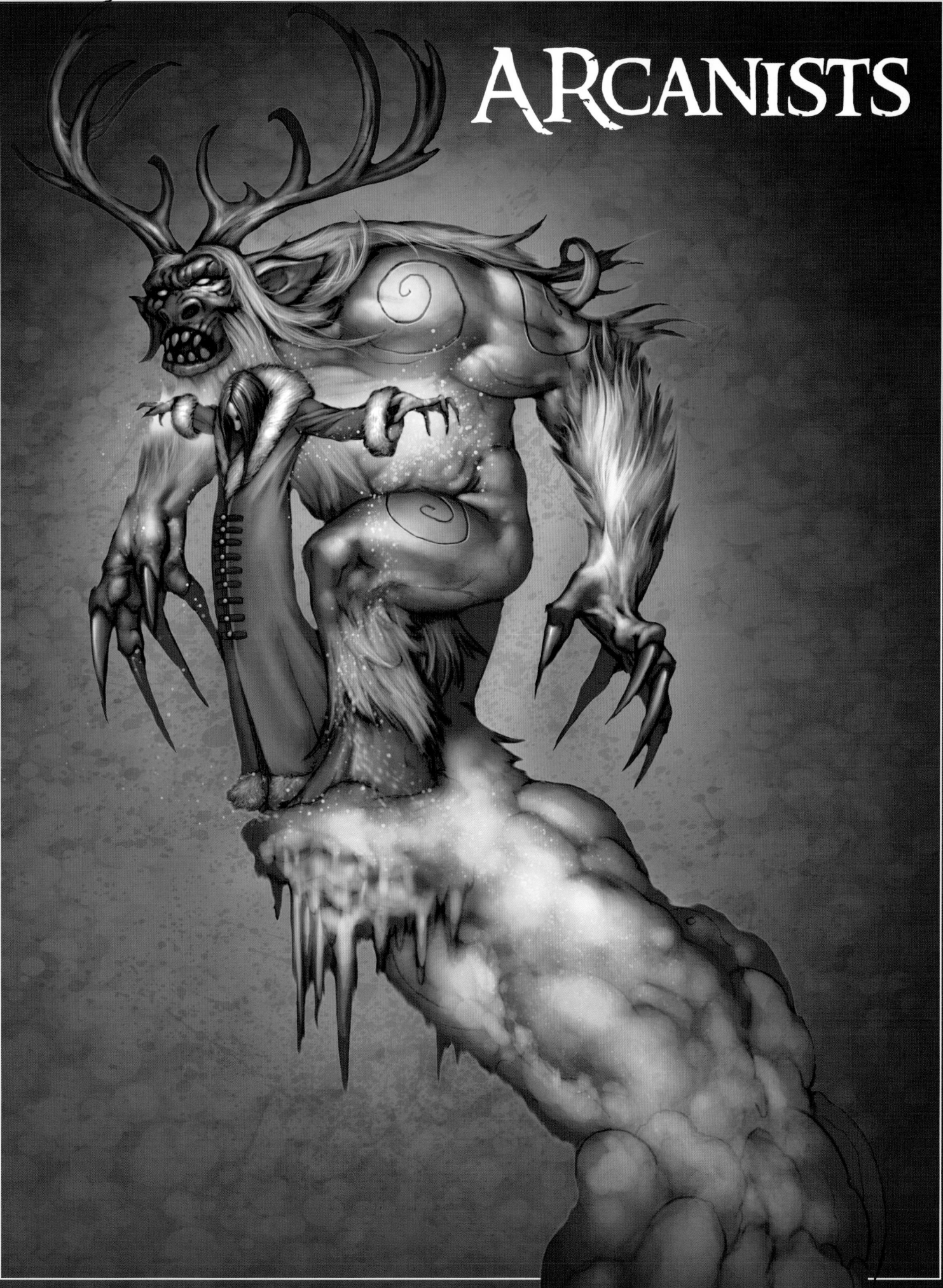

ARCANISTS

The clockwork horse reared up, jetting a blast of steam into the night air, and Colette DuBois' heart was won.

"Look at it, Cassandra! Is it not beautiful? Is it not exquisite?" She turned to her companion with a mischievous gleam in her crystal blue eyes. "Is it not mine? Why is it not mine?"

Cassandra rolled her eyes, an act that would have given any of her male admirers – which is to say any man who had ever seen her – weak knees and an overwhelming urge to compose romantic verse and shook her head. "*I* am going to check on the deliveries," she said, feigning a petulant tone. "Ramos' man said he wanted these out before midnight. Once you're done admiring the tin pony-"

Colette gasped as she peered through the stage door of The Star theatre to the cobblestone lane beyond. "Not just one, but a team of horses, Cassandra! A veritable team! A wonder of the age!" Damp night air was falling, and she fastened the jade clasp on her fur cape quickly as she talked. "You go down. Deal with Ramos' messenger. Butter him if he's a man, or oil his pistons if he's a machine. I will be along presently, just as soon as I persuade the gentleman in that carriage to give me the name of his craftsman, and a letter of introduction."

"But-"

"You are quite right, dear friend. What would I do without you? I simply cannot-" Colette opened a box on the stand by the door and removed the contents, "-be seen in public without a new hat." She pinned the small-brimmed, high-crowned topper with a purple silk wrap onto her chignon and checked her appearance in her purse-mirror with the same winning smile that had the punters flocking to The Star in droves. "They'll all be wearing these by the weekend, Cassandra, mark my words."

She shooed her friend away with quick flicks of her white silk gloves. "Go, go, go. We cannot keep our underground guest waiting," and then she stepped out into the lane, tucking her more unruly brown curls under her hat. She had removed her stage makeup after the evening's performance and had applied something more subtle, if no less striking. Her long hoarcat cape played out behind her as she arranged her face into a perfectly lipsticked moue. Whoever owned those marvelous creations wouldn't know what had hit him.

The team of four clockwork horses stood at the end of the lane, pawing at the cobbles and shaking their heads in perfect mechanical mimicry. As Colette approached, the amber gaslight of the streetlamps revealed the workmanship to be pure artistry. Sweeping equine curves of polished brass detailed with the most remarkable filigree-encased clockwork so intricate and mesmerizing in its action that Colette resolved to acquire one even if it meant placing a mortgage over The Star itself. She raised a gloved hand to the face of the nearest, gently stroking the gleaming muzzle as only the faintest of whirring sounds came from within. It snorted, a fresh cloud of steam coming from some internal reservoir, along with the warm tang of engine oil. There was no maker's mark or name she could see, and she followed the bridle and harness back toward the coach.

If the horses were made to appeal to more delicate and detailed tastes, then the coach was surely made to attract a more ostentatious-prone audience. No less ornate, it was, however, hugely proportioned in iron and brass, bedecked with gold trim and ivory rails, with wheels that would not have looked out of place on a frontier locomotive. No horses of flesh and blood could ever hope to pull this rolling townhouse, but even the slightest motion of the clockwork mares had the coach rocking gently on its industrial springs. There was no driver she could see, but the reins fed into a complicated arrangement of tubes and pistons at the front.

The door was open, the steps extended, and a warm glow within fell onto the cobbled lane without.

Never one to decline such a clear invitation, even one that an unaccompanied lady should on no account accept, Colette banished discretion to the aether and peered into the coach, Upon seeing a hand, she paused for a moment as the body was still hidden in shadow, waiting until she was motioned forward.

Within, velvet seats lined the walls and shielded gaslamps brushed gold over the magnificent fittings and heavy silk brocade curtains. A mahogany folding table sat nested in the center. All it needed was a fireplace and a butler, Colette mused, turning to greet her host.

And his gun.

Instinctively, her hand went to a concealed pocket on her scarlet dress, but a quick motion of the gun stopped her, and then she saw who held the weapon.

"Ah," she whispered, incredulity banishing the alarmed expression on her face to the same place as her discretion.

The man's unshaven face betrayed nothing but hatred. He was stick-thin, old and hunched with a choleric look. Black eyes like bullet holes sat too close together under graying eyebrows that met in the middle. His filth-brown city coat and tattered, gray tweed suit that had known more owners than cleanings looked as out of place in these surroundings as an urchin at the Governor's Ball.

"Black Cyrus," spat Colette, as her wits returned. She arched an eyebrow. "I had hoped that if I ever saw you again, you would be dead. It is cold comfort that you only smell as if you are."

The carriage door slammed shut and Colette rocked back on her heels as the carriage jolted forward. Her natural grace and practiced dexterity kept her upright, although Cyrus had to steady himself on a handrail, although his gun never wavered.

Without a word, he reached forward with his free hand, waving it over her dress and cape. A polished silver ring gleamed on his dirt-stained thumb – no doubt he had taken it from the same gentleman who had owned the coach. The ring emitted a tone like a bell and, every time it did, the hand unerringly found a hidden pocket, and he quickly retrieved a Soulstone. In moments, Black Cyrus had relieved her not just of a fortune but of her best means of defense. He was not done, however, and before the coach had reached the end of Two Mile Ride, he had also taken every mirror she possessed, and a great many other objects of varying degrees of sharpness hidden in linings, laces, or loops.

Cyrus sat down with a hacking, dry cough that it took her a moment to realize was laughter. He stuffed the stolen items in a reddish woolen sack. "Always know yer enemy, luv. I'm certain I taught ya that."

Colette sat, lacking other obvious options. Without her Soulstones, she was no match for a gun, and without her mirrors, she lacked a way to call her girls or easily escape. This was quite the situation.

Outside the coach's windows, the gas lamps of the Guild Guard station on Meeple Mews streaked past. The horses seemed to know where they were going.

"Enemies it is, Cyrus," she said, with an icy calm she was far from feeling. "I should be thankful – I run out of those Stones so quickly. What's it been – ten years? What do you want?"

"Innit obvious, luv? Yer head on a stick'll do, you traitorous, ungrateful wretch! Oh, you've 'ad it comin', gerl, for a long time. After everything I done for ya, everything I taught ya. You stabbed old Cyrus in the back – the back! – and stole it all, so ya did! You think I'd forget that?"

"The money was mine, Cyrus. I earned it, with every graft and steal and con you pushed me into. You just took it off me and called it expenses. I was only a girl, I didn't know any better. At first." She shrugged decorously. "And I didn't stab you in the back. I was trying to stab you in the chest, but you started to run like the weasel you are."

"And now, luv, you're gonna give it all back. Wiv interest, eh?" He shook the woolen bag. "This is just fer starters."

"I'm not stupid, Cyrus. I know you won't let me leave this coach alive, and you've got everything I had. What else can I give you?"

The coach lurched as it turned into the rutted cobbles of Clapper Lane. They were heading for the river, then.

"The secret."

She frowned, unsure if she'd heard correctly. "The secret?"

"Don't play coy wiv me, luv. Don't make me 'urt ya. Look at ya. A gerl like you, all lady of the ball? Yer own theatre? The Governor General hisself what comes ta see ya? You? Running yer own smugglin' scam? Yeah, I knows about that." He spat, and stabbed the gun at her. "You've got a secret, a'right, and I want it. Whatever power you magic'd 'ere or whatever secret thingumyjig you got, I want it. Whatever can make ya queen of this pissant town,

s'gonna make me a lord up in 'ere. I already got me this lovely coach an' four, see? Now, give!"

Colette started to laugh, low at first, but soon she was wracked with fits of laughter, tears welling up in her eyes, although there was no humor in her bitter mirth. Cyrus ground his blackened teeth in anger.

"Oh, Cyrus," she said, when the laughter had subsided. "You misunderstand so completely, I almost don't know where to begin." She cast her eyes around, and spotted a sealed pack of cards on the table. "Let me speak a language we both understand. May I?"

He snorted, which turned into a series of hacking coughs that eventually subsided. He opened a brass panel in the wall beside him. Bejeweled dials and levers gleamed in the gaslight, and he adjusted them, keeping one eye on Colette. The coach picked up speed. "For old time's sake, like, I'll let ya do whatever ya want till we reach Hurrycross Bridge. Then I'll kill ya. You tell me yer secret, an' I'll make it quick, like. Hold out on old Cyrus, and I'll make it 'urt. I'll take it out you in blood."

Chain Cars

Break a law, unable to pay a debt, cross the Guild, any of these things can buy a one way ticket to Malifaux. The mode of transportation? Chain car. These steel and black iron railcars, etched with arcane runes, transport unwilling guests of the Guild through the Breach into Malifaux.

Inside are men and women whom the Guild owns, body and soul, destined for lives of servitude and unimagined dangers until their debts are paid. All are shackled and bound by heavy chains to thick steel pillars in the center of each car. Cutthroats and thieves sit side by side with individuals whose only crime was to spit on the street where a Guild official's wife happened to cross. All share the same ashen pallor and sunken features brought on by a combination of their previous incarceration and the grim realization of the life awaiting them. Thus is the price of justice.

On midnight cargo runs, the convicts and unwilling contractors destined for Malifaux are dragged through the eldritch portal between worlds. Either to die in body in the Soulstone mines or to die in soul in a sanctioned brothel, the chain car's grim environment foreshadows horrors awaiting the condemned. Malifaux is a hard place and sentences are rarely lived to completion. Some never make it to their new lives. They find a way to end it all or lash out in rage, punishing another for their own fear of what is to come.

Perhaps the poor souls who die in the chain cars are the lucky ones. They are spared the horrors their fellow passengers will all too soon experience. Regardless, their lives sustain the Guild one way or another, since to fuel the train, its Soulstones must stay charged.

She slipped her gloves off, opened the pack of cards and shuffled. She riffled them on the polished surface, arching their backs in a dovetail, before cutting the deck and placing it between them on the table.

"Ain't nothin' you know I didn't teach ya, luv. Ain't no new tricks under the sun."

"We're not under your sun, Cyrus. We're under mine." Colette held her breath. Would this work? If not, she was as good as dead. "Let's play Queen's Return. Deal me a card?"

Cyrus eyed her for a moment and then, the gun steady, leaned forward and flipped the top card. The Queen of Hearts.

Colette pulled down the casement window a fraction, kissed the card leaving a lipstick rose and tossed it out to be swallowed by the night. She sent a silent prayer after it.

She shuffled the deck again, working a few flourishes into the routine – not to impress Cyrus, who snorted, "You'll 'ave ta get up earlier'n that, luv," but to steady her shaking hands – and cut the deck into four even piles.

"There are many powers in Malifaux, Cyrus. They're the ones who always rise to the top, all by themselves." She flipped the top card of each stack, placing them beside their piles; four Kings.

"Here are four. Each of them runs his own little kingdom." She tapped the four stacks of cards. She flipped the new top cards in each stack over, all Jacks. She placed them beside the Kings. "And just below King comes his knaves, Cyrus. Sturdy, uncompromising men who go armed into the night and reduce the King's troubles. Would you be a knave, Cyrus, or do your ambitions stretch further?"

She picked up the four stacks of cards, shuffling them together, leaving the Kings and Jacks on the table. "And this is Malifaux, all the dreamers and hopers and wanderers. I sometimes think Malifaux is built of all the dreams of those who come here, but it's older than any of us. What does that say about our dreams?

Or us?" She paused, and with a superbly disguised thumb flick, an Ace of Hearts jutted out from the middle of the deck, face up. "And this is me."

"Aces 'igh or low, luv?"

"That would be telling. Catch." She tossed the deck, and Cyrus caught it, eyeing her suspiciously, but she had made no move for his gun. "Look through it."

"What for?"

"You'll know when you see it."

"Don't do nothin' stupid, gerl." He gnawed a sore-ridden lip. "Awright." With his free hand, and with surprising dexterity, he flipped the cards one by one up over the deck exposing their face and then slotting them in at the bottom. After he had gone through about two thirds of the deck, he stopped. It was the Queen of Hearts, with a lipstick rose on it. Colette tried not to smile; it was working! But still, only a third of the way from the bottom of the deck? A long way to go.

Cyrus shrugged. "You palmed it at the window, dint'ya?" He pulled his own window down an inch and flicked the Queen out of the car with a smirk.

Outside, the sound of the wheels faded as the Lane opened out into Governor's Quadrant, then were lost as the coach raced past a patrol of thundering iron Peacekeepers, emitting steam as they lumbered through the square.

Colette retrieved the pack and shuffled it hand over hand while she talked. "Control. Power. Freedom. What man doesn't seek these things?" With another flick of her wrist, the Ace of Hearts emerged once more, and she placed the pack between the four Kings and their Jacks, slapping her card face down on the top. She left her finger on it. "And here is where I sit in Malifaux – at least, according to you, Cyrus. At the center of it all, with my control and power and freedom, and all the people below clamoring to see me and my girls."

The coach lurched again as it turned into the busy thoroughfare of Southing Boulevard. The bridge wasn't far, now. What was taking so long?

She handed the deck to Cyrus. "Look through it, like you did before. Please," she added, with an indulge-me smile it took all her stage skills to fake.

Scowling, he started to flip through the cards single-handed again. "My patience is wearing precious thin, luv. I think-" He stopped, about a third of the way from the top. The Queen of Hearts winked up at him with her lipstick eye. He grunted. "S'a decent trick, gerl. Dun't mean nothin', though. Ain't gonna save yer 'ide." He took the card and placed it in his top coat pocket.

Colette again reclaimed the pack. "Control, power, and freedom. But am I really in control of where I am and what I do, or am I at the beck and call of others?" She lifted the nearest King, and there was the Ace of Hearts, underneath. She lifted the Ace, put it back into the deck and shuffled.

The next King. "And do I have any real power, or is there always someone standing over me?" She lifted that King up, and again, there was the Ace of Hearts. She shuffled it back into the deck once more. "And do I really have any freedom in this city of Kings and dreamers, or is it all just an illusion?"

She sat back and made a go ahead gesture to Cyrus. He lifted the third King carefully, and chortled – there was nothing under it.

"I am not without my wiles," Colette said, gesturing at the last King, "but sooner or later, all illusions must end."

Cyrus snatched the last King up and threw it with a snarl across the coach. The Ace of Hearts lay on the polished wooden tabletop.

The rattling of the coach eased, and Cyrus leered as the coach moved from cobbles to the smooth, wide flagstones of Hurrycross Bridge. "And end it does, luv. A sorry tale, to be sure, but I don't buy a word of it, and here comes the endin', courtesy of old Cyrus."

Colette gathered the cards, shuffled the deck, and placed it in the center of the table, her fingers shaking. Her hands were clammy. It was now, or never. "One last flip through the deck, Cyrus. For old time's sake. That's all I ask. We're not across the bridge yet."

With the gun pointing directly at her, Cyrus bowed with as much malevolent condescension as he could muster and, grinning, flipped the top card over. His hand immediately shot to the top pocket of his coat, and came away empty.

The Queen of Hearts, with lipstick stain, sat on the table. Colette closed her eyes in relief.

"What's it mean? 'Ow you doin' that?"

She smiled. "It means there are new tricks under the sun, Black Cyrus."

There was a heavy thump from the roof of the carriage and Cyrus bolted up, confusion in his coal-black eyes. "Who's 'at? Who's up there?"

"Why, it's the Queen of Hearts. Luv. And about time, too!" Colette added loudly.

Cyrus was showered with broken glass and screamed in pain as a sabre, as slender and lithe as the girl who wielded it, stabbed down through the skylight and pierced his arm.

He dropped the gun and fell back heavily, his shoulder slamming into the panel of levers and dials. The coach jolted sideways, knocking both of them off their feet. There was a loud, grinding crash of stone and metal, and the coach halted abruptly.

Cyrus was first to his feet. He flew to the door, opened it, and leapt out – only for a gloved hand to grab his collar from above. He was swung once, twice, screaming in fury, and then the hand let go and he disappeared from sight.

Colette heard a distant splash a few moments later. She tried to stand, but the wreckage of the folding table had her pinned. "What took you so long?" she shouted. "Lend me a hand in here."

Cassandra's head appeared upside down in the doorway, but her expression was grim. Colette realized why when the coach tipped forward with a groan of brass.

"You're about to go over the side of the bridge!" Cassandra yelled. "Hurry!"

The coach tipped even further, and Colette could hear the clockwork snorts of the horses dangling in their harnesses, pulling the coach over. There was no time to free herself. Blurting out a very unladylike word that surprised Cassandra, Colette pushed a very obvious-looking lever on the panel.

There was a twanging noise. The coach immediately righted itself with a thud as the rear wheels touched back down. Colette closed her eyes, dejected, counting the four far-away splashes of the beautiful clockwork horses falling one by one into the river below.

Cassandra helped her out, Colette retrieving the reddish woolen bag as they left.

"Back to The Star?" asked Cassandra, concealing her sabre under a long cloak as a crowd gathered at the far end of the bridge. Cloaked figures with deep hoods kept back at a hand sign from the dancer.

Colette nodded, rubbing her aches and pains. She'd had worse on stage, but the loss of the horses hurt far more. "We don't have much choice, Cassandra. I expect there will be a very angry messenger demanding we get his goods out tonight, and my girls need their rest before tomorrow's matinee." She set her head high, adjusted her slightly bruised hat, and the crowd parted before her and Cassandra as they set off back along the midnight streets of Malifaux. "After all, the show must go on. For now."

Breach Running

Earthside conjurers not in the good graces of the Guild are willing to pay a fortune for Soulstones and Malifaux artifacts. Alternately, Malifaux residents are willing to trade such treasures for any rare item, from medicine to fruits from Earth, even strange texts unearthed in ruins excavation (another booming new industry). To address these demands on both sides of the Breach, enterprising individuals began smuggling, or Breach Running as it is called, almost as quickly as the City was re-opened. This ability to circumvent the Guild's strangle-hold on the Breach, and all traffic passing through it, has frustrated the Guild ever since. From the elite who simply want to avoid the Guild's excessive portage taxes, to individuals of low moral fiber, all make use of the secret flow of goods into and out of the City. The means by which smugglers ply their trade are almost as varied as the smugglers themselves. Whatever the smuggler's motivation, the Guild's punishment for smuggling, which it metes out with relish, is a public neck stretching.

This threat does little to deter men and women from all walks of life from Breach Running. From the noble-minded smuggling needed medicine to cutthroat opium suppliers trading in opulent sums for Soulstone, all share a defiance of the law and the determination to meet a need. They go about their business, getting their goods to the Breach via river, coach, and rail. Ingenious false bottom containers disguise smuggled goods, enabling them to slip unnoticed through the Breach. Body Skipping, the practice of swallowing Soulstone to smuggle it out through the Breach, is another common technique. The best breach runners are skilled in rift dowsing, a strange type of divination used to find smaller Breaches between Malifaux and Earth. The rare skill allows smugglers to avoid the heavily patrolled main Breach but comes with its own perils.

COLETTE DU BOIS - MASTER

Colette began as a cheap pickpocket, using her charm, grace, and quick fingers to lift valuables from men with more than enough wealth to sustain them both. Although beautiful, and quick to prey upon the careless advances of men hoping to lure her into a night of private debauchery, Colette would never succumb to the lowly activities of a lady of the night. Instead, she gave in to the inner drive to always fulfill an insatiable ambition. Burlesque shows and cheap sleight of hand tricks allowed her to mesmerize dozens of men at a time, all eager to garner her attention and favor.

Mere parlor illusions were quickly forgotten when she arrived in Malifaux. Passing through the Breach, she knew almost immediately that her skills of legerdemain were just the hint of a truer power. Once more following her ambitions to be ever better, she acquired her first Soulstones, and her potential was fully realized. Her arcane thirst proved nearly as insatiable as her own drive and determination, yet her illusions became more and more real and her skills more diverse and phenomenal. Colette quickly understood how to drain a Soulstone and use its spiritual energy to fuel her explosive displays.

Unlike other masters of the arcane arts, however, Colette gathered a troupe of girls with similar skills and made no secret among them about the use of Soulstones. They worked in a secret pact to learn the uses of sorcery and hone the art by which they might acquire more power, wealth, and subsequent freedom.

Legendary accounts of their burlesque and magician's shows have spread beyond the City's borders and have migrated Earthside, leading more and more travelers to come, no longer just to stake their own claim in the wilds of Malifaux, but to see the fabulous girls dance, perform unbelievable shows of magic, and gaze upon wondrous advances in technology as mechanized dancers, human-sized dolls, dance upon the stage alongside their beautiful flesh and blood counterparts.

Colette and her girls thought they had found true success when they were given great payment for excess Soulstones acquired in the quiet and dim moments after each show. It wasn't long after, however, that Colette discovered her success and power came with a much higher price. Although famous, and truly rich, she now struggles to keep

her powers a secret from the Guild officers that come to see her perform every evening. The Arcanist Movement relies upon her to move their illicit wares in the black market, leaving her no time to enjoy the freedom she's earned.

All eyes are upon her and her freedom is nothing but an illusion.

30MM BASE

M&SU MEMBER, MASTER, SHOWGIRL

Wk/Cg	Ht	Wp	Ca	Df	Wd
4/-	2	6	7📖	6📖	6

TALENTS:

Abilities

Artificial Soulstone: The first Soulstone this model discards each turn is not deducted from its Crew's Soulstone Pool. The Soulstone may not be discarded to summon a model.

Special Charm: ⚫4. Friendly Arcanist models receive +2 **Wp**.

The Show Must Go On: Once per Encounter, when flipping to determine if the Encounter ends, after seeing the result, this model's Controller can choose to have the flipping player re-flip.

Slow to Die

Soulstone Augury: When this model discards a Soulstone to flip a card, the flip receives ⚫.

Union Labor: Crews containing this model can hire M&SU Members from any Faction at no additional cost.

Actions

(0) Soulstone Infusion: Discard one Soulstone. This model receives **Reactivate**. This Action may be taken once per turn.

(1) Illusionist: Switch this model and one friendly Showgirl within 18".

(1) Soulstone Manipulation: Either discard one Soulstone and draw two Control Cards, or discard two Control Cards, and gain one Soulstone. This Action may be taken once per activation.

Triggers

Ca (📖📖📖) Mannequin Replacement [Disappearing Act]: Sacrifice defender instead of burying it after it fails to resist this Spell. Summon one Mannequin into base contact with the defender before it is removed from play.

Ca (🦋) Sleight of Hand [Disappearing Act, Discharge Soulstone]: After resolving this spell, and the defender fails to resist it, gain one Soulstone.

Df (📖📖) A Blinding Flash: The model that attacked this model receives **Slow**. Switch this model and one other friendly Showgirl within 18".

SPELLS:

(0) "Now You See It..."
(CC: 15📖 /Rst: - /Rg: C) Target one friendly Mechanical Dove within 3". One other friendly Showgirl within 18" of this model Switches with the Mechanical Dove. Sacrifice the Mechanical Dove.

(0) Trick of the Hat
(CC: 15📖 /Rst: - /Rg: C) Discard one Soulstone. Summon one Mechanical Dove. The Summoned Mechanical Dove may activate immediately after the end of this model's activation.

(1) Death Defying
(CC: 13🦋 /Rst: - /Rg: C) Discard one Soulstone. Switch this model and one other friendly Showgirl within 18". This model heals **Wd** equal to the number of **Wd** remaining on that Showgirl. Kill that Showgirl. This Spell may only be **Cast** as a **Slow to Die** Action.

(1) Disappearing Act
(CC: 13📖 /Rst: Df /Rg: 8) Discard one Soulstone. Bury target non-Master model. Place target model within 6" of this model during the Start Closing Phase, or in base contact with this model if this model is removed from play.

(1) Discharge Soulstone
(CC: 14📖 /Rst: Df /Rg: ⤳12) Discard one Soulstone. This Spell ignores cover and inflicts **Dg** 2/3/5 which ignores **Armor**. If the target model is killed by this Spell while within 6" of this model, gain one Soulstone.

(1) Magician's Duel
(CC: 10📖 /Rst: Ca /Rg: ⫻ 3) **Dg** 2/3/5. Targets with **Use Soulstone** receive -2 **Ca** resisting this Spell. If the target is killed by this Spell, gain one Soulstone.

MECHANICAL DOVE - TOTEM

A beautiful accompaniment to Colette Du Bois' magnificent stage performances, her mechanical doves rarely fail to elicit awestruck gasps from audiences. The intricately assembled Constructs are both aesthetic and technical masterpieces. The platinum feathers were individually hand-crafted, the beak and claws shaped in polished brass, and two sparkling sapphires for eyes. Within this unequalled work of art beats a complex heart of clockwork machinery, giving the dove artificial life.

First time visitors to Ms. Du Bois' shows are unprepared for the mechanical dove's ability to fly like the flesh and bone bird it was designed to mimic. On stage, it is revealed on a metal perch, watching Ms. Du Bois' movements with interest, convincing the audience it is simply a complex puppet of some sort. At the climax of her act, she gestures into the audience and the bird leaps into the air, circling the crowd three times before settling back onto its perch. Gasps of delight and surprise drown out the metallic click of the dove's wings until it lands, then thunderous applause fills the air.

Just like her Coryphée dancers, Ms. Du Bois deftly avoids questions about the artist who designed the dove for her and where she had it built, knowing that, in part, her show's draw is the lure of the unknown. Giving out such trade secrets would be like robbing herself of future profits, something Ms. Du Bois would never do willingly.

30MM BASE

SOULSTONE COST: 2

CONSTRUCT, INSIGNIFICANT, TOTEM (COLETTE)

WK/CG	HT	WP	CA	DF	WD
10/-	1	4	4📖	5	3

TALENTS:

Abilities

Flight

From the Hat: Up to three Mechanical Doves may be connected to Colette at a time.

Harmless

Soulstone Powered: A friendly Showgirl model within 3" of this model may sacrifice it when that model could use a Soulstone. The Showgirl gains the benefit of having discarded a Soulstone even if she does not have the **Use Soulstone** Ability. If the Soulstone was used to flip a card, by a model other than Collete, the flip receives 🃏.

Actions

(1) Detonate Soulstone: (⚡)2. Models must win a **Df → 14** Duel or suffer **Dg** 2. Sacrifice this model after resolving damage.

SPELLS:

(1) Magical Extension
(CC: * /Rst: * /Rg: *) This Spell may be cast only once per activation. Cast one of the connected Master's **(1)** Spells. During this casting, this model may use a Soulstone to change its casting total while casting this Spell.

MOBILE TOOLKIT - TOTEM

Repairing mining machinery and Constructs in the field is a constant challenge for Miners & Steamfitters Union mechanics. The remote and often isolated location of many mines requires these mechanics to spend weeks in the field, rotating between sites in an effort to prevent inevitable breakdowns. Because access to tools and materials can be several days' ride away, most mechanics carry their supplies and tools with them, either by wagon, on horseback, or using the ingenious mobile toolkit.

This squat, mobile, multi-drawer Construct is capable of carrying dozens of tools in its sturdy frame. It is resistant to wear and tear when on the road for extended periods of time and utilizes a fraction of the resources a wagon or beast of burden would require to transport the same amount of materials. Responding to vocal commands, this little workhorse can identify and dispense the appropriate tool the mechanic needs and is equipped with two arms configured to receive a number of tool attachments, allowing it to assist the mechanic in his or her maintenance work.

Because of the time spent alone travelling between mines, some mechanics come to regard their mobile toolkits as confidants and friends. They attribute personalities to their Constructs and even name them as they would a trusted horse or mule. While endearing, many folks look askance at a mechanic when he refers to his walking toolbox as "Sally".

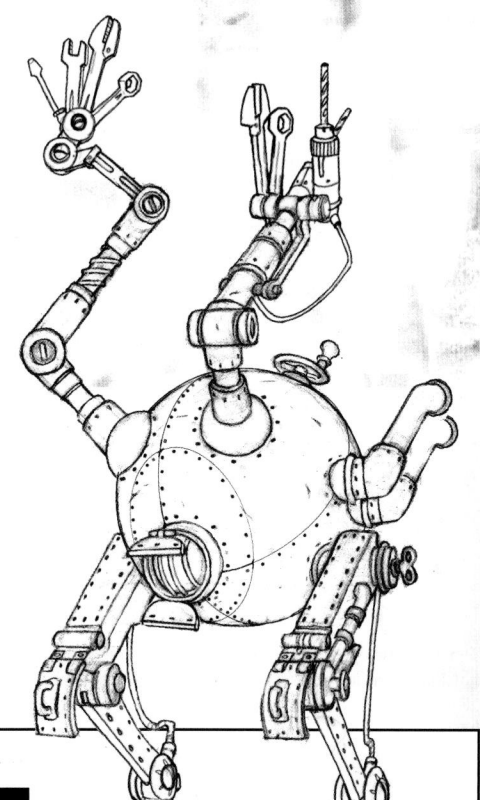

30MM BASE   **SOULSTONE COST: 3**

CONSTRUCT, TOTEM (RAMOS/C. HOFFMAN)

WK/CG	HT	WP	CA	DF	WD
4/-	1	3	3📖	3	3

TALENTS:

Abilities

Companion (Master)

Easy to Wound 1

Handy: At the end of any model's activation, if this model is not in base contact with its connected Master, this model's Controller may Push it into base contact with its connected Master. While in base contact with its connected Master, this model may not be damaged by (☠) or ☠ effects.

Immune to Influence

Actions

(1) Controlled Detonation: Kill target friendly Construct within 12". Target generates (☠)2, **Dg** 2 before being removed from play. Target model does not activate any Ability which generates a (☠) when it is killed.

(1) Lab Equipment: This model or one other target friendly model within 6" gains +📖 **Ca**.

(2) Weld Together: Target friendly Construct within 2" makes a Healing Flip.

SPELLS:

(1) Magical Extension
(CC: * /Rst: * /Rg: *) This Spell may be cast only once per activation. Cast one of the connected Master's **(1)** Spells. During this casting, this model may use a Soulstone to change its casting total while casting this Spell.

KAERIS - HENCHMAN

Anasalea Kaeris is a woman who asks only once.

Before her arrival in Malifaux, Kaeris had already earned a reputation as being a patient woman, whose attention to detail and ability to get results quickly and efficiently were without peer. Her skills at removing unwanted problems were sought after by several unofficial organizations, each trying desperately to convince her to work for them exclusively. Despite generous offers, Kaeris remained steadfast in her neutrality, the balance between these powers more important than any paycheck they could write.

A trip through the Breach changed all of that.

Invited by a group calling itself the Arcanists, who had followed her career Earthside, Kaeris came to Malifaux. She met with Victor Ramos, speaking on the Arcanists' behalf, who explained that she had been asked here to help them in their efforts to shatter the Guild's hold over these lands and its treasures. The Arcanists needed someone with no ties to the Miners and Steamfitters Union or its membership.

Kaeris did not answer right away, but rather let the offer simmer as she explored Malifaux's wonders. She saw the oppression in the Guild's mining operations, marveled at the pioneering drive and hope of settlers striking out from Promise to make a life for themselves in a new world, even experienced the horrors of the City's Quarantine Zone. She felt she knew a bit of this place now, but what intrigued her most was the access everyone had to the rarest of resources Earthside – magic.

She learned more of the nature of magic and the aether and its effect on people, wondering if she had even a spark of talent which she could one day fan alight. Then she thought about the Guild's stranglehold over Earth's access to the Breach, how it snuffed out the light of equality and balance she had strived for years to help achieve.

Meeting with Ramos again, she took the job on the condition he and he alone would teach her magic. To their mutual surprise, Kaeris possessed more than just a spark of talent. Since then, she has patiently absorbed all he has taught her, her arcane talents growing steadily. Ramos has recently designed a Soulstone-powered harness to both boost and focus her abilities as she continues her studies, keeping the potential wildfire of her potential contained to a slow burn.

Kaeris now puts both her mundane and magical talents to work in eliminating obstacles to the Arcanists' plans, hand-selecting assets she is confident can achieve her objectives, approaching each of them with a single question: "Are you in?"

30MM BASE

SOULSTONE COST: 8

HENCHMAN 5, SPECIAL FORCES (M&SU ASSET)

WK/CG	HT	WP	CA	DF	WD
5/8	2	6	6 📖	5	9

IGNITE	
RG	⌐10
CB	6 📖📖📖
DG	1/2/3 ♣

TALENTS:

Abilities

Cleansing Fire: This model may choose to ignore any damage it would suffer from a ♣. If this model ignores the damage it heals 1 **Wd**.

Flaming Armor: Armor +1. Models hitting this model with melee **Strikes**, or melee Spells suffer 1 **Wd** and receive one Burning Counter.

Flight

Gunfighter [Ignite]

Kindling: This model draws one Control Card whenever it kills an enemy Construct.

Special Forces Leader (M&SU Asset): Crews led by this model may only hire M&SU Members or M&SU Assets.

Smoldering Heart: When declared the target of a Duel, this model may suffer 1 **Wd** to receive +3 **Wp** until that Duel is resolved.

Weapons

Ignite: Models damaged by this Weapon receives one Burning Counter.

Actions

(+1) Casting Expert

(0) Inner Fire: Inflict 1 **Wd** on this model, Draw one Control Card.

(0) Resource Management: (ϒ)12. All M&SU Members or M&SU Assets suffer 1 **Wd**. This model heals a number of **Wd** equal to the total number of models affected.

Triggers

Ca (📖📖) Surge

Cb (📖📖) Turn it Up [Ignite]: After inflicting damage on defender with this Weapon, **Strike** another target model in range at a cumulative -1📖 **Cb** with this Weapon.

SPELLS:

(1) Accelerant
(CC: 12📖📖 /Rst: - /Rg: (ϒ)10) Models with Burning Counters suffer **Dg** 1/2/4. A model affected by this Spell may instead choose to take no damage, remove all Burning Counters, and receive **Paralyzed**.

(1) Flame Wall
(CC: 13📖 /Rst: - / Rg: 12) Place two 50mm markers touching one another at least 1" from any model. These markers are obscuring **Ht** 5, and hazardous (**Dg** 3) and lasts until the End Close Phase. This Spell may only be cast once per activation.

(1) Immolate
(CC: 15📖 /Rst: Wp /Rg: 12) **Dg** 3/5/6. This Spell may only be cast on a model with a Burning Counter. If target model is killed, replace it with one 50mm marker. The marker is obscuring **Ht** 5, and hazardous (**Dg** 3).

(1) Overheat
(CC: 12📖 /Rst: - /Rg: 12) Kill target friendly Construct. Models within (ϒ)3 of the killed Construct receives one Burning Counter.

CASSANDRA, MAGICIAN'S APPRENTICE - MINION

Cassandra is possibly the greatest celebrity in Malifaux, perhaps drawing more men to see her perform than even her great friend, Colette. Cassandra was once a rival of Colette's, singing, dancing, and acting her way to the top. She has spread the widely accepted rumor that Malifaux offers her the freedom to entertain in a way that critics and audiences wouldn't allow in the more stagnant Earthside parlors, decaying in squalor.

A select few that know her best have learned hints of a darker truth that she might have fled here, not to forge a lifestyle of excess, but to escape one of subjugation and cruelty. She never speaks of her past when probed, sometimes even losing her typical wit and charm in agitation.

She takes her beauty for granted, rarely noticing the stares she receives from admirers. Yet she can speak with the bawdy men fresh out of the depths of the mines as if she had spent the day among them, and her sharp tongue can strike as deeply as the saber she wields like a well-trained and seasoned Guardsman.

As the two senior showgirls have embarked upon a new adventure, smuggling rare goods and Soulstones for the Arcanists, the Star has very rapidly become the underground hub of activity. Cassandra's role has become even more important to both Colette and the Arcanist Movement as she regularly leads the troupe of girls through the labyrinth beneath the city. No matter the stench of decay or the

dangerous confrontations they've endured, Cassandra has never uttered a complaint, always standing between the others and whatever obstacle they face.

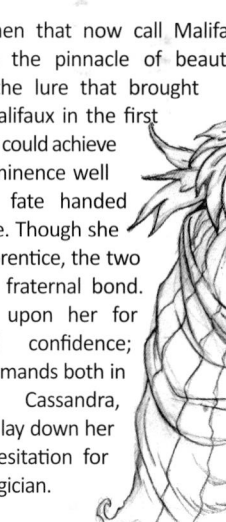

Among the men that now call Malifaux home, she is the pinnacle of beauty, representing the lure that brought them all to Malifaux in the first place, that they could achieve a level of prominence well beyond what fate handed them Earthside. Though she is Colette's apprentice, the two have a strong fraternal bond. Colette leans upon her for support and confidence; Cassandra commands both in abundance. Cassandra, though, would lay down her life without hesitation for the Master Magician.

Colette is protective of all of her girls. Cassandra protects Colette.

30MM BASE   **SOULSTONE COST: 9**

SHOWGIRL, UNIQUE

WK/CG	HT	WP	CA	DF	WD
5/8	2	5	6📖	6	7

SABER

RG	⫸ 1
CB	7📖
DG	2/3/4

TALENTS:

Abilities

Celebrity: For the first two turns of the Encounter, this model may only be targeted by ranged **Strikes** and Spell attacks. This Ability ends if this model makes an attack.

Confident: This model's Controller may Push it up to 6" before the first Start Activation Phase of the Encounter.

Grande Finale: This model may activate once after the end of the last turn, but before Victory Points are calculated for the Encounter.

Magician's Apprentice: This model gains **Use Soulstone** when hired by a Crew that contains Colette Du Bois.

Actions

(+1) Nimble

(0) Blonde Act: ⚫1. Defense Flips receive ⊟ until the end of this model's activation.

(0) Southern Charm: Attack and Damage Flips targeting this model receive ⊟.

(0) Sword Dance: This model may interrupt its movement Actions at any point to make one Saber **Strike**. After resolving the **Strike**, it may finish the movement Action.

(1) Dance Partner: Place this model in base contact with a friendly Coryphée or Coryphée Duet in play within 18" or Switch places with a friendly Coryphée or Coryphée Duet in play within 18".

(1) Sultry: This model gains **Harmless**.

(1) Understudy: Cast one **(1)** Spell belonging to a friendly Showgirl within 12". This Action may be taken once per activation.

Triggers

Ca (📖📖) Embellish [Breathe Fire]: After defender fails to resist this Spell, defender must make a **Wp → 12** Morale Duel.

Ca (♥) Swirl of Motion [Breathe Fire, Sublime Performance]: Push this model up to 4" after it successfully casts this Spell

Cb (📖♥) Magician's Prop [Saber]: After hitting defender with this Weapon, **Cast** a **(1)** Spell on defender. This Spell's Casting Flip receives ⊟.

Cb (♥) One Fluid Motion [Saber]: After damaging defender, Push this model up to 4".

SPELLS:

(0) Sublime Performance
(CC: 14📖 /Rst: - /Rg: C) Gain +♥ to **Ca** and **Cb**.

(1) Breathe Fire
(CC: 13📖 /Rst: Df /Rg: ⤳6) **Dg** 3/3♣/5♣♣. This Spell may be cast while this model is engaged. If so, its **Rg** is ⫸ 2 when cast.

(1) Elegance
(CC: 12📖 /Rst: Wp /Rg: 6) Heal target enemy model 3 **Wd**. Gain one Soulstone if target heals at least 2 **Wd**. This may be cast once per turn by this model.

CORYPHÉE - MINION

On occasion, Ms. Du Bois' burlesque is replaced with more sophisticated entertainment, the ballet. Collette's performers are more than vaudevillian actors. They are classically trained dancers, performing with delicate Constructs to demonstrate the grace and beauty of both the human and Construct form. These real and artificial performers create a performance unlike any other on Malifaux. Some come to witness the spectacle of Constructs in intricate performances, while others are held rapt by the pure beauty of it all, never once considering the Coryphée performing the dances alongside humans as less than experts at their craft.

Ms. Du Bois deftly evades any inquiries regarding her Coryphées' cost. She is able to turn requests for the name of the artist capable of creating such masterpieces into discussions about technique and where their skills could be further improved. By keeping the secret of her clockwork troupe, she further enhances its mystique and fills the seats nightly.

Few know the graceful figures they witness on stage have the potential to be as deadly as they are beautiful. With a few alterations, these clockwork entertainers are transformed into deadly combatants. The Coryphée's delicate porcelain mask worn during performances is stowed away, showing the featureless metallic head, and its brass hands are removed, replaced with long blades.

A Coryphée's *pas seul* choreographs speed and lethality in equal measures, its motions almost mercurial as it nimbly strikes its foes. It weaves through complex steps, lashing out with its blades while avoiding the clumsy efforts of its enemies. Few would argue the skill needed to design a Construct as beautiful and functional as the Coryphée, and those who do often find themselves as its next dance partner.

Building on the talents of a single Coryphée, a duet of these amazing Constructs reaches a new height of technical achievement and beauty. Where one Coryphée's performance is a masterpiece, its ability to play off the talents of its counterpart is nothing more than miraculous. Both hit their marks, the gestures and movements of each a mirror image of the other.

This perfection is amazing to behold, and the audience is lost in its symmetrical perfection. With lethal grace, the Coryphée duet dances a complicated staccato, their dress sabers flashing in the stage lights as they cut and whirl. Eventually the ballet must come to an end, its awe-inspiring synchronicity etched forever in the minds of those who witness it.

40MM BASE   **SOULSTONE COST: 7**

CONSTRUCT, RARE 2, SHOWGIRL

WK/CG	HT	WP	CA	DF	WD
8/-	2	4	5📖	6	4

BLADES
RG	⚔	1
CB	6📖	
DG	2/3/4	

TALENTS:

Abilities

Always in Motion: This model may not be targeted by **Charge** Actions.

Arcanist Asset: This model may only be hired by Crews containing Arcanist Masters.

Bulletproof 2

Evasive 3

Mercurial: This model's Defense and Resist Flips receive ➕.

Pass Through

Sidestep Harm: This model receives ➕ to Defense Flips when disengaging.

Weapons

Blades: Paired.

Actions

(+1) Instinctual

(1) Dance Partner: Place this model in base contact with another friendly Coryphée or Coryphée Duet in play within 18". Or Switch places with a friendly Coryphée or Coryphée Duet in play within 18".

(1) Dance Together: Sacrifice this model, and one other Coryphée within 2". Replace this model with one Coryphée Duet in base contact with it before it is removed. Any **Wds** or effects on each individual Coryphée are applied to the Coryphée Duet. The Coryphée Duet may not take a **Dance Apart** action this turn.

(0) Lost in Dance: This model receives +2 **Wp**.

(0) Soul Dancer: Gain **Use Soulstone**.

(0) Sword Dance: This model may interrupt its movement Actions at any point to make a Blades **Strike**. Once the **Strike** is resolved, finish the movement Action.

Triggers

Ca (🦋) Swirl of Motion [Blinding, Orchestral Crescendo]: After successfully casting this Spell, Push this model up to 4".

Cb (📖📖) Enchanting Performance [Blades]: After damaging defender with this Weapon, it loses any Talent which provides immunities to **Wp** Duels.

Cb (🦋) Hypnotic Movements [Blades]: After damaging defender, it receives ➖ to its Resist Flips.

Cb (🦋) One Fluid Motion [Blades]: After damaging defender, Push this model up to 4".

SPELLS:

(0) Sublime Performance
(CC: 14📖 /Rst: - /Rg: C) Gain +🦋 to **Ca** and **Cb**.

(1) Blinding
(CC: 12📖 /Rst: Wp /Rg: ⚔ 2)
Dg 2/3+**Slow**/3+**Paralyzed**. Push this model up to 3".

(1) Orchestral Crescendo
(CC: 12📖 /Rst: Df /Rg: (↑)2) Non-Showgirl models suffer 2 **Wd**.

CORYPHÉE DUET - MINION
SOULSTONE COST: PLACED

CONSTRUCT, SHOWGIRL

WK/CG	HT	WP	CA	DF	WD
9/-	2	6	6📖	7	8

BLADES

RG	///	1
CB	7📖	
DG	2/3/4	

TALENTS:

Abilities

Always in Motion: This model may not be targeted by **Charge** Actions.

Bulletproof 2

Evasive 3

Mercurial: This model's Defense and Resist Flips receive ➕.

Pass Through

Sidestep Harm: This model receives ➕ to Defense Flips when disengaging.

Weapons

Blades: Paired. This Weapon's Damage Flips receive ➕.

Actions

(+1) Fast

(+2) Subconscious Actions: This model may take three different **(0)** Actions during its activation.

(0) Live for Dance: This model makes a Healing Flip.

(0) Soul Dancer: This model gains **Use Soulstone**.

(0) Sword Dance: This model may interrupt its movement Actions at any point to make a Blades **Strike**. Once the **Strike** is resolved, finish the movement Action.

(1) Dance Apart: Sacrifice this model. Replace it with two Coryphée in base contact before this model is removed from play. Any effects on this model are applied to each Coryphée. Any **Wds** on this model are distributed as evenly as possible between the two Coryphée. Neither Coryphée may take the **Dance Together** Action this turn.

Triggers

Ca (🦋) Swirl of Motion [Blinding, Orchestral Crescendo]: After successfully casting this Spell, this model Pushes up to 4".

Cb (📖📖) Enchanting Performance [Blades]: After damaging defender with this weapon, it loses any Talent which provides immunities to **Wp** Duels.

Cb (🦋) Hypnotic Movements [Blades]: After damaging defender, it receives ➖ to all Resist Duels.

Cb (🦋) One Fluid Motion [Blades]: After damaging defender, Push this model up to 4".

SPELLS

(0) Sublime Performance
(CC: 14📖 /Rst: - /Rg: C) Gain +🦋 to **Ca** and **Cb**.

(1) Blinding
(CC: 12📖 /Rst: Wp /Rg: /// 2)
Dg 2/3+**Slow**/3+**Paralyzed**. Push this model up to 3".

(1) Elegance
(CC: 12📖 /Rst: Wp /Rg: 6) Heal target enemy model 3 **Wd**. Gain one Soulstone if target heals at least 2 **Wd**. This Spell may be cast once per turn by this model.

(1) Orchestral Crescendo
(CC: 12📖 /Rst: Df /Rg: (ɾ)2)
Non-Showgirl models suffer 2 **Wd**.

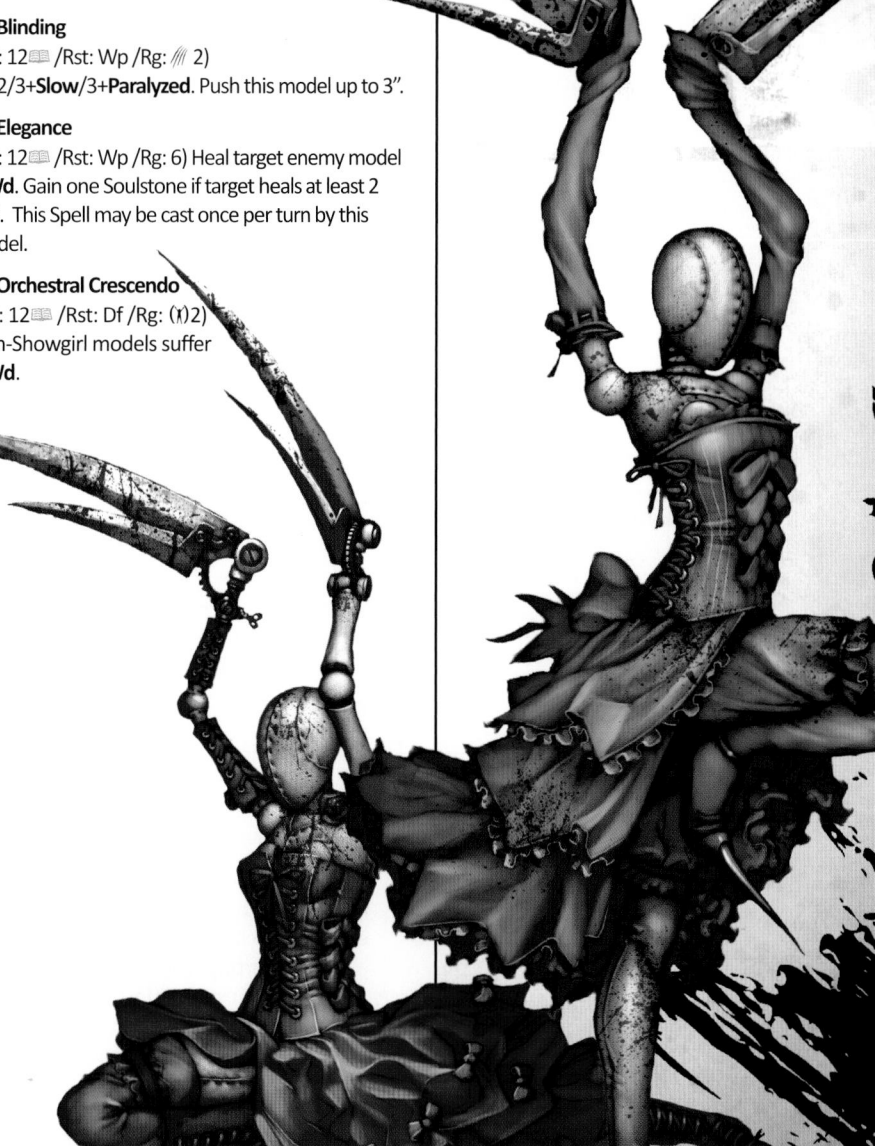

Gunsmith - Minion

Consummate professionals, Arcanist Gunsmiths embody the adage that sometimes the threat of violence is more effective than actual violence itself. These highly trained assets operate within the Miners and Steamfitters Union, discouraging union breaking by disgruntled members or Guild agitators that have slipped into mine sites and quarries.

A Gunsmith's presence at a site is never announced by the Union bosses. The rumors of their existence are enough to keep all but the most dedicated anti-union activist in line, though the bosses will sometimes let slip where a Gunsmith may be headed in an effort to defuse a situation before it explodes into an effort to break up the Local.

Because they rely heavily on their own talents when on an assignment, Gunsmiths are skilled in all aspects of their trademark weapon – a custom-built pistol based loosely on the Guild's own Peacebringer revolver. These heavily modified weapons are virtually silent, easily concealed, and have a broad selection of specialized ammunition a Gunsmith may have reason to need in the field. Gunsmiths with access to only a limited number of tools can effect repairs or on-the-fly modifications to their weapons thanks to the extensive training they receive before being assigned to their first "situation".

A Gunsmith never draws his pistols if there is the chance he can resolve a situation without using them. The ability to bring tense encounters to peaceful conclusions with their mere presence ensures that knowledge of the Union's involvement, and more importantly, any Arcanist involvement, by the wrong parties is avoided. But, when words are not enough, a Gunsmith has no trouble turning the threat of violence into the real thing.

30MM BASE   **SOULSTONE COST: 6**

SPECIAL FORCES (M&SU ASSET)

WK/CG	HT	WP	CA	DF	WD
5/6	2	4	5	4	7

CUSTOM PISTOL

RG	☞10
CB	5📖
DG	1/3/4

TALENTS:

Abilities

Concealed Weapon: Models targeting this model must win a **Wp** → **13** Duel to target this model with ranged **Strikes** or ranged Spells until it takes a **Strike** Action or casts a ranged Spell.

Duty: This model's Controller cannot be changed.

Gunfighter [Custom Pistol]

Hard to Kill

Intimidating: This model is **Terrifying** → **12** to **Ht** 1, Insignificant, **Harmless**, and **Pitiful** models.

Ruthless

Smoldering Heart: When declared the target of a Duel, this model may suffer 1 **Wd** to receive +3 **Wp** until that Duel is resolved.

Weapons

Custom Pistol: Paired. At the start of this models activation, choose one of the following effects for each **Strike** made with this weapon:

 Armor Piercing: Ignore **Armor**.

 Explosive: Custom Pistol damage becomes 1/2♣/3♣. Damage Flips against living targets receive 🃏.

 Silver: Damage Flips against Undead targets receive 🃏.

 Wooden: Damage flips against Neverborn targets receive 🃏.

Actions

(0) The Hard Way: This Action may be taken only while this model has suffered 1 or more **Wd**. This model's Melee and Ranged Attack Flips receive 🃏🃏.

Triggers

Cb (📖📖) Experimental [Custom Pistol]: Change this Weapon's **Dg** to 2/4/6.

SPELLS:

(2) Leadstorm
(CC: 14 /Rst: Df /Rg: ☞(x)6) **Dg** 4.

LARGE STEAMPUNK ARACHNID - MINION

The reliability of the Steampunk Arachnid design has spawned a number of offshoot applications. The most impressively sized of which is the Large Steampunk Arachnid. Intended as a response to the Guild's development of large Constructs with decidedly offensive capabilities, the Large Steampunk Arachnid provides the punch available in a Steamborg but at a dramatically reduced drain on Arcanist resources.

The primary armament of this imposing Construct is its circular sawblade. This frightening weapon is capable of slicing through an armored opponent with unsettling ease. Its well-armored frame ensures it is able to withstand most attacks and deliver crippling damage to whatever it is sent to engage.

What it lacks in the finesse of its smaller cousins, the Large Steampunk Arachnid makes up for in sheer power, brutally charging into danger and laying about with its massive claw while hampering the maneuverability of its enemies with well-placed snares. The potent combination of defensive and offensive capabilities makes the Large Steampunk Arachnid a proven resource in preventing the loss of Arcanist assets in Malifaux.

40MM BASE

SOULSTONE COST: 5

CONSTRUCT, RARE 2, SPECIAL FORCES (M&SU ASSET)

WK/CG	HT	WP	CA	DF	WD
4/8	2	5	5📖	5	7

CIRCULAR SAWBLADE

Rg	⫻ 2
Cb	5
Dg	2/3/5

TALENTS:

Abilities

Arachnid

Armor +1

Weapons

Circular Sawblade: This Weapon ignores **Armor**.

Actions

(+1) Melee Expert

Triggers

Cb (📖) Brutal [Circular Sawblade]

Df (📖) Spare Parts: Draw one Fate Card after an attacker misses this model with a melee **Strike** or melee Spell. Show the card to all players. Keep the card if it is a 📖 or Joker, otherwise discard it.

SPELLS:

(1) Cut Away

(CC: 12📖 /Rst: Df /Rg: ⫻ 2) Target model gains **Armor** -1 if it has an **Armor** of +1 or more. This Spell is cumulative.

MALIFAUX RAPTOR - MINION

Trained in a number of roles, Malifaux raptors support Arcanist operations throughout Malifaux. Because of their large size and ability to defend themselves from other airborne predators, Arcanists use them as messengers, carrying missives that may otherwise be intercepted if sent via stagecoach, telegraph, or aethervox.

In addition, these creatures are frequently employed to harass and distract, allowing Arcanist agents the opportunity to escape the Guild or providing the edge needed to overpower an opponent. A flock of these birds of prey can prove a formidable weapon as well, sharp talons and beaks slashing and tearing at exposed skin or eyes. Even the threat of such an attack can cow the bravest soul into surrender.

In the hands of a talented handler, the raptor can be used as a scout, seeking out and circling targets until help arrives. Guild agents have orders to shoot birds circling their positions on sight in the eventuality they are marking the location for an Arcanist ambush.

New rumors suggest that the birds are learning how to disarm weapons or pluck small objects like Soulstones from the hand. A raptor capable of stripping a Guardsman of his pistol is a potential threat the Guild would like to see stopped before the Arcanists perfect the maneuver.

40MM BASE

SOULSTONE COST: 2

BEAST, INSIGNIFICANT

WK/CG	HT	WP	CA	DF	WD
8/10	1	4	2	6	4

TALONS	
Rg	 1
Cb	4
Dg	1/2/3

TALENTS:

Abilities

Easy to Wound 1

Flight

Flock: When activating this model, simultaneously activate all friendly Malifaux Raptors within 4" that have not already activated this turn.

Pack Mentality 2: This model loses Insignificant while it is within 3" of two or more friendly Malifaux Raptors.

Trainable: This model may be hired only by Crews containing Marcus, Zoraida, or at least one Guild Austringer, regardless of faction restrictions.

Actions

(2) Diving Attack: This model **Charges** an enemy model ignoring LoS, terrain, and intervening models. If the **Charge** fails, this model's activation immediately ends.

Triggers

Cb (🦷) Distract [Talons]: Instead of flipping for damage with this Weapon against an enemy defender, place the top three cards from target's controller's discard pile on top of their Fate Deck in any order.

Cb (📖) Enrage [Talons]: After resolving a Damage Flip with this Weapon, target gains the Beast Characteristic until the end of the Encounter or until the model's controller discards two Control Cards during its activation.

MECHANICAL RIDER - MINION

The Mechanical Rider's earth-trembling charge is a welcome sight to its allies. The rider appears out of nowhere, screaming a challenge to the Arcanists' enemies before unleashing her assault. Building up a tremendous head of steam, the mechanical mount hurls her at her enemies, scattering them with the attack.

Delivering fatal blows with her saber, she maneuvers through combat, pushing into the thickest of the fighting where she demands a toll be paid with her foes' blood. She appears to relish the slaughter, riding down retreating combatants or impaling them with a chain spear rather than accept their surrender.

Once the mount's impetus stops, the rider fights by lashing about with her weapons as the mount readies for another burst of speed. Its inner mechanisms are designed to channel a considerable amount of power to its initial charge, but the creature needs time to re-energize before it can rush the enemy again. This lull in its speed does not hamper the mount's performance in close quarters, however. It is capable of defending itself and its rider until it is ready to charge again, riding down enemies unable to move from its path in time. She is deadly to almost all who encounter her, and the Arcanists are grateful for her intervention, but even they wonder who she is and why she is willing to put herself in danger for them.

50MM BASE

SOULSTONE COST: 8

CONSTRUCT, UNIQUE

WK/CG	HT	WP	CA	DF	WD
6/10	3	6	5	4	9

SABER

RG	///// 2
CB	6 📖
DG	3/4/5

CHAIN SPEAR

RG	⤳ 8
CB	6
DG	1/2/5

TALENTS:

Abilities

Armor +1

Immune to Influence

Power Cycle: At the start of each Activation Phase, this model gains the benefits of the current turn's Stage below. This model benefits from only one of the three Stages at any time.

> **Powering Up Stage (Turn 1-2):**
> **(+1) Nimble**
> **Pass Through**
> **Full Power Stage (Turn 3-4):**
> **(+1) Melee Expert**
> **Cb (📖) Brutal [Saber]**
> **Powering Down Stage (Turn 5 and later):**
> **Armor +3**
> **Hard to Kill**

Wicked: This model's **Strikes** against disengaging models deal damage in addition to ending the Action.

Actions

(2) Flurry [Saber]

(2) Mounted Combat: Push this model up to its **Cg**. This model may interrupt the Push to make one Saber **Strike** which receives ⚑ to the Damage Flip. Continue the Push after resolving the **Strike**.

Triggers

Cb (🔗) Drag [Chain Spear]: After this Weapon inflicts damage on the target, Push target 4" directly toward this model.

SPELLS:

(0) Power Manipulation
(CC: 9 /Rst: - /Rg: C) This Spell must be cast before taking any other Action during the model's activation. Nominate a turn number two higher or lower than the current turn number. This model's **Power Cycle Stage** is now set for that turn number.

PERFORMER AND MANNEQUIN - MINION

Anyone can belt out a few off-key tunes to an inebriated audience. The dime-a-dozen saloon girls and hack entertainers stuffing boomtown saloons and dance halls prove this. However, for talented female artists seeking a name for themselves, no better venue exists in Malifaux than Colette Du Bois' Star Theater.

Women seeking employment at the Star must possess more than just a pretty face. Auditions are required for any employee, and during those auditions, a candidate must demonstrate her singing and dancing skills as well as any unique stage talents she might have. Only after proving she has the ability to keep up with the other Star performers is an applicant granted probationary status as an understudy. Those understudies who demonstrate they have what it takes are offered full placement in the show as befits their skills and talents. Not only are these women trained in stagecraft, but also the most ancient of dances – seduction.

Colette's performers are no mere prostitutes, however. They are trained Arcanist operatives, using their wiles to infiltrate and gather information which they pass back to Colette's contacts within the Arcanist organization in exchange for autonomy in running the Star. Colette does not take this

relationship with the Arcanists lightly. She knows they use her talented performers as a means to an end, but she would rather burn the Star to the ground than give up the freedoms she has earned for both herself and the women who have put their futures in her hands.

30MM BASE

SOULSTONE COST: 6

MERCENARY, SHOWGIRL

WK/CG	HT	WP	CA	DF	WD
5/-	2	5	5📖	5	5

POISON RING	
RG	🗡 1
CB	4
DG	0/0/1

CLOCKWORK DERRINGER	
RG	↗6
CB	4
DG	2/3/4

TALENTS:

Abilities

Dresser: The listed Soulstone Cost is for this model and one Mannequin.

High Class: This model costs two additional Soulstones instead of one when hired as a **Mercenary**.

Irresistible: Enemy Models must win a **Wp → 12** Duel when targeting this model with an attack or the Action fails. This may not be ignored by any Talent.

Precious: When this model is killed, target friendly Showgirl within 4" of this model receives **Reactivate**.

Weapons

Poison Ring: Poison 2. This model may use either **Wp** or **Cb** when attacking with this Weapon.

Actions

(0) Mesmerizing: Target model within 6" makes a **Wp→Wp** Duel with this model. If the target loses, it receives **Slow**.

(1) Poison Gift: Target **Paralyzed** model within 2" suffers **Poison 4**.

Triggers

Ca (♥) Fatal Distraction [Seduction]: After applying the effects of this Spell to the target, this model may take a melee or ranged Strike against target.

SPELLS:

(1) Expensive Gift
(CC: 13📖 /Rst: Wp /Rg: 6) Target model with Use Soulstone discards one Soulstone. Gain one Soulstone.

(1) Seduction
(CC: 12📖 /Rst: Wp /Rg: 4) Target model's Resist and Defense Flips receive ⊟ ⊟.

(1) Siren Call
(CC: 12📖 ♥ /Rst: Wp /Rg: ↗15) Move target enemy model its **Wk** toward this model. If the target moves within this model's melee range, it receives **Paralyzed**.

MANNEQUIN - MINION

Colette Du Bois does not invest in her performers lightly. The challenging auditions and personal interviews ensure the women she hires are the best, brightest, and most loyal that Malifaux has to offer. Once hired, these fortunate entertainers learn that, in addition to their generous salaries, they have been assigned a mannequin as a helpmate behind the scenes.

Mannequins are required to fulfill a number of roles for their assigned performer. Because the cast of the Star make most of their own costumes, at its most mundane, a dormant mannequin can serve as a dressmaker's dummy. While operating, they may be called upon to carry stage equipment, serve as porters for the performers' heavy costume trunks, even stand in as a "volunteer" while the ladies practice their acts.

Mannequins also serve as dressers for the performers, helping with costume selection and preparation for each evening's performance. During the show, they stand offstage with their performer's next costume change in patient hands, rushing to help her make the change in half the time a less efficient human assistant would be able to.

Ms. Du Bois is intensely protective of her performers, and by extension, their mannequins. She prefers to keep the existence of these Constructs a secret, content to let the public see only her Coryphées on stage.

30MM BASE

SOULSTONE COST: –

CONSTRUCT, INSIGNIFICANT, OBJECT 2, SHOWGIRL

WK/CG	HT	WP	CA	DF	WD
4/-	2	8	5	3	3

TALENTS:

Abilities

Armor +3

Clumsy: This model suffers -2 **Wk** when activating in any terrain without the open trait.

Companion (Showgirl)

Fixable: Friendly Showgirls within 2" of this model gain the following Action: "(1) Fix Mannequin: Target Mannequin heals 1 Wd."

Harmless

Performer's Clothes: This model may only **Link** to Showgirls.

Actions

(-1) Slow

(0) Soul Dancer: Gain **Use Soulstone**.

(0) Link: This model and target model in base contact with it are **Linked**. After the model this model is **Linked** to completes a **Walk** Action or ends its activation, Push this model into base contact with the **Linked** model. A model can be **Linked** to only one model at a time. **Link** ends if the two models are not in base contact at the Start Closing Phase.

Triggers

Ca (♪) Full of Pins [Beautiful Clothes]: After defender fails to resist this Spell, target suffers an unmodifiable **Dg** 1/2/4.

Ca (♥) Jealousy [Beautiful Clothes]: After defender fails to resist this Spell, **Cast Beautiful Clothes** on another model within range.

Ca (▤) Overload [Beautiful Clothes]: After defender fails to resist this Spell, it suffers 3 **Wd**. Sacrifice this model after resolving the **Wd**.

Ca (✕) Tangled [Beautiful Clothes]: After defender fails to resist this Spell, it receives **Slow**.

SPELLS:

(1) Beautiful Clothes
(CC: 11 /Rst: Wp /Rg: ∥ 2) Target model cannot target this model with **Strikes** or Spells.

(1) Mirrors
(CC: 14♥ /Rst: - /Rg: ✪2) Friendly Showgirl models, including this model, suffer no damage from Weak Damage Flips.

(1) Tricks of the Trade
(CC: 14 /Rst: - /Rg: C) Discard one Soulstone or sacrifice this model. Gain one of the following effects:

- Target friendly Showgirl within 3" makes a Healing Flip.
- Friendly Showgirl within 12" is Placed in base contact with this model before it is removed from play.
- Friendly Showgirl within 3" gains **Use Soulstone**.
- Target friendly Showgirl within 3" receives +♥ to her **Ca**.

SILENT ONE - MINION

The Cult of December's priestesses were at one time equal to their male counterparts. Both enjoyed His favor, faithfully following His laws and commands. Through their tireless dedication, the cult enjoyed a swelling in its ranks as new members were drawn by the honeyed messages of the priests and priestesses.

Before long, December's message to the priesthood changed. It foretold of a mortal vessel into which it would pour more of its essence than any of its faithful had yet enjoyed, and that vessel would speak to His followers in His voice, ushering in a time where He would be master of the land. Unfortunately for the priestesses, the message also foretold the vessel would be a woman.

Faith is no match for unbridled ambition. Conspiring in secret, the male priests devised a plan to force December to choose one of them as His vessel. In one well-orchestrated motion, they seized the cult priestesses, cut out and devoured their tongues. Their thought was that without a tongue, the women would be unable to speak with December's voice, and He would be required to nominate one of their membership, instead. Although the priestesses, now called Silent Ones by the cult, retained their magical connection with December, they were treated as little more than common slaves, cast down from the positions of status they once held.

Until Rasputina's sudden appearance, the male priests dominated the Cult's hierarchy. Her dramatic rise saw a shift of power as the tables were quickly turned on the once-feared male leaders, and the Silent Ones were liberated from their servitude. Freed of this bondage, the Silent priestesses now follow Rasputina with undying loyalty, fanatically devoting themselves to her as both their savior and December's chosen vessel. Wielding the powers of winter, the Silent Ones serve as Rasputina's chosen handmaidens and bodyguards, tasked with critical duties and missions as the vessel sees fit.

30MM BASE

SOULSTONE COST: 6

RARE 2

WK/CG	HT	WP	CA	DF	WD
3/5	2	4	6📖	3	6

FROZEN TOUCH

RG	🗡 1
CB	3📖
DG	1/1/6

TALENTS:

Abilities

Bulletproof 1

Counterspell: After this model is targeted by a Spell it may discard two Control Cards or one 📖 suit Control Card to cancel the Spell before starting totals are generated.

Frozen Heart: This model is immune to Morale Duels.

Ice Mirror: When casting a Spell, this model may draw LoS and range from a friendly model with **Frozen Heart** within 6". These Spells receive -3 **Ca**. Spells with the ⌐ icon may not be cast through a model in melee using **Ice Mirror**.

Perfect Mirror: Spells cast through this model with **Ice Mirror** receive -1 **Ca** instead of -3 **Ca**.

Shatter 3: (ɪ)2. **Dg** 3 when this model is killed.

Actions

(+1) Casting Expert

(0) Freeze Heart: Target model within 8" receives **Frozen Heart**.

Triggers

Ca (📖📖) Surge

Ca (📖📖) Thirty Below [Ice Wind]: Enemy models suffer 3 **Wd** from this Spell instead of 2 **Wd**.

SPELLS:

(0) Ice Wind
(CC: 13📖 /Rst: Df /Rg: (ɪ)2) Models with **Frozen Heart**, including this model, heal 1 **Wd**. Models without **Frozen Heart** suffer 2 **Wd**.

(1) Freeze
(CC: 13📖 /Rst: Df /Rg: ⌐10) **Dg** 2/3♥/4♥.

(1) North Wind
(CC: 14📖 /Rst: - /Rg: ❶3) Models with **Frozen Heart** receive +3 to the **Rg** of their Abilities, Spells, and ranged Weapons. ❶ and (ɪ) ranges are not increased.

(1) Turn to Ice
(CC: 14📖 /Rst: Df /Rg: 12) This Spell may not target models without **Frozen Heart**. Reduce the **Df** of target model to 1. Damage Flips against target model receive ⊟⊟. Target model may not **Wk** or **Cg**, be Pushed, or make disengaging strikes.

SNOW STORM - MINION

Few forces of nature can rival the fury of a winter's storm. Freezing winds, blizzards, ice storms all strike with an intensity rarely seen in other weather, leaving a wake of destruction buried beneath sheets of white. When this raw force is channeled into a form and made to manifest, it does so with terrifying results.

As the soul-wave reached Rasputina, she sensed it contained the power to transform her in ways she had never dreamed of. She feared combining the wave's power with the might of December that she bore would tear her apart. As the wave struck, Rasputina diverted the power she would have absorbed and bound it to the soul of one of her devoted Silent Ones, her command of all things winter shaping the spirit's manifestation.

The Silent One, Snow, was changed by this binding. Her skin took on a bluish tinge and grew ice cold while her raven black hair was bleached of color, whitening in seconds. The spirit's manifest form, with its curling rack of horns and claws the length of icicles, embodied the raw primal power of winter. Rasputina took one look at the spirit and dubbed it Storm.

Snow and Storm share a unique relationship. As prison and prisoner, the nature of their binding prevents them from being apart for long, and their time together has turned a relationship filled with animosity into something more akin to friendship and

respect. Neither is able to speak but instead share an empathic connection that borders on the telepathic. Together, they are willful and independent, only reluctantly following Rasputina's commands. Snow, however, follows her commands and compels the Storm which heeds every slightest request made by Snow, much to Rasputina's frustration.

50MM BASE — **SOULSTONE COST: 11**

GRAVEROBBER, SPIRIT, UNIQUE

WK/CG	HT	WP	CA	DF	WD
6/7	3	5	5📖	6	6

ICEY TALON
RG	⚔ 2
CB	6📖
DG	3/3/6

TALENTS:

Abilities

Bulletproof 3

Float

Frozen Heart: This model is immune to Morale Duels.

Middle of the Storm: This model and models in base contact receive soft cover.

Shatter 4: (⚡)2. **Dg** 4 when this model is killed.

Actions

(+1) Instinctual

(0) Eat your Fill: This model may immediately take this Action after it kills a model with a melee Strike or melee Spell. This model heals all **Wd** and then ends its activation.

(0) Form Ice: Push a friendly Ice Golem or Ice Gamin within 8" into base contact with this model.

(0) Freeze Heart: Target model within 8" gains **Frozen Heart**.

(0) Frightening Winds: This model gains **Terrifying →12**.

(0) To the Bone [Icy Talon]: This model's Damage Flips with this Weapon receive ➕.

(1) Foul Weather: (⚡)12. Nominate a table edge. All models are Pushed 2" directly toward the nominated table edge. This model may be Pushed up to 6" directly toward the nominated table edge.

(1) Sleet: ⚫6. Models without **Frozen Heart** receive -2 **Cb** when making ranged **Strikes** and ranged Spells and cannot **Charge** without first winning a **Wp →** 12 Duel. Models with **Frozen Heart**, including this model, receive soft cover.

(2) Flurry

Triggers

Ca (📖⚔) Overpower [Ice Tornado]: If defender failed to resist this Spell, after resolving the Spell, **Cast** it again on the same target.

Cb (⚡📖) Grip of Winter [Icy Talon]: This Weapon receives ➕➕ to its Damage Flip.

SPELLS:

(0) December's Command
(CC: 8📖 /Rst: - /Rg: (⚡)4) Push models with **Frozen Heart** directly into base contact with this model.

(1) Ice Pillars
(CC: 10📖 /Rst: - /Rg: 12) Place two 50mm bases in base contact with one another and at least 1" from any model. These bases are Ice Pillar terrain with the following traits: **Ht** 5, breakable (hardness 3), and impassible. This Spell may be cast once per Crew, per turn.

(1) Ice Tornado
(CC: 12📖 /Rst: Df /Rg: 6) **Dg** 2/3♥♥ /3♥♥♥.

Soulstone Miner - Minion

Innovation is a hallmark of Ramos' Miners and Steamfitters Union. Constantly designing new ways to implement Construct technology, Ramos' workshop has introduced several new inventions into the Union's Malifaux operations in recent months. One of the batch, the Soulstone Miner, is already exceeding expectations in the field.

Intended to alleviate some of the pressures and dangers Union members face in the Soulstone mines, the miner is fitted with a massive drill allowing it to dig through solid rock. In addition, an ingenious device allows the miner to sense nearby charged Soulstone by analyzing the fluctuating resonations of its powering Soulstone. An unintended consequence of this device enables the miner to charge its own depleted Soulstones when a soul departs a nearby body. This resource has proven invaluable in cave-ins where trapped miners were unable to escape, but provided the necessary recharge to a Soulstone Miner, allowing it to dig its way free of the rubble thereby preventing the loss of a very expensive piece of equipment and additional deaths.

Signaling a push to automate mining operations, the Soulstone Miner allows mining crews to dig faster and deeper without the potential loss of life. The question Union members who have seen these Constructs at work ask is how long before they are deemed obsolete and replaced completely by the machines?

40MM BASE   **SOULSTONE COST: 6**

CONSTRUCT, RARE 2, SPECIAL FORCES (M&SU ASSET)

WK/CG	HT	WP	CA	DF	WD
5/8	2	5	4📖	5	6

ROCK DRILL

RG	⫸ 2
CB	6📖
DG	2/3/4

TALENTS:

Abilities

Armor +1

Limited Soulstone Use: This model may discard Soulstones only when required by its Talents or Spells.

Regular Maintenance: When this model has 3 **Wd** or less, this model gains Insignificant.

Scout

Weapons

Rock Drill: This Weapon ignores **Armor**.

Actions

(all) Mine Soulstone: Reduce **Df** to one and suffer 2 **Wd**. Gain 1 Soulstone. This model may only use this Action once per turn.

(0) Overdrive: Discard one Soulstone. This model gains **(+2) Melee Master**. This model suffers 2 **Wd** at the end of this activation.

(1) Tunneling: Place a 30mm Tunneling Marker in base contact with this model, then bury this model. During the Start Closing Phase, move the Tunneling Marker up to 8", ignoring terrain and models. During the Start Activation Phase, you may remove the marker and place the model in that location. When this model is placed, end this Ability, it gains Insignificant until the next Draw Phase.

Triggers

Ca (📖📖) Surge

Cb (✗📖) Syphon Essence [Rock Drill]: After killing a model with this Weapon, gain one Soulstone.

SPELLS:

(1) Shatter Stone
(CC: 12📖 /Rst: Df /Rg: ⫸ 2) Discard one Soulstone. **Dg** 2/3♠/4♠♠.

(2) Extract Soul
(CC: 12✗📖 /Rst: Df /Rg: 4) Target model with 2 **Wd** or less remaining is killed. Gain one Soulstone.

Neverborn

Neverborn

The ground around the abandoned quarry was the color of dried blood, and creeping shadows striped it inky black as the sun was swallowed by the hills to the west. A cold wind blew up from the Badlands, drawing a veil of dust across the rusting hulks of the ancient machines that had once worked the stone. The setting sun and the wind at their backs, four figures moved into the open.

From where the boy and his friend stood, atop the cliff face high above the quarry floor, the four figures looked like beetles, and the boy said so. He liked drawing beetles. He had to pluck their legs off to stop them running away, of course.

"Look closer," said his friend, and the boy did.

Long shadows against the umber sky made it hard to see, but the boy's eyes were good, and if he squinted just right, he could make out – yes, holsters, hats and badges.

Were they lawmen, he asked his friend, and his friend told him they were. The boy liked lawmen. They hunted outlaws.

"Would you like to play a game with them?" his friend asked. "They would like that."

The boy smiled and nodded. "As long as I get to win."

Virgil stopped, halting his fellow Death Marshals with a gesture. Ahead lay Bedlam Quarry, a huge bowl of rock filled with shadows and dust. At its center rose two enormous, rusting pylons. Still and lifeless, it had last been worked long before the Breach had first

opened; by whom, no one knew, or much cared. But Virgil was a grizzled and gaunt veteran of the Guild, the scars on his weathered face, all the medals he would ever have or need, and eighteen years of service told him something was very wrong here.

"I know this place." The quiet, cautious voice of Lucas interrupted Virgil's thoughts, and then he realised the young man had hit the nail on the head. Virgil knew it, too.

"I thought you'd never been out here," he asked, but Lucas slowly shook his head. In the fading evening light the lad's thin, sunken face made him look like one of the Undead he usually hunted. The polish on Lucas' Guild badge might still be fresh from the quartermaster's store, but he was one of the most level-headed rookies Virgil had ever known. Most came gunning out of the Academy eager to put Malifaux to rights, one corpse at a time, thinking they were Death himself. Most didn't make it, but most didn't have the rattlesnake calm of Lucas.

"Neither've I," Cody added gruffly from behind the wild tangle of black hair and beard that framed a face known to every bartender in Malifaux, "but I know what I know, and I know them towers."

"This is gonna sound nuts, chief," said Lucas, "but I think I dreamed about this place."

A chill ran down Virgil's back. Then Cody spat into the dust and nodded. "Greenhorn's right. Last night, back in the City. Didn't think nothin' of it, 'til right about now."

Virgil turned. "Dead Eye?"

Their fourth companion, a silent, hulking giant wearing an eye patch and a sour look, said nothing. Instead, he unslung the coffin from his back in one smooth move and readied it, telling Virgil all he needed to know.

They all hipped their coffins, carrying them lightly in one hand as if they weighed nothing at all.

"We all had the same dream?" asked Lucas, tight-lipped. "That ain't possible."

"We hunt dead men," Virgil replied, tugging his hat down and setting out for the quarry, his fellow Death Marshals falling in behind him. "Don't tell me what ain't possible."

Virgil knew now that the tip-off about Resurrectionist activity all the way out here was most likely bunkum, but he was having trouble remembering which of his informants in the Malifaux underworld had approached him with it. He had no trouble remembering the directions to the quarry, nor the certainty that there was an Undead menace growing out here, but the more he thought about it, the less sense it made and the harder it became to picture the face of the man who'd told him. It was disappearing from his mind, like a dream on waking.

Someone had tricked them. No - someone had tricked *him*. They were going to regret it, before they died.

"Spread out," he ordered, drawing his Peacebringer. "Might be Ressers. Might not."

"Ambush?" asked Lucas, as the men strode four abreast across the blood-red dirt.

"Didn't no one tell ya, greenhorn?" cackled Cody, drawing his own pistol and planting a kiss on the underslung blade. "This whole darned world's an ambush. Turn you inside out if ya let it, so just fill yer hand and walk on."

His laughter echoed off the towering cliff walls as they headed down the haul road into the crumbling ruins of Bedlam Quarry.

Four men waited for them, standing still as statues in the middle of the track running through the old workers' huts.

Virgil had led his Death Marshals down the switchback road, past the waste heaps, dried up settling ponds, and the shattered foundations of old brickworks. Strange machines lay half buried by the side of the road, fused by rust into somber monuments that loomed in the swirling dust and gathering dark. Some had been broken apart. Many an Arcanist had come here hunting for forgotten lore, and most, so the stories said, had wound up going mad. Some said it was the relentless wind keening among the eerie corpses of brass and iron or maybe the isolation that caused it, but less fanciful men blamed the water. Either way, the quarry had got its name.

The huts were a shanty town of corrugated iron and timber, decayed and broken like rotten teeth. Strips of rusted iron clanged and creaked in the gusting wind as the Death Marshals picked their way through the pools of shadow. Then the road opened, and there they were.

Although the last of the setting sun was full on them, their faces were dark masks. They wore long, tattered riding coats. No guns he could see, although their hands were hidden. Virgil shouted a challenge, but it was the wind that rose in answer, howling down out the Badlands in a stinging slap of dust. He lost sight of the four men, and when the wind died, they were gone.

Well, if that's how they wanted to play it. "Cody, Lucas. Take the right. I want them alive."

"They'll be alive, chief," said Cody, ducking under some jagged planks of wood as Lucas fell in behind. "They just won't be happy 'bout it."

Both men were quickly lost in the swirling dust and deepening shadow. Phantom cries and whispers threaded around as the wind drew voice from the creaking ruins. Virgil turned to the barrel-chested giant beside him. "Stay back. I'll move up and flush 'em out. When you see 'em, nail 'em. Leave one alive. We'll get those masks off 'em and see what's goin' on here."

As he turned to go, Dead Eye put a meaty hand on his shoulder. "Not masks, chief."

Like it mattered. "What, then?"

"The backs of their heads."

"They were facin' us, Dead Eye. Not even you could see the other-"

"Backs of their heads, but from the inside. Those men ain't got no faces."

Virgil paused. Ressers brought the dead back to life, but they kept the heads intact. More or less. He shook his head; he had no time for ifs or maybes. "You get a shot, you take it."

Holding his coffin in one hand and his Peacebringer in the other, Virgil darted off into the gathering dusk.

As Virgil disappeared, Dead Eye moved back behind the crumbling brickwork of an old wash house. The road where the four men had stood was still empty. The wind grew again, tugging with dusty hands at pieces of rusted ironwork, sending stones and dry weed tumbling, rattling old wood like broken bones. The ruins were alive, and those faceless men could be anywhere.

With a twisted smile, Dead Eye reached up and moved his eye patch from his right eye to his left, blinking that right eye in the sudden light. For every hunted man who thought his pursuer was half-blind, there came a moment of cold clarity, usually followed by the end of the hunt. Dead Eye hadn't gotten his name because of the patch he wore; he only wore it to give the men he hunted a fighting chance.

He could see Virgil, now, moving like a cat from shadow to shadow. Cody and Lucas were away off to

the right, but something large was trying not to be seen amid the splintered wood of a roofless tool shed to the side of the road.

Trying, and failing.

The shed would get in the way, he reckoned, but a brace of shots would sort that out. A little Dead Eye two-step.

He hefted his pine coffin, judging the distance and the wind. The Death Marshals' trademark tool of office was often misunderstood. Much lighter than seemed possible, yet heavy when they needed to be, the magic that filled them made them as deadly as they were striking.

He stood, hurling the coffin high in the air above the road, then fired his invitation to dance. Wood splintered at the far side of the shed, and the dark shape bolted from cover, away from the impact and toward the road.

The forward step...

The coffin arced overhead, unseen. Dead Eye shot it – just so – and the lid jerked open in mid-air. The figure froze as a brilliant blue light flared above it. With a heavy thud, the coffin slammed down, swallowing the man underneath. It bounced once and landed on its back, and the roll flipped the lid shut.

...and the closing step.

"Get in," growled Dead Eye in grim satisfaction, striding forward with his Peacebringer at his side. The wind howled its applause.

Dead Eye planted one boot on the coffin lid. Best see what he'd boxed. But when he toed it open, there was nothing to see in the blinding blue light.

He kicked the box shut and crouched, sweeping around the dark ruins with eye and pistol. He hadn't missed, so where was it?

Applause turned to screeching laughter as the wind snatched movement from every dark corner of his eye.

Nothing could get out the pine box once a Death Marshal put it in. Nothing.

The laughter rang in his ears as he turned this way and that, phantom figures moving everywhere he looked. What was happening? Where was his man?

The darkness swam around him as if he'd been struck on the head, and he reeled, feeling sick and confused. Then everything was moving at once, the road heaving up at him while vengeful shadows darted and dashed between the shifting walls.

He cursed and waved his pistol wildly, but his sight betrayed him again, and his gun jumped from one hand to the other.

He clenched his eyes shut, but the shadows had gotten in there, too.

The world reeled and the night turned inside out. Dead Eye shook his head violently, staggering. He glanced upwards, but up was down, and the swirling dust above yawned like a chasm. He fell to his knees, gasping.

The silhouette of a man stood before him, and Dead Eye grasped him. "Help me," he begged.

The dark figure eased its long, clawed fingers around Dead Eye's mind, and spoke. "You cannot trust your eyes," it said. "Give them to me."

He knew what he had to do.

"Virgil wanted 'em alive," Lucas whispered, his back pressed against a cold sheet of corrugated iron. On the other side, only just rising over the wailing wind, crunching sounds as one of the masked men crept across broken glass.

Cody winked and grinned, his Peacebringer cocked and raised. "He only needs one."

Lucas shook his head, and pressed an eye up to a rust hole. It took a moment for him to spot the man, crouched by a busted stove, both hands up at his face. The skin was abnormally pale and so bright that Lucas wondered if the moon was out, but then he saw what the man was doing. He snapped back from the rust hole like it was red hot.

Cody's frown asked the question, and Lucas had to wait a moment to answer, his mouth dry. "Man's eating his own fingers. Strippin' 'em down to the bone."

A look of uncertainty flashed across Cody's pug-like face, but only for a moment. "Fool can't shoot, then. On three, greenhorn. One-"

Cody sprang forward through the opening in the gap-toothed ruin before Lucas had a chance to move. Cody's Peacebringer made the iron walls ring like a bell once, twice, and three times, and then Lucas was through the gap. The man lay sprawled in the rubble, his chest a dark mess, his white eyes staring up at the hidden sky.

"Dammit, Cody-" Lucas began, but Cody turned on him, fury in his eyes.

"What if he'd had his piece drawn, ya damned fool? What'd you go spinnin' that yarn about his fingers for?"

Lucas glanced down and saw the man's hands. The fingers were unharmed. "I know what I saw..." he began, then something about the man's eyes caught his attention. He stepped closer and bent down for a better look.

The wind whistled through the rust holes, drowning out Cody's brimstone ire as the iron structure began to ring like a glass. Lucas shook his head to clear the noise – sounded like a child's voice, high and far away – and tilted the dead man's head toward him. The eyes shone like Soulstones in the gloom, but there was something moving behind them. They were bulging and stretching. Something inside was straining to get out. Lucas reached out a gloved hand.

At his touch, both eyes burst like grapes. A swarm of black spiders poured out the empty sockets and swept up Lucas' arm. Leaping to his feet with a yell, he swatted at them, scattering broken bodies and twitching legs, but there seemed to be no end to them. And then they swarmed over his shoulders and face and into his mouth in a hideous kiss. Horrified, he tried to spit them out, but it was too late, and his scream choked and died as they surged down his throat.

As quickly as it had begun, it was over. Coughing and hacking and slapping at himself, Lucas realized the spiders had gone. The only remnant was a strange crawling sensation in his head, as if they had got in under his skull. The whispering voice on the wind was laughing as he straightened up and looked at Cody, a frozen look on his companion's face.

Lucas started laughing, too.

"Want to clue me in, partner?" hissed Cody.

Of course. It all made sense, now.

"What's with the jumpin' and the yellin'? There's three of 'em out there-"

"We all dreamed about this place, remember?"

"That don't mean jack! Now-"

"We're still dreaming. Don't you see? None of this is real." Lucas raised one hand and put the muzzle of his Peacebringer to his palm. "Watch."

Cody's yell was drowned out by the thunder of the gun.

Blood and bits of bone and flesh sprayed the inside of the iron-walled room. Lucas raised the shattered stump and grinned at Cody, who was backing away. "See? Nothing happened. I'm fine. It's all just a dream."

He put the blood-splattered muzzle of the gun under his chin. "Just a dream," he whispered.

He had heard the gunfire and heard the whispers on the wind. He knew that his companions were gone and that soon, whatever they were would be coming to make sport of him.

In the gathering storm, Virgil found Dead Eye, sprawled lifeless in the road. He took in the raw, empty sockets and blood-stained hands and walked on. The whispers followed.

Inside a rusted, iron shack, walls black with blood, he found the headless corpse of Lucas. The empty corners echoed to the laughter of the wind.

A short distance away, he came upon Cody, or what had been Cody. Virgil had once seen a French baker making one of those fancy loaves the Europeans were fond of. He'd taken strands of soft dough and wound them around one another, folding them back on themselves in a complex knot. It looked like someone had done the same to Cody; his parts had been rearranged – turned inside out. There was no blood, but somehow that made it worse.

Then a mouth opened, deep within a nameless fold of flesh, and an inhuman moan escaped through teeth that looked like melted wax. Virgil emptied his pistol into the thing, and could only hope he'd killed it.

He re-armed, pistol and box, and looked up. Four shapes that looked like men stood abreast, untouched by the storm. They started toward him.

He didn't move. The wind howled, and dust peppered his face.

The four shapes drew closer, their forms abandoning their pretense of humanity and twisting into nightmares.

Still he didn't move, didn't shoot, didn't run. The wind raged, and the voice borne on it changed.

It sounded angry.

"I'm not going to fight," Virgil growled, stock still as the four shapes reached out for him.

Anger, black as a thundercloud, and clear as lightning. Clear enough to trace. Virgil's head snapped up. Not far away, the bones of a brick boiler house stood black against the dusk. The source of the whispers.

He rolled, ducking the outstretched claws of the nightmares and rose, throwing the pine coffin true as an arrow. It was light when it left his hand, but heavy when it landed. It slammed into the remnants of the brick wall like a locomotive, collapsing it in a cloud of dust.

The coffin had barely come to rest when Virgil arrived at full tilt. He leapt, landing on the box and rode it down the fresh scree of bricks, springing clear at the bottom. A figure moved, partially buried, and Virgil hauled him clear.

"So he gets angry when someone refuses to play his game," he roared, drawing back his Peacebringer with its razor sharp blade, "just like a..." The words died on his lips as he realized he was holding a small, blond-haired boy in a white night gown. "...child?"

Incredibly, the boy didn't look afraid. He looked annoyed. "S'not fair. You said I would win."

With a chill that slowed the blood in his veins, Virgil knew the boy wasn't talking to him. There was a sound behind him, and he brought his Peacebringer scything down towards the boy's neck-

-and then he was rising, held in a grip of iron, his legs flailing. The boy forgotten, Virgil saw fresh blood spray into the night air and realized with a distant regret it was his own. Looking down, he lived long enough to see the claw that protruded from his chest and his own heart fluttering feebly in its grasp before the black talons crushed it to a pulp.

The Death Marshal's corpse landed at the base of the iron tower, some thirty yards away. The boy paid it no attention. He was frowning at the hulking monster before him, a horror of teeth and claws brewed from the very stuff of nightmares.

And then he smiled, the sort of open, guileless smile only a child can manage. "I did! I did win!"

He embraced his friend before climbing up to sit on its massive shoulder. He clapped his hands. "That was fun!" he said. "So, what'll we do now?"

Contract Towns

The success of the Guild's contractor programs in Malifaux has led way to what the Guild calls contract towns. Residents of these towns are not contractors in the usual sense; instead, they function as property renters and maintainers of the buildings and equipment sponsored and built with Guild funds.

The towns are given imaginative names such as Contract Town #1, #2, #3, and so forth by the Guild. Their residents, on the other hand, invariably give each town a name that matches its personality. The towns of Edgewater, Mason's Gap, and Sunset are known to the Guild as Contract Towns #15, #7, and #11, respectively.

Each town has a town council and mayor, the latter of which is a contractor for the Guild. The position of mayor in a contract town is an unenviable one. They are directly responsible for the town being profitable enough to fill the Guild vaults, and any disruptions in a contract town's functioning could cost the mayor his contract, which is immediately payable in full to the Guild. Mayors unable to fulfill their contractual obligations to the Guild find themselves with a debt contract that may take years to repay.

The Dreamer - Master

As Nytmare began to speculate the possibilities and formulate the machinations by which he might achieve his true immortality, he happened upon the mind of a young boy. This boy dreamed remarkably elaborate and complex images amidst puzzling mazes of thought. Equally remarkable, just as Nytmare attempted to twist the boy's thoughts into the fearful night terror upon which he could feed, the boy's dream-self looked directly upon the mighty creature for only a moment and then reclaimed the dream, twisting it away from Nytmare. The Dreamer certainly had no fear of the beast as he smiled upon it and turned away, creating a beautiful and vibrant garden of color and sound.

Nytmare never had such an experience. He was immediately fascinated and awed by the boy. He would not have admitted it, but he might have felt genuine pangs of fear of that boy.

He toyed with the child for days. He could do nothing to scare the Dreamer, and he had no power over the boy's hauntingly brilliant and intricate dreams. Feeling himself weaken at not having fed properly on the anxiety of the innocent, he withdrew from the boy, resolving to first rejuvenate and eventually return, unlock, and consume the boy's mind.

As Nytmare departed the boy's dream, the Dreamer followed him. As Nytmare severed their dream-connection, he could not have imagined it was possible, but the boy manifested his dream-self in Malifaux, believing it to be just another extension of his own labyrinthine dreamscape. It is, to him, nothing more than a dream, and he has no awareness that he has bridged the great divide between worlds, escaping the twilight barrier of dreams.

The boy likes to play games, and the nightmarish creature has become his favorite playmate. While the Dreamer

30MM BASE

SOULSTONE CACHE: 0

MASTER, SPIRIT

WK/CG	HT	WP	CA	DF	WD
3/-	1	8	7🐾	2	3

TWIST REALITY	
RG	⌐12
CB	6
DG	1/2/4

TALENTS:

Abilities

A Ghost in Malifaux: This model may ignore any (☓) and 🌑 effects and damage from ⚑.

Gunfighter [Twist Reality]

Harmless

Master of Dreams: A Crew containing this Master gains one Soulstone to the Crew's Soulstone Pool at the start of the Encounter for each Nightmare it hired, up to a maximum of five. A Crew containing this Master may not hire Mercenaries in Scraps.

My Teddy Bear: A Crew containing this Master ignores the **Rare 1** limitation on Teddy. Teddy models hired by a Crew containing this model gain the Nightmare Characteristic.

Pleasant Dreams: Bury any number of friendly Nightmares instead of deploying them during the Deployment Phase.

Release Nightmares: When this model is killed or sacrificed, you may place any number of friendly buried Nightmares, within 6" of this model before it is removed from play.

Shadowy Form: This model cannot be targeted by an enemy Action while it is within 3" of a friendly Nightmare that could have been targeted by the Action.

Shared Actions: This model and a friendly Lord Chompy Bits may use a maximum of three general AP per turn between them. **Pass** Actions do not count against this total.

Actions

(+1) Instinctual

(0) "I Can Fly!": This model's **Wk/Cg** becomes 7/- and it gains **Flight**.

(0) Night Terrors: (☓)6 friendly Nightmares gain **Terrifying → 13**, or increase their **Terrifying** to 13 if they already have the Ability.

(0) Nightmare Friend: Bury this model and replace it with a friendly buried Lord Chompy Bits.

(0) Unhinge: Target model with **Wp** 4 or less within 3" of this model receives **Paralyzed**.

Triggers

Ca (🐾🐾) All My Friends [Frightening Dream]: This model's Controller may place any number of friendly buried Nightmares within 6" of this model.

SPELLS:

(0) Daydreaming
(CC: 17🐾 /Rst: - /Rg: C) Discard two Soulstones. Summon one Daydream.

(0) Inflict Dreams
(CC: 14🐾 /Rst: Wp /Rg: 12) Target model's Defense, Casting, and **Wp** Flips receive ⊟ when defending against Nightmares.

(1) Calm Dreams
(CC: 11🐾 /Rst: - /Rg: C) Bury any number of friendly Nightmares within 6".

(1) Frightening Dream
(CC: 10🐾 /Rst: - /Rg: C) Place one friendly buried Nightmare within 6" of this model.

(1) Rapid Eye Movement
(CC: 14🐾🐾 /Rst: - /Rg: 6) Target friendly Nightmare gains (2) **Flurry**.

believes they're playing an innocent game of tag, the living near him see the reality as something vile as creatures drawn from their own dark subconscious come alive to confront them. A favorite game of the child's is called "The Monster" in which he and his towering playmate chase the others and "gobble them up", like a game of tag, but with horrible consequences. He's now come to call the Nytmare "Lord Chompy Bits". He's gone by many names. This fits as well as any other.

Although a mere apparition on Malifaux, the boy is known in quickly growing legend as The Dreamer. The power he possesses over the twisting imagery of his dreams has followed him here, and he controls the laws of reality. He ravages Malifaux, reshaping rocks, plants, and even

living beings into grotesque parodies of their former selves.

So far, when the boy finds himself in true danger, Lord Chompy Bits has been there, too, to fight his battles in Malifaux. As an additional fear for Lord Chompy, the master of nighttime terrors, he has heard that other masters of Malifaux magic, the Neverborn, seek him and the boy, intending to unlock their secret and use that power for themselves.

Now, pursued by Neverborn and human alike, Nytmare has found himself in a strange position in which he must protect the boy while desperately attempting to unravel the boy's mastery of reality.

But he is an ancient creature. He knows fear better than most.

Lord Chompy Bits - Master

The strong imaginations of children allow them to have spectacular and fascinating dreams, often reflecting their dawning understanding of the world as well as the fears they harbor about the unknown.

Humans are familiar with dreams beginning and ending within the mind of their owners, but one mysterious creature might be responsible for many Earthside fears and superstitions ranging from the Boogeyman to the Beast. Although he never manifested the traditional mastery of Malifaux magics, this enigmatic creature somehow developed the ability to span the aether between worlds and enter the minds of the innocent. He tormented them. He manipulated their subconscious thoughts and twisted their dreams, infusing their nights with images of their own greatest fears.

In Malifaux, he might only be regarded as a hulking and deformed creature, sharing many attributes of a large Nephilim. Yet, in the dream-world, he is both a god and a devil, feeding upon the fear only he is able to instill as he can twist and reshape the images there, bending that dream-reality to his will.

He is the haunting image of dreams. He is Nytmare.

The Nytmare is older than most would believe, including the Neverborn. He is a creature of solitude, exploring the depth of his victim's fears and anxieties, torturing children with perhaps every moment of his horrible life.

Those fears not only sustain him, they make him strong and vibrant. He has come to believe that he might be eternal and the powerful imagination of a child might unlock a great magic never before witnessed.

50MM BASE

SOULSTONE COST: SUMMONED

MASTER, NIGHTMARE

WK/CG	HT	WP	CA	DF	WD
4/6	4	5	5 🐾	4	10

SIX-INCH TEETH			TEN-INCH CLAWS		
RG	🔪 1		RG	🔪 3	
CB	6 🐾		CB	5 🐾	
DG	2/3/5		DG	2/4/6	

TALENTS:

Abilities

Delight in Pain: This model heals 1 **Wd** when a living model is wounded by a melee **Strike** within 4".

Dreamer's Revenge: If this model is killed or sacrificed, its Controller may place a buried friendly The Dreamer within 6" of this model before it is removed from the table.

One Master: This model is included in any Crew hiring The Dreamer and always starts the Encounter Buried. This model may never be in play at the same time as a friendly The Dreamer. When this model is brought into play, this model's Controller must bury a friendly The Dreamer and this model activates immediately. Any time a friendly The Dreamer is brought into play, bury this model and activate the Dreamer immediately. Totems connected to The Dreamer in this Crew are connected to this model as well.

Prey on the Weak: This model ignores **Harmless** and **Pitiful**. This model receives +2 **Dg** to Damage Flips against **Harmless** or **Pitiful** models.

Shared Actions: This model and The Dreamer may use a maximum of three general AP per turn between them. **Pass** Actions do not count against this total.

Terrifying → 14

Wicked: This model's **Strikes** against disengaging models deal damage in addition to ending the Action.

Weapons
Six-Inch Teeth: Poison 2.

Ten-Inch Claws: Paired.

Actions
(+1) Melee Expert

Triggers

Cb (📖🐾) All Done [Six-Inch Teeth, Ten-Inch Claws]: After damaging defender, bury this model and replace it with a friendly buried The Dreamer.

Cb (🐾🐾) Flay [Ten-Inch Claws]

Cb (✗🐾) Disembowel [Six-Inch Teeth]: When damaging defender with a Six Inch Teeth **Strike**, kill defender unless its controller discards two Control Cards or two Soulstones. Only models with the **Use Soulstone** Ability may discard Soulstones.

Cb (🌀🐾) Onslaught [Six-Inch Teeth, Ten-Inch Claws]: After damaging defender with a melee **Strike** with this Weapon, immediately make a melee **Strike** with this Weapon targeting the defender.

SPELLS:

(0) Dreamer's Daydream
(CC: 12 🐾 /Rst: - /Rg: C) Discard two Soulstones. Place a Daydream within 8" of this model. Immediately activate this Daydream following this model's activation. The Daydream may only take **Walk** and (0) Actions this turn.

Daydream - Totem

The Dreamer has no friends. He draws pictures and tells stories of faraway places filled with wizards, and he unflinchingly tells tales of big scary monsters – some with broad wings and long claws, some of giant flying teddy bears, some with many eyes that watch children while they sleep. He frankly scares the other children who have come to avoid him altogether. His parents chastise him for his elaborate storytelling and for the constant complaints of the schoolmarm regarding his staring into space and ignoring her lessons.

Sharp cracks of a ruler upon his knuckles have not put an end to these distractions, and his parents have become weary of the constant war between their authority and his perpetual daydreaming.

The Dreamer assures them that he is not daydreaming, even while he stares absently beyond them, oblivious to their frustrations. When they are gone, he quickly resumes talking to a playmate that isn't there, dreaming of adventures they share in faraway lands, and of the big monster they play hide-and-go-seek with.

The doctors say the child's daydreams are harmless "imaginary friends," and encourage his parents to have patience. His parents argue that he has involved conversations with his "friends", often breaking out into laughter and sometimes arguing with them. They hope it is nothing more than an overactive imagination that he soon outgrows. So far, his nighttime and day dreams are increasing and becoming more elaborate.

30MM BASE   SOULSTONE COST: 2

INSIGNIFICANT, NIGHTMARE, SPIRIT, TOTEM (THE DREAMER)

Wk/Cg	Ht	Wp	Ca	Df	Wd
6/-	1	4	4🦇	5	2

TWIST REALITY

Rg	➹12
CB	4
Dg	1/2/4

Talents:

Abilities

Change into Nightmare: If this model is killed or sacrificed by an enemy model's **Strike** or spell, its controller may place one buried Nightmare within 6" of it before it is removed from the table.

Companion (The Dreamer/Lord Chompy Bits)

Dreamer's Reality: This model may **Cast Magical Extension** twice per activation. Its controller must discard one Control Card in addition to paying the AP to cast it a second time. This model may not **Cast Magical Extension** unless The Dreamer is in play.

Dreams: Crews containing The Dreamer may hire up to three Daydreams. The Dreamer/Lord Chompy Bits can connect up to three Daydream Totems instead of one.

Float

Gunfighter [Twist Reality]

Actions

(0) Calm Nightmares: Bury friendly Lord Chompy Bits within 6" and replace it with a friendly buried The Dreamer.

(1) Disturbing Whispers: ⚫6. Non-Nightmare, non-Master models receive -1 **Wp** when defending in a Duel.

(1) Call Nightmares: Sacrifice this model. Place one or more friendly buried Nightmare models within 6" of this model. This model's controller must discard one Control Card for each Nightmare model placed after the first.

(1) Lead Nightmare: Target friendly Lord Chompy Bits or friendly Nightmare within 12" Pushes 4" directly toward this model.

Spells:

(1) Magical Extension
(CC: * /Rst: * /Rg: *) This spell may be cast only once per activation. Cast one of the connected Master's **(1)** spells. During this casting, this model may use a Soulstone to change its starting total.

Collodi and Marionette - Henchman

What passes for reality in Malifaux has a way of seeping into Earth's collective subconscious, creating the stuff of ghost stories and legends for centuries to come. Collodi and its awful marionettes are one of those legends whose origins begin not on Earth, but in Malifaux.

In the days of Old Malifaux, Collodi was a wooden puppet brought to life by ancient magics. Its sole purpose was to entertain and delight without thought to its own happiness, which it did faithfully for decades. When Old Malifaux collapsed, Collodi was left alone and without purpose. It did not realize the children it had brought joy to for so many years were not coming back. Several years passed. Then Collodi experienced something it had never experienced before. It felt.

At first it did not know what was happening. A gaping emptiness filled its thoughts, and it knew a void deep down that no amount of searching would fill. It came to know what this feeling was - loneliness. It missed the children's smiles as they delighted at the stories performed for them. The absence of their laughter haunted its every moment. Finally, the loneliness was too much for it to bear, and it began once again to carve. The marionettes it carved bore the likenesses of the children whose faces it remembered. It built a stage and performed for its new children under the open sky. For a brief time, the marionettes gave

Collodi comfort, and it could imagine their laughter once more. But soon it was lonely again. It took its creations and wandered far and wide, even finding Earth for a time through a tear between worlds, seeking any sign of life for which it could perform.

When humans began settling Malifaux a century ago, Collodi rushed to perform for the arriving children. The first settlers were terrified of the animated wooden puppet and chased it from their towns with torches and axes. Shunned by those it had waited centuries to entertain, Collodi felt its second emotion - hate. It hated the humans for denying it what it had waited so long to feel and vowed they would know the emptiness of being without their children just as it had felt for so long.

Today, Collodi's painted wagon roams Malifaux, conducting performances much as it did long ago. It takes care to hide its wooden features from prying eyes, letting its marionettes be the stars of the show. Children flock to the traveling stage, laughing at the marionettes' antics and delighting at their colorful costumes. None notice the uncanny resemblance many of the marionettes bear to children from neighboring towns, all of which have disappeared after a visit from Collodi's travelling show.

30MM BASE

SOULSTONE COST: 8

CONSTRUCT, HENCHMAN 7, SCAVENGER, SPECIAL FORCES (DOLL)

Wk/Cg	Ht	Wp	Ca	Df	Wd
2/5	2	6	6 ♟	5	9

WOODEN TALONS	
Rg	⚔ 1
Cb	6 ♟
Dg	2/3/5

TALENTS:

Abilities

Living Puppets: Friendly Dolls lose Insignificant while with 12" of this model.

Marionettes: Crews hiring this model must hire at least one Marionette. After another model hits this model with a Strike or spell targeting this model, this model's controller may nominate a friendly Marionette within 6" to become the target before resolving the effects of the **Strike** or spell.

Perfect Machine: This model may ignore any effect that specifically targets Constructs.

Holding the Strings: Friendly Marionettes within 6" may immediately activate after this model's activation ends.

Puppet Master: ✪4. Friendly Dolls receive +2 **Wp.**

Special Forces Leader (Doll): Crews led by this model can only hire Dolls.

Actions
(+1) Casting Expert

(0) Doll Friends: One friendly Doll within 6" of Collodi activates after this model's activation ends.

(1) A Puppet's Soul: (χ)4. Sacrifice any number of Dolls. Gain one Soulstone per Doll sacrificed.

(2) Puppet Show: (χ)4 Friendly Dolls receive **Fast.**

(2) Mend Puppets: (χ)4 Friendly Dolls make a Healing Flip.

(2) Puppet Tools: Discard one Scrap Counter within 6", or carried by this model, Summon one Marionette.

Triggers
Cb (♟ χ) All Wound Up (Wooden Talons): After resolving damage, defender receives **Slow.**

SPELLS:

(1) Breathe Life
(CC: 15♟ /Rst: - /Rg: 15) One friendly Doll, plus one friendly Doll per ♟ in the casting total gains one of the following: **(+1) Melee Expert, (+1) Ranged Expert**, or **(+1) Casting Expert.**

(1) Disassemble
(CC: 14♟♟ /Rst: Df /Rg: 6) Target Construct is sacrificed unless its Controller discards two Control Cards. If the model is sacrificed, gain Scrap Counters equal to target's base size.

(1) Long Strings
(CC: 13▤ /Rst: - /Rg: 8) Target friendly Marionette loses **Collodi's Dolls** and **Pull Strings** until the End of the Encounter.

(2) Filled with Stones
(CC: 12♟ /Rst: - /Rg: 3) Target friendly Doll gains **Armor +2, Hard to Kill** and -1/-1 **Wk/Cg.** This lasts until the end of the Encounter.

Marionette - Minion

30mm Base **Soulstone Cost: 2**

Construct, Rare 4, Special Forces (Doll)

Wk/Cg	Ht	Wp	Ca	Df	Wd
5/7	1	5	3	5	3

Wooden Claws	
Rg	//// 1
Cb	4 🐾
Dg	1/2/4

Talents:

Abilities

Attached Strings: This model is sacrificed if a friendly Collodi is killed or sacrificed. If a friendly Collodi is buried, this model is also buried and is placed within 4" of a friendly Collodi when that friendly Collodi returns to play.

Collodi's Dolls: This model may only be hired by Crews containing Collodi. This model may not move further than 8" from a friendly Collodi. Any effect that moves this model may not move it further than 8" from a friendly Collodi. If this model starts its activation further than 8" from a friendly Collodi, immediately Push this model directly toward a friendly Collodi until it is no further than 8" away.

Hard to Wound 1

Weapons

Wooden Claws: Paired.

Actions

(0) Retract: Push this model into base contact with a friendly Collodi.

(0) Tell No Lies: Neither this model, nor its target may Cheat Fate or Use Soulstones during this model's next **Strike**.

(1) Pull Strings: This model moves up to its **Wk**. Move a friendly Collodi into base contact with this model after the move.

(2) Flurry

Triggers

Cb (🐾 ✗) All Wound Up (Wooden Claws): After resolving damage, defender receives **Slow**.

Alp - Minion

The mischievous Nightmares known as Alps delight in creating havoc. These foul creatures insinuate themselves into the lives of ordinary folk, playing cruel pranks while sowing mistrust and fear among their victims. An Alp can feel the tension of its intended targets as a palpable force, growing in intensity until it reaches a point where nerves are drawn as taut as bowstrings. This is when the Alp's truly horrible intentions are revealed.

The Alp targets its nervous victims, preferring to take them while they are fast asleep. Sitting atop their chest, this little monster delights in draining its prey of their vitality and life force, literally stealing it away with each labored breath they struggle to take. Their strained nerves serve to flavor the vitality with hints of paranoia and fear, a delicious bouquet indeed.

Although it prefers its victim asleep when it feeds, some may be wide awake when it encounters them. It is prepared for this and is capable of reducing even the wariest or lightest sleeper to such an exhausted state that they can only struggle to stay awake for so long. To fall asleep alone with an Alp is to invite a slumber from which one can never awaken. While sitting on the victim's chest, the Alp then slowly leeches its life force, eventually draining the body and suffocating it at once before moving on to its next meal.

30MM BASE

SOULSTONE COST: 3

NIGHTMARE

WK/CG	HT	WP	CA	DF	WD
5/8	1	4	4	4	3

KISS	
RG	⫻ 1
CB	4
DG	1/1+Slow/3+Slow

TALENTS:

Abilities

Exhaustion: Enemy non-Nightmare models suffer 1 **Wd** when taking a **Wk** or **Strike** Action within 1" of this model.

Feed on Dreams: Enemy models receiving **Slow** while within 3" of this model suffer 1 **Wd**, even if they are already **Slow**.

Never Wake Up: If a model is killed by **Feed on Dreams** within 6" of one or more Alps, the Alp closest to that model summons one Alp.

Smother: Enemy models activating within 4" of 1 or more Alps must win a **Wp → 12** Duel that receives ⊟ for each Alp after the first within 4". If the model loses the Duel it receives **Slow**.

Tarnkappe: An enemy model targeting this model from further than 6" receives ⊟ ⊟ to attack Flips against this model.

Actions

(0) Blood Gift: Reduce this model's current **Wd** to 1. Target friendly Neverborn model within 4" of this model makes a Healing Flip. This model cannot take this Action if it has only 1 **Wd** remaining.

(0) Yawning: (⋊)6. Models with **Fast** must win a **Wp → Wp** Duel or suffer 4 **Dg**.

(1) Disturbing Whispers: ⬤6. Non-Nightmare, non-Master models receive -1 **Wp** when defending in a Duel.

SPELLS:

(1) Steal Breath
(CC: 11✘ /Rst: Wp /Rg: 8) Target receives **Slow**.

Black Blood Shaman - Minion

Revered by other Nephilim, black blood shamans practice a primal magic, the origins of which are lost to the ages. These mysterious entities tap into the primordial power of the Nephilim's black blood to fuel their rituals and create potent charms and poisons.

The knowledge necessary to become a black blood shaman is passed down orally from generation to generation and only to a Nephilim worthy of such honor. The bestowing of this honor comes after days of bloody trials, each more violent than the last. Only the strongest of Nephilim can endure each of the trials. Surviving, alone, demonstrates that its blood courses strongest of all the contenders.

Once the new shaman has learned the sacred rites and rituals from its predecessor, its first act is to ritually slay its teacher, offering up its blood as a sacrifice to the Nephilim spirits of might, violence, and dominance. When the ritual is concluded, the shaman dons the holy raiment of its station, never to reveal its face to another living soul again.

The Guild has recently become aware of the existence of black blood shamans. They have been seen accompanying other Nephilim on raids against settlements and Guild strongholds, whipping the attackers into crazed frenzies and poisoning the blood of the defenders with slashes of their wicked ritual knives.

30MM BASE

SOULSTONE COST: 6

GRAVEROBBER, NEPHILIM, RARE 2

WK/CG	HT	WP	CA	DF	WD
5/-	2	5	6🗡	4	8

RITUAL KNIFE

RG	⚔ 1
CB	4🗡
DG	1/1/1🌳

TALENTS:

Abilities

Black Blood

Blood from the Dead: This model may use its Corpse Counters as Blood Counters for its Talents and spells.

Blood Sense: When a living or Undead model is killed within 3", this model gains 1 Blood Counter.

Ride Nephilim: Reduce the Casting Cost of **Carry** to 1 AP when a friendly Nephilim casts it on this model.

Weapons

Ritual Knife: Poison 3.

Actions

(+1) Instinctual

(0) Blood in the Air: (🗡)8. Friendly Nephilim may Push up to 4" toward this model.

(0) Blood Offering: This model suffers 4 **Wd**. This model gains one Blood Counter.

(0) Spill Black Blood: Inflict up to 6 **Wd** on this model or a target friendly model with **Black Blood** within 3". Non-Neverborn models within 1" of the model suffer 1 **Wd** for every 2 **Wd** suffered by target model.

Triggers

Ca (🗡🗡) Bloody Mess [Inject Blood, Taint Blood]: This model gains one Blood Counter after successfully casting this spell.

SPELLS:

(0) Blood Frenzy
(CC: 12🗡 /Rst: - /Rg: (🗡)4) Friendly Nephilim gain **(2) Flurry**.

(0) Blood Magic
(CC: 10🗡 /Rst: - /Rg: 6) This model or friendly model within 2" of this model suffers 3 **Wd** or discards a carried Blood Counter. Target friendly non-Master Neverborn model selects one of the following effects:

- **Charge** Actions require only 1 AP. If the **Charge** fails, the model's activation immediately ends.
- One of target's basic melee weapons gains **Poison 2**.
- Target model receives **Fast**.
- Target model gains **Black Blood**.

(1) Inject Blood
(CC: 13🗡 /Rst: Df /Rg: ⚔ 2) This model discards one Blood Counter. Target model without **Black Blood** suffers Dg 2/3/5. Target model with **Black Blood** heals 2 **Wd** instead.

(1) Potent Blood
(CC: 12🗡 /Rst: - /Rg: 6) Target model's **Black Blood** inflicts +1 **Dg** .

(1) Taint Blood
(CC: 12🗡 /Rst: Df /Rg: 6) This model discards one Blood Counter. Target model gains **Black Blood** and Nephilim. Inflict 1 **Wd** on this model during the Resolve Effects Step, this Spell does not end until the next Resolve Effects Step.

Coppelius - Minion

Man still struggles to understand how the nightmares he has endured have their origins more in the dark recesses of Malifaux than within the dim depths of his own troubled subconscious.

The Ortegas recently had the great fortune of capturing a young Nephilim. They questioned the creature vigorously and mercilessly, probing for further insight into all Neverborn practices. They worked some truth from it until their questions turned to the activities of the walking nightmares. It refused to speak despite their ungentle encouragement. When they mentioned the name Coppelius, it went mad, howling and screaming as it clawed at its own face - the only thing its manacled hands could reach. Its interrogators backed out of the cell, leaving the creature to writhe in unbridled terror.

When the howling ceased many hours later, the Guild officers reentered the cell. The Nephilim's body rested where they had bound it, but its flesh had been torn and shredded as if it had flayed itself to death. Strangely, the creature's eyes were torn from their sockets. Stranger still, a thorough search of the cell never uncovered the eyes.

Their shock only mounted when they studied the corpse. Rather than random lacerations in its own hide, it had carved tiny, barely discernable words into its flesh, from its neck down. Translators have determined most of the message to read, "...Don't you know yet? He is a wicked man who comes...[Something unintelligible] in their eyes till they bleed and pop out of their heads. He takes the eyes...as food for his children."

Only one human adolescent claims to have seen Coppelius and survived. Unfortunately, since her encounter with the creature, she refuses to speak. In writing, she only briefly mentions his appearance, and never the deed, of which the mere mention sends her into a temporary catatonia.

But she writes of their encounter, "The most hideous figure could not have filled me with deeper horror. He is large and thin with long limbs. His head, we thought, was like a normal man's. But it was round, his eyes blank, and his mouth was like a horrible creature wriggling about trying to eat the eyes he stole. His whole appearance was loathsome and repulsive, but we were most revolted by his huge hands, and fingers that stretch toward the eyes."

The Guild has issued several warrants for his arrest.

30MM BASE   SOULSTONE COST: 9

NIGHTMARE, UNIQUE

Wk/Cg	Ht	Wp	Ca	Df	Wd
6/-	2	6	6 🐾	5	10

LONG CLAWED FINGERS

Rg	⚔ 2
Cb	6 🐾
Dg	1/2/5

TALENTS:

Abilities

Deeply Disturbing: When this model gains an Eye Counter, living models within 3" of it must conduct a **Wp → 12** Morale Duel.

The Dying Dream: This model inflicts 4 **Wd** on the model that killed or sacrificed it before it leaves play. Eye Counters carried by this model when it is killed or sacrificed are discarded.

Float

Night Stalker: ●4. Models forced to fall back after losing a Morale Duel suffer 3 **Wd** in addition to falling back.

Terrifying → 13

Unexplained Connection: Crews containing C. Hoffman may hire this model at no additional Soulstone cost.

Weapons

Long Clawed Fingers: Poison 2. Gain one Eye Counter when inflicting Severe damage with this weapon.

Actions

(+1) Melee Expert

(0) Savor Delicacy: Discard one Eye Counter. This model or a friendly Nightmare within 2" makes 2 Healing Flips.

(0) Unhinge: Target model with **Wp** 4 or less within 3" of this model receives **Paralyzed**.

Triggers

Cb (✗ 🐾) Remove Eye [Long Clawed Fingers]: After hitting a defender with this weapon, instead of flipping for damage, this **Strike** inflicts Moderate damage. This model gains one Eye Counter.

Cb (🐾) Slumber [Long Clawed Fingers]: After hitting a defender with this weapon, do no damage. Defender receives **Paralyzed**.

SPELLS:

(0) The Crescent Moon
(CC: 14 🐾 /Rst: - /Rg: C) Discard one Eye Counter. Summon one Alp.

(1) Hallucinations
(CC: 10 🐾 /Rst: Ca /Rg: 6) Gain one Eye Counter if the target is living or Undead. Living models immediately fall back.

(1) Sleep, My Friends
(CC: 13 🐾 🐾 /Rst: Wp /Rg: (ϒ)3) All non-Master models receive **Slow**.

174

Insidious Madness - Minion

Whether driven to it by experiences of euphoric beauty or horrifying malevolence, or witnessing a loved one suffer from it, at some point, everyone visiting Malifaux has been touched by madness. As physical manifestations of its terrible power, the Woes of Madness sow discord and insanity wherever they are encountered. Their mercurial forms are in a state of constant flux, continually sprouting and absorbing thick tentacles, inhuman eyes, and wet gibbering maws.

To hear the chilling whispers emanating from those ever-changing mouths brings a Madness' namesake, dissolving the will and sanity of those it comes in contact with only to replace it with paranoia, mania, dementia, or a litany of other mind-destroying afflictions. Few completely recover from such an encounter, their psyche damaged to one degree or another by the assault.

Madness basks in the despair and hopelessness it inflicts on its victim's friends and loved ones as they watch the victim's mind collapse. This indirect assault on their sanity ensures Madness' influence will spread slowly through Malifaux, gripping its human residents with fear and paranoia. These two emotions weaken the resolve of rational men and women, allowing the Woe to insinuate itself into their psyches and shatter them from within.

30MM BASE　　　　　**SOULSTONE COST: 4**

NIGHTMARE, RARE 3, SPIRIT, WOE

WK/CG	HT	WP	CA	DF	WD
8/8	2	5	2	6	3

NEVERBORN WHISPERS	
RG	↝10
CB	*
DG	1/2/2+Slow

TALENTS:

Abilities

Delirium: This model's Controller may sacrifice it after determining initiative activation order, but before activations begin. The Controller of this model re-flips their Initiative Flip. The new Initiative Flip receives ⊞.

Float

Hysteria: Falling back models within 3" of this model may not Rally at the start of their activation unless they win a **Wp → Wp** Duel.

Psychosis: ⓧ2. A model must win a **Wp → Wp** Duel with this model when it declares this model the target of a **Strike**, or the starting flip for the Strike receives ⊟⊟.

Weapons

Neverborn Whispers: This weapon's Attack Duels may be made with either; **Wp → Df** or **Wp → Wp**, Controller's choice. Models wounded by this weapon lose any immunities or bonuses involving **Wp** Duels.

Actions

(1) A Danger to Yourself: A model within 4" of this model must win a **Wp → Wp** Duel or suffer 2 **Wd**.

(1) Induce Phobia: This model gains **Terrifying → 12**.

(1) Psychopathic Episode: ⓧ4. All models, including this model, receive ⊟ to **Wp** Duels.

175

Lelu - Minion

Lelus are the Woes of Self-Deprecation. Despite their massive physique, other Nephilim and their sibling Lilitu, treat these Neverborn with contempt and disgust. They lack the predatory drive necessary to stand their ground against their betters, instead serving as their lackeys and vassals, constantly reminded of their worthlessness. All wear a bonding torc, a collar marked with the name of the Nephilim or Lilitu to which they belong. This perversely gives a Lelu some measure of comfort – after all, what Neverborn would wish to claim ownership over a creature completely devoid of value?

Those not of the black blood, on the other hand, provide an outlet for their depression. They take great delight in forcing their will upon the few creatures they deem weaker and less valuable than themselves, typically humans. They prefer to strike when their prey is most vulnerable, raising their spirits at the expense of others. Because of their need to pass along their suffering, Lelus forestall their own misery by extending their victim's torment as long as possible. Even the inevitable feeding is painfully slow and purposeful, providing a Lelu a sense of dominance over another living being. The feeling is fleeting, however, and before long, the Lelu finds his mind trapped in a cage of his own self-loathing.

30MM BASE **SOULSTONE COST: 7**

NEPHILIM, NIGHTMARE, RARE 2, WOE

WK/CG	HT	WP	CA	DF	WD
4/6	2	4	5	5	9

CLAWS	
RG	🩸 2
CB	5 🐾
DG	2/3/5

VAMPIRIC BITE	
RG	🩸 1
CB	7 🐾
DG	1/2/4

TALENTS:

Abilities

Black Blood

Bond (Lilitu): This model may simultaneously activate with any friendly Lilitu regardless of distance between the models.

Flight

Regeneration 2

Same Malignant Force: If this model is healed from any source other than a friendly Lilitu, one friendly Lilitu heals the same number of **Wd**.

Thoughts Twisted: Target non-Neverborn within 2" of this model suffers 2 **Wd** in the Resolve Effects Step.

Two Sided: During the Resolve Effects Step this model suffers 3 **Wd** if there are no friendly Lilitu models in play.

Weapons

Claws: Paired. **Poison 2.**

Claws, Vampiric Bite: This Weapon's Attack Flips receive ➕ while this model has 5 **Wd** or less remaining.

Actions

(+1) Melee Expert

(0) Drain Blood: This model may immediately use this Action after killing a living or Undead model. This model gains one Blood Counter.

Triggers

Cb (🐾 🐾) Flay [Claws]

Cb (✖ 🐾) Thirst [Vampiric Bite]: After hitting a defender with this weapon, do no damage. Instead, inflict 1 **Wd** then this model immediately casts **Drink Blood** on the defender. The Casting Flip receives +3✖ **Ca.**

SPELLS:

(0) Drink Blood
(CC: 12✖ /Rst: Wp /Rg: 🩸 1) **Dg** 2/3/6. This model heals a number of **Wd** equal to the damage inflicted by this spell.

(1) "Punish Me!"
(CC: 12🐾 /Rst: Wp /Rg: 6) Target model loses **Hard to Wound** and **Hard to Kill** until the Start Closing Phase.

(1) Summon Lilitu
(CC: 18🐾 /Rst: - /Rg: C) This model or one friendly Nephilim within 6" of this model discards two Blood Counters. Sacrifice one friendly Nephilim within 6" of this model. Summon one Lilitu.

Lilitu - Minion

Lilitus are the Woes of Forbidden Delight. A Lilitu's tantalizingly exotic beauty seems so inviting at first blush. A glance from one is filled with lurid suggestions, clouding the minds of mortal men with dark imaginings. Their intoxicating voices draw the weak-willed to their side where they can whisper the hope of uncountable joys to explore in exchange for impossible promises. Few realize the peril they have put themselves into until it is too late and their promised payments come due.

A Lilitu's demeanor changes abruptly when she learns her victim cannot deliver on its commitment. The honeyed words so very recently dripping from her tongue are replaced with an arrogant disappointment as she metes out horrible violence upon the victim. The Lilitu's gentle caresses become searing pain as she uses her barbed lash to flay victims to the bone.

Lilitus take great delight in breaking their victims, drawing sustenance from the sadistic pain they inflict both bodily and mentally. Not only do they enjoy the punishments they deliver to their victims, but they treat their own siblings, the Lelu, in an equally domineering manner.

30MM BASE **SOULSTONE COST: 7**

NEPHILIM, NIGHTMARE, RARE 2, WOE

WK/CG	HT	WP	CA	DF	WD
5/8	2	5	6 🐾	6	7

BARBED WHIP

RG	⚔ 4
CB	5 🐾
DG	1/2/4

TALENTS:

Abilities
Black Blood

Bond (Lelu): This model may simultaneously activate with any friendly Lelu regardless of distance between the models.

Dark Beauty: +2✗ Ca when **Casting** or **Channeling Lure**.

Float

Irresistible: Enemy models must win a **Wp->12** Duel when targeting this model with an attack or the Action fails. This may not be ignored by any Talent.

Sadist: This model's Damage Flips receive 🎴🎴 when damaging a model with less than half of its **Wd** remaining.

Same Malignant Force: If this model is healed from any source other than a friendly Lelu, one friendly Lelu heals the same number of **Wd**.

Twisted Thoughts: Target friendly Neverborn model within 2" of this model heals 2 Wd in the Resolve Effects Step.

Two Sided: During the Resolve Effects Step this model suffers 3 **Wd** if there are no friendly Lelu models in play.

Wicked: This model's strikes against disengaging models deal damage in addition to ending the Action.

Actions
(+1) Casting Expert

(0) Drain Blood: This model may immediately use this Action after killing a living or Undead model. This model gains one Blood Counter.

Triggers
Ca (🐾🐾) Double Take [Lure]: After defender fails to resist **Lure**, completely resolve the spell then cast **Lure** on the same target.

SPELLS:

(1) Emotionally Exposed
(CC: 13 🐾 /Rst: Wp /Rg: 12) Models receive +4 **Wp** in Duels when they target the target of this spell.

(1) Impure Thoughts
(CC: 14 🐾🐾 /Rst: Wp /Rg: 4) Apply one of the following to the target model:
- Target model receives **Paralyzed**.
- Select one of the target model's basic melee weapons. Target suffers a Damage Flip that receives 🎴🎴.
- Target model discards two Control Cards or one Soulstone. Only models with **Use Soulstone** may discard Soulstones.

(1) Lure
(CC: 12 ✗ 🐾 /Rst: Wp /Rg: 18) Push target model its **Wk** toward this model. If the Push ends with the target in this model's melee range it makes a melee attack against the target.

(1) Summon Lelu
(CC: 18 🐾 /Rst: - /Rg: C) This model or one friendly Nephilim within 6" of this model discards two Blood Counters. Sacrifice one friendly Nephilim within 6" of this model. Summon one Lelu.

Nekima, The Dark Sibling - Minion

If not for her insatiable thirst for blood, Nekima would have ascended to supremacy over all Nephilim. Instead, her murderous desires led her down a very different path than that of her sister, the ever-conniving Lilith.

As the oldest and strongest of the Nephilim, every indication pointed to Nekima claiming dominance over the Nephilim when the time was right. She waited, honing her murderous talents until her slightest gesture could flay the skin from a man's bones. Her skills demanded fear-borne respect from everyone around her. Everyone but her sister, that is.

Lilith's martial prowess was second only to her sister's, but where Nekima's sole purpose was slaughter, Lilith's talents lay in a more subtle path. With the Great Breach's first opening, Lilith began to plot. While Nekima raided and slew what she saw as weak-fleshed invaders, her sister watched and listened, eventually interjecting herself into their midst, learning the secrets needed to break through the humans' protective magic and close the Breach.

When the time came, Lilith's work bore fruit and the destruction of the first human settlers to Malifaux began. Nekima could not count the number of lives she ended that day, such was the bloodlust which overcame her. When she returned to herself, she found her sister sitting where she should be, in command of the Nephilim. She cursed herself for a fool, realizing now how oblivious she had been as Lilith had surrounded herself with enough loyal supporters to give even a warrior such as herself pause. She was forced to take a knee before her younger and less powerful sister, her massive wings snapping with barely suppressed rage at the betrayal.

Since that day over a century ago, Nekima has been gathering a following of her own, those Nephilim dissatisfied with Lilith's rule. Her mind is focused on one thing: the day when she has enough backing to challenge Lilith for leadership and victoriously rip her heart from her chest.

Someday, Nekima will come forward to reclaim her birthright, and she will drench the Nephilim in rivers of internecine blood in the challenging.

50MM BASE

SOULSTONE COST: 13

NEPHILIM, UNIQUE

WK/CG	HT	WP	CA	DF	WD
6/10	3	6	4	4	12

NEVERBORN GREATSWORD

RG	⚔ 3
CB	7
DG	3/4/6

TALENTS:

Abilities

Black Blood

Blood Sense: When a living or Undead model is killed within 3" of this model, this model gains one Blood Counter.

Enraged by Insolence: If a Nephilim within 8" and LoS of this model is killed by an enemy model, this model may Push up to 4" directly toward that enemy model. This Ability has no effect if a Terror Tot Nephilim was killed.

Flight

Irresistible: Enemy models must win a Wp->12 Duel when targeting this model with an attack or the Action fails. This may not be ignored by any Talent.

Nephilim Princess: (✹)6. Nephilim models gain **Regeneration 1**.

Nurture Nephilim: Friendly Nephilim within 10" of this model receive +4 **Ca** when **Casting** or **Channeling Grow** or **Mature**.

Regeneration 1

Terrible Beauty: (✹)6. Enemy models gain -2 **Wp** in Duels as the defender.

Weapons

Neverborn Greatsword: After final Duel totals are determined, but before triggers are activated, this model may add any one suit to the Duel total. This weapon's Damage Flips receive ◼.

Actions

(+1) Instinctual

(+1) Melee Expert

(0) Blood Offering: This model suffers 4 **Wd**. Gain one Blood Counter.

(0) Growth Spurt: (✹)6. Non-Master Nephilim gain **Flight**.

(0) Nephilim Heart: (✹)6. Select **Wp, Ca, Df,** or **Cb**. All non-Master Nephilim receive +◪ to the selected statistic.

(0) Spill Black Blood: Inflict up to 6 **Wd** on this model or a target friendly model with **Black Blood** within 3". Non-Neverborn models within 1" of the model suffer 1 **Wd** for every 2 **Wd** suffered by target model.

Triggers

Cb (◪◪) Bloody Fate [Neverborn Greatsword]: After damaging defender, draw one Control Card, then discard one Control Card if the defender was not killed by the **Strike**.

Cb (⚑◪) Throw Aside [Neverborn Greatsword]: After damaging defender, Push defender up to 3". If the defender ends the Push touching terrain, it suffers **Dg** 2.

Cb (📖◪) Meat for the Young [Neverborn Greatsword]: After hitting enemy defender, inflict no damage. Push defender up to 6" directly toward a friendly Nephilim within 10".

Cb (✕◪) Rip in Half [Neverborn Greatsword]: After killing an enemy model, all enemy models within 6" of this model immediately make a **WP → 11** Morale Duel.

Malifaux will have
it's revenge
- Lilith

Stitched Together - Minion

Bad dreams have a way of clinging to a person's thoughts even after waking. Sometimes, they even follow the dreamer into the waking world, visible out of the corner of the eye or faintly heard when the mind wanders. Eventually, these half-seen stalkers fade away, drawn back into the in-between place to await the next spirit to drift by.

The Dreamer's singular talent allows some nightmares to remain in the waking world to wreak havoc long after they should have faded from reality. Stitched Together are one of these persistent nightmares. Horrible burlap puppets overstuffed with rotten meat and offal, these creatures stalk the living, relishing the fear they create. Their crudely stitched faces are twisted parodies of maniacal glee, blank button eyes staring inhumanly into the eyes of those unfortunate to encounter one.

Because they haunt waking dreams, Stitched Together are keenly aware of what scares their victims the most, using that fear to cow them into despair before tearing them into pieces with their fiendishly hooked 'hands'. They are nearly impossible to kill; the terrible contents inside their rough shells extending their parodies of life. They constantly hunger for meat to replace this continually decaying supply and happily take their pound of flesh from whichever hapless soul they stumble across.

30mm Base

Soulstone Cost: 5

Doll, Nightmare, Rare 3

Wk/Cg	Ht	Wp	Ca	Df	Wd
4/6	2	6	5🦋	4	7

Hooks

Rg	/////	1
Cb	4	
Dg	1/2/4	

Talents:

Abilities

"Does Not Die!": When this model would be killed, it instead remains in play with 1 **Wd** remaining. This model cannot be sacrificed or buried until the Start Close Phase, and if this model already activated this turn it gains **Reactivate**. Sacrifice this model during the Resolve Effects Step.

Rotten Contents: When this model suffers 1 or more **Wd** from a melee **Strike**, flip a Fate Card. If the flipped card is a ✗, living models within (✗)2 of this model suffer 2 **Wd**.

Actions

(0) Creepy Fog: 🔘4. **Ht** 5 obscuring, for all models, including this model, until the Start Closing Phase.

(0) Gambler: Discard one Control Card. Target an enemy model within 6" of this model with a **Wp → Wp** Duel. If the target loses, the target's Controller discards one Control Card and this model's Controller draws two Control Cards.

(1) Gamble your Life: Target an enemy model within 6" of this model with a **Wp → Wp** Duel. The loser of this Duel suffers an **Dg** 3/4/7, which may be Cheated.

Triggers

Ca (🦋🦋) A Dark Place [Deepest Fear]: Defender damaged by this Spell receives **Slow.**

Spells:

(1) Abduction

(CC: 13✗🦋 /Rst: Df /Rg: 2) Bury target **Ht** 1 model. Place the buried model within 6" of this model at the Start Activation Phase. If this model is removed from the board, place buried target in play within 1" of this model before it is removed from play.

(1) Deepest Fear

(CC: 10🦋 /Rst: Wp /Rg: 6) **Dg** 1/3/5, ignoring **Armor.**

Wicked Doll - Minion

" With a click, click, click and a drip, drip, drip, the tiny doll came a-calling.

It rapped, rapped, rapped and tapped, tapped, tapped, but no one did reply.

With a click, click, click and a drip, drip, drip, the tiny doll was left a-waiting.

It pulled, pulled, pulled and pushed, pushed, pushed, but the locked doors did deny.

With a click, click, click and a drip, drip, drip, the tiny doll climbed upward.

It skritched, skritched, skritched and scratched, scratched, scratched, and the window did welcome.

With a click, click, click and a drip, drip, drip, the tiny doll stalked deeper.

It crept, crept, crept and crawled, crawled, crawled, for deeds unwholesome.

With a click, click, click and a drip, drip, drip, the tiny doll climbed the blankets.

It slashed, slashed, slashed and stabbed, stabbed, stabbed, and its victims did succumb..."

30MM BASE

SOULSTONE COST: 3

CONSTRUCT, INSIGNIFICANT, SPECIAL FORCES (DOLL)

WK/CG	HT	WP	CA	DF	WD
5/7	1	5	3	6	2

SEWING CLAWS	
RG	1
CB	4
DG	1/2/4

TALENTS:

Abilities

A Voodoo Doll: This model may be summoned with **Create Voodoo Doll**. When summoning this model, its controller does not need to sacrifice other Voodoo Dolls or Wicked Dolls in play.

Doll House: This model loses Insignificant while within 3" of a friendly Zoraida, Bad Juju, or two or more friendly Wicked Dolls.

Sewn in Poison: While in base contact with this model, friendly models' melee **Strikes** gain **Poison 1**.

Wicked Intentions: Any time an enemy model activates within 2" of two or more Wicked Dolls, it must win a **Df →14** Duel or may not take any Action other than **Walk** or **Pass** Actions during that activation.

Weapons

Sewing Claws: Paired.

Actions

(all) Malice: Sacrifice this model. Target model within 3" of this model suffers 2 **Wd** and receives **Slow**.

(0) Hags's Toys: Place this model within 2" of Zoraida or a friendly model with the **Puppet Master** Ability.

(0) Murderous: This model may immediately use this Action after killing an enemy living or Undead model with a melee **Strike**. Summon one Wicked Doll. End this model's activation.

(0) Stitchwork: This model or a friendly Doll within 3" of this model makes a Healing Flip.

Triggers

Cb (X) A Little Drop of Poison [Sewing Claws]: Poison 2.

181

Aethervox

Niklaus Dudek is considered one of the greatest minds of the age in the field of arcane research. His greatest invention is widely believed to be the Aethervox. The Aethervox is a deceptively simple machine consisting of a wood frame, metal dials, and an odd collection of tubes, wires, and hundreds of etched brass for gears spinning within. The device runs on what Dudek calls "spirit energy", the ever present aether of Malifaux.

Currently, there is only one true station on the aetherwaves. This Guild-controlled broadcast has a variety of programs, the majority of which are official news reports interspersed with musical scores. In addition to this broadcast, the Arcanists maintain a few mobile transmitters, broadcasting their own underground anti-Guild propaganda. The Guild destroys these so-called Aether Underground stations as soon as they are found.

Aethervoxes are expensive to construct, which limits them from becoming widespread. Entire townships may have a single receiver, if they are lucky. Some of the City's wealthier residents have their own 'Vox, and the Governor General keeps one in his office. In the Slums, it is common for the poor to gather at saloons and drown their sorrow while listening to programs carried on the aether.

When a station's broadcasting day ends on the Aethervox, its signal is replaced with static. The low buzzing is sometimes broken by whispering voices. Alien languages, obscene threats, and dire missives bleed through from somewhere, sometimes with disturbing consequences. It's told that the voices drove Edgar Ryan to murder his family. Monica Stonewall, wife of the affluent Horatio Stonewall, was found in their home hanging dead above their private 'Vox. Her husband said she had laughed hysterically at the 'Vox for weeks, typically beyond the broadcast day. Most residents of Malifaux recall the night that the news was broadcast twelve hours early. The program accurately reported the events that would transpire later that day. Malifaux residents have not forgotten the transmission received by every Aethervox last Conjunction Eve, at the moment the moons aligned. Every Aethervox turned itself on, hissing static erupting from the speakers. The entire city was chilled by the inhuman scream in the static that lasted for three minutes before the 'Voxes cut out again.

OUTCASTS

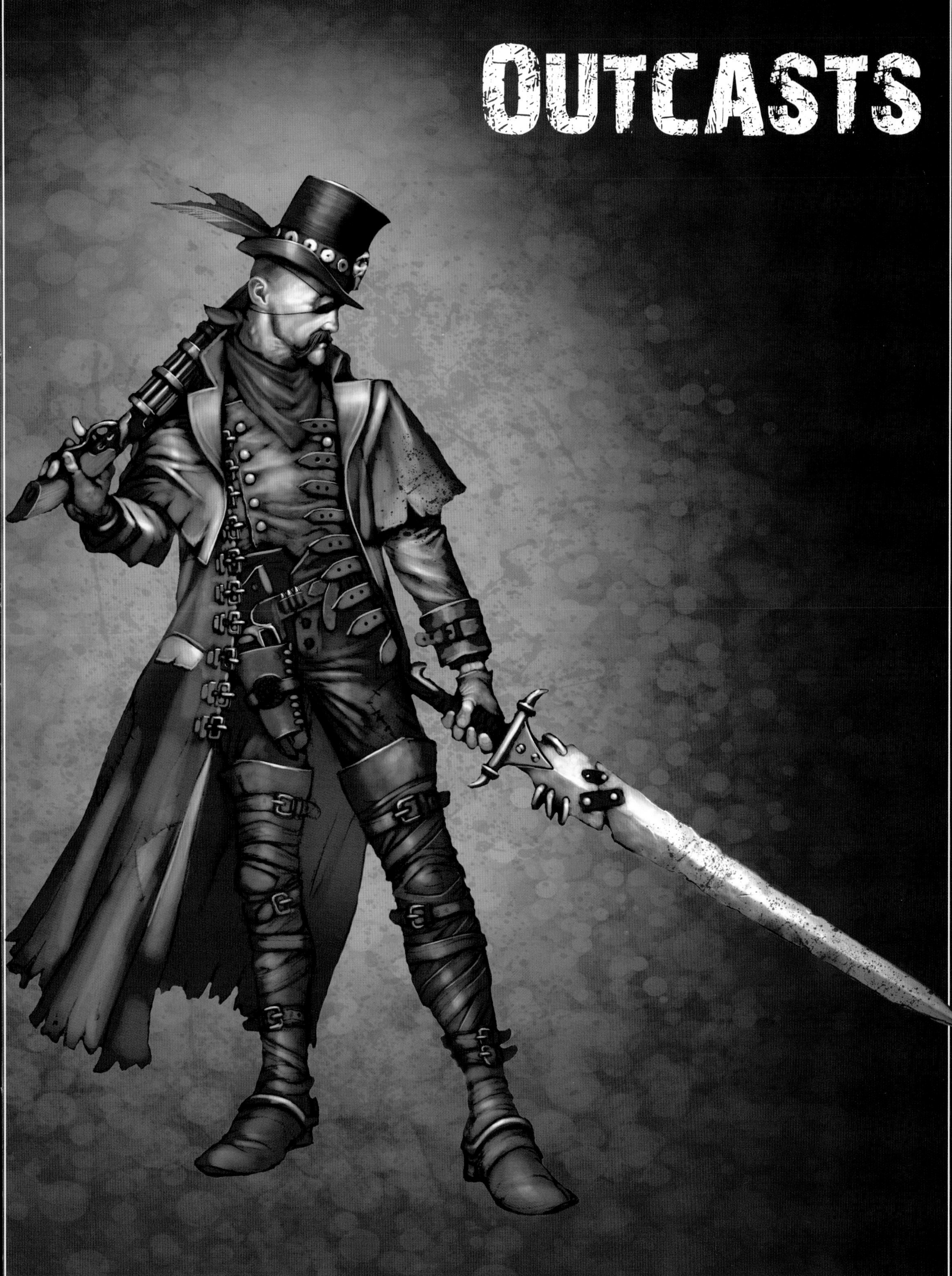

OUTCASTS

Squatting on his haunches, Mischa shielded himself in a tumbledown pile of debris that might once have been a home. Most areas in the Quarantine Zone were in one state or another of disrepair. To find crumbling blocks of empty homes and businesses, leaning drunkenly against one another or out over the streets, was common to those exploring the massive ruin that was the City, but these particular blocks were in even worse shape.

Here, ruined cobble streets were strewn with the debris of collapsed buildings, while the remaining structures needed only a nudge to bring them crashing down as well. The sheer volume of detritus both simplified and complicated his job at the same time, allowing him to move virtually silently and unnoticed through the rubble but forcing him to keep his eyes and ears scanning for threats doing the same. His alertness had caught the sound of activity ahead, the scrape of metal on rock telling him no mere beast lay in his path.

So he waited.

Despite orders to the contrary, Mischa usually left his helmet clipped to his belt when scouting. Leaving the head unprotected was a foolish risk, the Captain chided him frequently. "The Freikorps invests as much in you and your skills as we do in the armor you wear, Mischa. Do not waste my investment."

Mischa understood the Captain's concerns but was paid for his results, not for his ability to follow Freikorps protocols. His perceptions were dulled when he wore the helmet, his ability to see and hear clearly were far better protection in this situation than the armor could ever be. Besides, he wasn't here alone.

Two hundred paces behind Mischa the remainder of the six-man squad waited for his *all clear* signal. He chuckled to himself at their efforts to keep silent as they hid among the rubble. Whatever was making the noise ahead wouldn't hear them, but to his sharp hearing, they might have well been banging pots and pans together, singing church hymns. He placed his finger over his lips and mimed a shushing motion, certain Frank or Cameron would see it.

The rhythmic metal on stone sound continued. Mischa crept slowly forward, leaving his hiding place for a better vantage point. He held his rifle loosely, ready to bring it to bear on whatever might present itself as a target. A few slow feet put him close enough to see where the racket was coming from.

"Dammit," he hissed.

The wreckage of two city blocks lay below him, swallowed by a massive sinkhole. Tunnel mouths honeycombed the sides of the sinkhole, some collapsed, others yawning wide. For a moment, he wondered what had caused the destruction, before his attention was drawn to the noise. Milling around the rubble like lethargic ants, several figures were working to clear the wreckage, some with their bare hands, others with shovels and picks. Mischa scanned the workers with the rifle's scope, all too aware of the deception of appearances in this place.

Resurrectionists.

He counted dozens of Undead down there, all working toward whatever goal their controller had given them. He tried to pick out the unholy creature who had given unlife to these poor souls, but the terrain made it impossible at this range. Instead, he made mental note of their positions and numbers, then carefully made his way back from the sinkhole's edge, very much glad he was not alone.

The smell of charred meat and burning timber stung Mischa's nose as he made his way down the side of the sinkhole to join the other Freikorpsmenn below, the echoes of his shot still chattering against the surrounding buildings.

The fighting had been thickest toward the center of the ruin, where an unbroken building corner had sheltered the Resurrectionist from attack until Mischa's bullet had found his head. Without their puppeteer controlling them, most of the Undead had collapsed in piles of decaying flesh and bone. A few remaining pockets of resistance fought on as Mischa made his way to the Captain, but the occasional fwoosh of Franklin's Flammenwerfer told him the mopping up was well underway.

"...to know what they were looking for, Cameron. And I want to know now. We've lost one man, and I would not have it be for nothing." The Captain turned as Mischa approached. He had already removed his own helmet, bald pate shining with sweat as he chewed on a cigar. Mischa wondered where Captain Von Schill kept those things while the helmet was on. "Ah, Trapper, well done with the Resurrectionist."

"Thank you, sir." His eyes drifted to where Alejandro lay, armor and the man it had protected torn open, and offered a silent prayer for the man's soul. Alejandro had thrown himself at one of the Undead creatures, this one half again as tall as a man, when it attacked Von Schill. His efforts had protected the Captain but cost the Freikorpsmann his life. "Orders?"

Von Schill paused a moment. "Ready Alejandro's body. I won't leave one of mine here for the carrion, or worse. After that, I want you to give Cameron what he needs. That whoreson was looking for something...something valuable I'd guess if he was all the way out here. I'm depending on you, Cameron, to find out what it was."

Mischa set about the sobering task given to him while Cameron started his own work. The Captain had already moved off to check on the other squad members.

The pair worked in silence for several minutes. Cameron skimmed through copious notes stuffed into a leather satchel and compared what he found to strange markings etched into the stonework around them while Mischa carefully removed Alejandro's armor, stacking it reverently to one side of the body.

Once the armor was removed, Mischa fumbled around in the dead Korpsmann's kit for a blanket, closed Alejandro's eyes, and swaddled the corpse as best he could in its own blanket. Although he was no priest, Mischa whispered the few words he remembered from prayers his father had said over the graves of men he'd attended back in Warzaw. "Grant him absolution, give him peace..."

Deep in study, Cameron did not register Mischa's approach. He stood for a moment and watched the Librarian work. Mischa wondered if the inclusion of such support helped or hindered the squad. He was an experienced fighting man, and getting used to the strangeness of Malifaux took time. The threats the Freikorps were hired to confront often required more than mundane weapons and tactics, but even so, he felt these arcane researchers better served them far from the front line. They provided useful intelligence and analysis of threats from their dusty stacks. When they were brought into the field as active support, all too often Mischa or the others found themselves saving the Librarian's bacon rather than the other way around. The Captain worked hard to ensure all of his mercenaries were contributing members of the Freikorps, but the bit of combat training Librarians were given before being sent out with a squad was, in Mischa's opinion, less than useful.

Oblivious to Mischa's presence, Cameron carefully examined what appeared to once have been the wall of some sort of structure. His finger followed an intricately carved line across the pieces of rubble, checking what he traced against a sketch in a small book of hand-written notes.

"Find anything?"

Cameron jerked to his feet, dropping the notebook as he fumbled for his hunting knife. "Wha...oh, whew. You startled me, Mischa."

"I could have done worse than that," Mischa observed as he handed the notebook back to Cameron. "You have to be more alert out here in the field, Cameron. This isn't the classroom."

The Librarian's ears reddened. This was only his second trip into the field since joining the Korps, but it was already the second time Mischa or one of the other men had been called upon to babysit him. "I know, damn it, I know. But don't you find all of this," his wave encompassed the sinkhole around them, "so very intriguing?"

Mischa kicked at a rock. "Other than getting out of here alive and with our paychecks intact...not really. I'm here to do a job, so are you."

Cameron straightened. "I am doing my job. Look, these carvings are writing of some sort, very different from what I know of the ancient Malifaux language. Right now, it's beyond me to decipher, but given time and the correct reference books..." Out came several sheets of paper and a stick of charcoal. He began to take rubbings of the engravings, muttering about ancient cultures and dialects.

"So you can't make sense of it here?"

"No, not without a clear point of reference as to where this language and that of Old Malifaux cross. Like the Rosetta Stone..."

Mischa sighed. "Did you check the body?"

The charcoal paused mid-rub. "The what?"

"The body. The accursed Resurrectionist's body. If he was here for something, maybe he knew what he was looking at?"

Cameron's ears reddened again. "I hadn't thought of that..."

Mischa wondered if there would ever be hope for him as a field operative. "Then maybe we should go check."

The body of the Resurrectionist lay where he had died. His eyes were open, a surprised expression – as if he could not believe he was dead – across his face. Cameron turned away from the grisly scene when they came across the body, dry heaving. Death was never pretty.

"So what are we looking for?"

"Huu...ahem. Look around for any sort of reference materials. Books, maps, notes, even pieces of marked stone that look decidedly different from those around them. I'll check the body." Mischa gave the Librarian credit for that bit of bravado.

The search was slow going. Mischa quickly gave up on looking for anything printed, having seen Cameron dig a wad of yellowing parchment from underneath the body, and focused on the rubble. Patience in the face of tedium was nothing new to him, having spent much of his life as a trapper. He stooped to pick up a promising looking piece of rock, looked it over, then tossed it aside. Nothing here looked much like anything else, he decided. *This is going to take a while.*

It was a few minutes later when he came across it. An area of ground had been cleared of debris, a long but shallow hole dug in the center. Mischa could make out the hint of a marble slab poking up out of the dirt in the hole. Several picks and shovels lay in and scattered about the hole, cast aside when the Undead had made their stand against the Freikorps. Beneath a shovel he found a small marble tablet, its surface chiseled with markings similar to those Cameron had found earlier. As he took a breath to call Cameron, Mischa realized he could read the tablet's symbols. He let out the breath, but instead of shouting to Cameron, he began to chant. As he did, something beneath the marble slab at his feet began to stir...

"Fascinating," Cameron whispered as he read through the Resurrectionist's notes. They summarized what appeared to be four years of painstaking research, essentially from the time the Breach reopened to now. He understood now what this place was – had been – in centuries past. He admired the twisted dedication of the man who had written these notes, understood the unquenchable yearning for knowledge and the paths it might lead a person. He had followed one such path to this point in time, wondering if his pursuit would end as bloodily as the Resurrectionist's.

Looking out at the rubble, he wondered what the collection of buildings had looked like when they were whole. Using the roughly-copied map he found in the notes, Cameron could almost envision the institution's layout, where the lecture halls had been – over there, a dormitory, there the "faculty" offices. Now, all that remained was whatever the elements had passed over.

Sighing, Cameron read more of the notes.

He could not find reference to what had befallen the people here, could not be sure how or why the sinkhole had formed, but did see that the man believed secrets were hidden here – somewhere. His random musings posited that the tunnels ringing the sinkhole led to a network of vaults and subfloors beneath the "college", but as far as Cameron could tell, he had not investigated them. Instead, the Resurrectionist had focused on the floor of the sinkhole, salvaging what he could while searching for some sort of weapon.

"Mischa!" He could see the Trapper a ways off, something held in his hands. "Mischa, we're looking for a piece of stone…a marble tablet…" his voice trailed off. "No! Don't read from…"

The ground at Mischa's feet erupted with plumes of dirt and broken chunks of marble. "Lord, no."

Fear gave Cameron's feet wings. He was at his companion's side in moments, dragging him away from the ominously silent hole. "Come on Mischa we have to go now!"

The Trapper shook the cobwebs from his head, he felt like he had been asleep for a week. "Cameron?"

"Ohno ohno. Now! We have to go now!" Cameron knew he was raving, but he was desperate to stop it. He could feel the malevolence leaking out of the pit.

He managed to lever Mischa onto his feet, slid an arm around him, and began to move back from the edge of the hole. Somehow, Cameron noticed, Mischa had held onto his rifle. He wondered if it would have any effect at all.

The pair had barely moved out of the cleared patch when a hand reached out from the hole.

It was rotting, much of the flesh had decomposed and fallen away, leaving exposed bones which scrabbled at the edge as it prepared to pull whatever it was attached to out. The hand was massive, capable of grabbing a grown man about the chest and probably crushing the life from him, Cameron thought.

Another hand joined the first, both coming out of the dirt and digging back into it. Cameron could not tear his eyes away despite his fear. Something shifted in the hole, and the thing levered itself free, extinguishing Cameron's burning curiosity.

The Undead giant stood twenty feet tall, skeleton peeking through its rotting flesh. Cameron thought absently that the centuries-old magic keeping it animated and awaiting a summons must have also slowed its decomposition before terror gripped him once again. It flexed its massive hands with grim purpose, fixing its dead sockets on Cameron and Mischa. It opened its massive jaw and let out a hiss, far more chilling than the bellow that would have escaped it in life.

The giant's appearance cleared Mischa's mind like a splash of cold water. "What the…get back, Cameron!"

"It's the college's 'guardian'. The Resurrectionist was looking for it here, thought he could summon and control it."

The guardian took a halting step toward them. It seemed to be waking up from its long slumber and needed some time to regain its faculties. Mischa was half-puling, half-pushing Cameron back from the guardian's tentative advance. He unslung his rifle and took aim at the thing's head. He knew that even if he failed to damage the Undead beast, which he anticipated, the other Freikorps would hear the shot if they did not already see the giant, and he hoped it would distract the thing long enough for Cameron to get to safety.

The rifle shot cracked loudly, echoing across the sinkhole. The bullet ricocheted off the guardian's skull, rocking it back and tearing away some of the necrotic flesh still clinging there. The attack seemed to galvanize it, banishing its lethargy. It came at Mischa then, moving much faster than its massive frame would suggest it was capable of, those terrible hands reaching toward him.

Cameron had scrambled up a broken wall to get a better vantage point. A bit away, he could see the Captain and the other Freikorpsmenn rushing toward the sound of Mischa's shot, but they would be too late. The guardian was nearly on top of Mischa, who was desperately trying to reload his rifle in time for a last defiant shot.

"No," Cameron whispered. He began to recite, the words rushing out of him in a torrent faster even than his earlier panicked shouting. They seemed heavier than the air around him, tearing ripples in it as they rushed toward the guardian.

The words tore at Mischa's ears, battering the defenses of his psyche as they hammered at the guardian's back. He moaned in pain, dropping his rifle as he grabbed at his head while the guardian's charge became a stagger, then collapse before it could reach him. It struggled to its feet, turning to confront its new assailant. Cameron kept up the litany as it stomped toward him, each of its steps more difficult than the last. He reassessed his opinion of the Librarian in that instant, realizing that the Captain always knew his men better than they themselves did.

Cameron's voice grew harsher, hoarse at his recitation. The pain was getting worse, but he knew if he stopped now, the guardian would crush him and then turn back on Mischa. The pain burned through him, and he misspoke a syllable, breaking the litany for an instant. The guardian stumbled forward, it could almost reach him.

"Jump!"

The brief training Von Schill required of all his Librarians took hold and Cameron leapt to one side, hurling himself off the wall and into the rubble. As soon as he cleared the wall he heard and felt the fwooosh as Frank let loose a torrent of flame. The other Freikorpsmenn had reached them.

Cameron scrambled to his feet as Von Schill and the others rounded on the guardian. The Flammenwerfer kept up a steady stream of flame, driving the now-burning Undead back from Cameron and Mischa, who had recovered his weapon and donned his helmet. James and Mischa kept up a steady stream of lead as rifle and pistol both found their marks. Then the Captain was there, barking orders at the three men, his custom weapon's rhythm lending to the symphony.

Despite the tearing at his throat, Cameron joined in, lending his solo to the symphony's crescendo, the Freikorpsmenn's armor dulling its effect on them. The guardian, however, felt the full brunt of his ancient litany once again and could not withstand this additional onslaught. Ribs shattered, wrist bones exploded in a shower of dust, even the massive hissing skull cracked and shattered, sending the giant creature crashing to the ground. It lay there motionless, as the last of the Flammenwerfer's blaze licked hungrily at its bones before dying out.

"Well done, men," Von Schill said from around his cigar, "all in a day's work."

"I think we've found a home, Cameron. Well done." Von Schill clapped the Librarian on the back as the two of them stood at the edge of the sinkhole.

They had discovered a small antechamber beneath the marble slab, from which a carved stone staircase was leading down. The network of tunnels above them had connected to this chamber when the college was at surface level, but now only a few chambers remained intact. Cameron still wondered what had preserved the chambers as the rest of the college collapsed into the sinkhole but knew how to graciously accept a gift when he got one. Within the intact chambers they discovered hundreds of tomes and scrolls, enough to keep the Freikorps Librarians busy for years.

"Sir, what are you suggesting?"

"I want the Freikorps to have a headquarters, far from the Guild's prying eyes. I think this site is an excellent choice to build one, don't you?" The predatory grin on Von Schill's face told Cameron the question was a rhetorical one. "Deep enough in the Quarantine Zone the Guild won't come looking for us for years, well-stocked with esoterica for my Librarians, and readily-repaired for solid defense. It's all about the resources, Cameron, and the Freikorps has them."

Von Schill pointed his cigar toward the pit. "I'll need you to head up the research team here, Cameron. You're the best I have when it comes to this sort of thing. Looks like your days in the field are over. Make me a list of what you'll need." He waved his arm and shouted at a crew clearing rubble, heading their direction "Not there, THERE!"

Superstitions

Bizarre behavior like greeting a chimney sweep with a smile or making a wish has become a common sight in cobblestone alleys. With so much arcane power in the air of Malifaux, it is not surprising that superstitions both old and new take on a new importance this side of the Breach.

One April evening at the Starlight Saloon, Richard Clarkston, out of a habit his mother instilled in him, tossed a handful of salt over his shoulder. His screams of horror echoed two blocks down as the patrons fled from the place. The salt had seared the flesh of an impish spirit apparently hovering unseen behind Mister Clarkson. The spirit did not take kindly to being burned by the mineral.

"Lighting three Soulstone Cigars on a single match is a sure way to summon Bête Noire", folks whisper in back street saloons.

Farmers close to the Bayou watch to see if their pigs root in circles or back and forth. The latter is a sure sign that Gremlins are near.

Little Silas Crookston's mother let him see his reflection on Conjunction Eve. Thirteen witnesses described the same shadowy set of hands appear and clutch at Silas' reflection within the mirror. The next morning, the little one was laid to rest, having suddenly stopped breathing in his bed sometime in the night.

And everyone knows not to step under a ladder...

HAMELIN THE PLAGUED - MASTER

There are several tyrant-entities, now nothing more than specters that inhabit the fringes of the world of Malifaux. As they slowly approach a true death, most retain only a vague awareness of the world they once tried to dominate and force into subservience. Yet they were each once fierce and impassioned in their plans. Each sought to escape the inevitability of death and defy Fate's grand plan that destined them to fall, as all living things must, to give way to another generation.

One sleeping tyrant-entity lay awake; its mind once more stirring and plotting, still unwilling to accept death. He no longer had the means to move about in the world of men, though his disembodied mind grew stronger, longing for a chance to escape the great subterranean Necropolis that confined him for years upon years. But He could hear the stirring of people in the new City built over the much more ancient and vast city of Malifaux that He knew. He heard them and had hope. He watched for signs and stretched out his will to manipulate and twist Fate again, bending it so that He could know freedom once more.

Hamelin was merely a man that inhabited the shadows and darkest corners of an alley when he lingered about the activities of men. He could not know that one night, in the dank darkness of the immense caverns of the ancient sewers below the City, once wide streets of an older, forgotten city would lead him to an opportunity most men would never experience. He was chosen by that Tyrant Specter as His vessel.

Now, Hamelin the Plagued walks again. He has brought the blight of a dark and deadly pestilence to the world of Malifaux. In the consumption of the flesh, He draws forth the power released at the expiration of each cell in the body, feeding off death. The former Hamelin's power, too, is now His, amplified so that the song he plays on the pan-flute or hums softly in the dusk, calls forth the innocent to do His bidding. Their will becomes supplanted by the weight of a mind that has longed to return to the world of the living for hundreds of years. Though He has waited for so long, now that He walks again, He is impatient to fulfill the destiny he has planned for Himself.

INSIGNIFICANT, MASTER, SOULLESS

WK/CG	HT	WP	CA	DF	WD
5/8	2	8	7🐾	5	12

BLACK STAFF	
RG	⚔ 2
CB	6
DG	0*/3/9

PIPES	
RG	↗10
CB	7🐾
DG	1/3/3*

TALENTS:

Abilities

Bully: This model cannot be targeted by **Ht** 1 or Insignificant models.

Indiscriminant Void: When this model is killed or sacrificed, Summon a Hamelin, the Plagued into base contact with a friendly The Stolen within 3", then sacrifice that model. Hamelin receives -4 **Ca** until the end of the Encounter.

Lure of Emptiness: Crews containing this model may only hire **Ht** 1, Insignificant, and Soulless models, but may hire them from any Faction at no additional cost. Crews containing this model may not hire Gremlins, Constructs, or Henchmen.

Nihilism: While this model is in play friendly models lose Insignificant. If this model is in play at the end of the encounter, no friendly models count as Insignificant

The Void: Beginning with the second turn, draw 0 Cards in the Draw Phase. Each turn, nominate an opponent. Draw one Card from the Fate Deck or the top of the discard pile each time the nominated opponent plays a Control Card. This model's Controller may ignore any enemy effects targeting this model which require them to discard Control Cards.

Voracious Rats: When this model or a model within 6" of it is killed, Summon one Malifaux Rat in base contact with the model before it is removed from play. The model does not generate Counters of any kind. No other models can be summoned as a result of the model being killed.

Weapons

Black Staff: When this Weapon inflicts Weak damage, this model suffers 2 **Wd**. Models wounded by this Weapon gain one Blight Counter.

Pipes: When this Weapon inflicts Severe damage on a model with **Wp** 5 or less, that model takes a **(1)** Action or a **Charge** controlled by this model's Controller.

Actions
(+1) Fast

(0) Fate is Meaningless: This model ignores any 🃏 or 🃏 to its flips during its next Action.

(0) Useless Toy: Sacrifice target friendly model within 6". This model receives 🃏🃏 to all Attack and Defense Flips during its next Action.

(1) Abandoned Soul: Sacrifice target friendly model within 6". Draw two Control Cards and heal this model 2 **Wd**.

(1) Lure Malifaux Citizen: Summon one The Stolen. This Action may be taken once per turn.

Triggers

Ca (✗ 🐾) Plague [Bleeding Disease]: After defender suffers wounds from this Spell, **Cast** this Spell again at -2 **Ca**.

Cb (🐾 🐾) Haunting Melody [Pipes]: After resolving this Weapon's Damage Flip, the defender model must win a **Wp** → this model's combat total or gain Insignificant until the end of the Encounter.

SPELLS:

(1) Bleeding Disease
(CC: 10 / Rst: Wp / Rg: 12) Target model suffers 1 **Wd** per Blight Counter on it.

(1) Inevitable Truth
(CC: 15🐾 /Rst: Wp /Rg: 8) While this model is within 12" of target model, target model may only target this model. This Spell ends when this model is killed, sacrificed, or casts this Spell again.

(1) Irresistible Lure
(CC: 14🐾 /Rst: Wp /Rg: (↑)12) Enemy **Ht** 1 and Insignificant models move their **Wk** toward this model. A model moving into base contact with this model suffers an unmodifiable **Dg** 0/3/6 Flip.

(1) Obedience
(CC: 13🐾 /Rst: Wp /Rg: 12) Sacrifice a friendly model within 6". Target non-Master model immediately takes a **Charge** or **(1)** Action controlled by this model's Controller.

(1) Understand the Soulless
(CC: 12🐾 /Rst: Wp /Rg: 12) Sacrifice a friendly model within 6". Target model receives Insignificant until the end of the Encounter.

OBEDIENT WRETCH - TOTEM

Even in its new body, the now-corporeal Hamelin the Plagued requires servants to aid in His conquest of Malifaux. Tied to the flesh, He cannot be in several places at once, instead relying on the weak-willed to do His bidding.

Hamelin's pan-flute summons many to serve, but a few come to His side of their own volition. These believers have witnessed the power He wields and have surrendered themselves to Him, offering their talents and skills for Him alone. Hamelin imbues his most devoted followers with a modicum of His power and transforms the wretched mortal into something more befitting His needs. The resulting Totem's creation burns the humanity that the wretch possessed in life, leaving only her commitment to Hamelin.

The wretch serves Hamelin as conduit for His malevolence, channeling magic and disease through her body. The wretch can only contain Hamelin's essence for so long, eventually succumbing to the plague festering within. Even in death, however, the wretch serves Hamelin's purpose, calling vermin forth to partake of its body and spread more of the pestilence throughout Malifaux.

30MM BASE   **SOULSTONE COST: 2**

INSIGNIFICANT, SOULLESS, TOTEM (HAMELIN, THE PLAGUED)

Wk/Cg	Ht	Wp	Ca	Df	Wd
4/6	1	4	5	4	4

TALENTS:

Abilities

Companion (Hamelin)

Inevitable Fate: When this model is killed or sacrificed, summon one Malifaux Rat into base contact with it before it is removed from play.

No Humanity: (X)6. When this model is killed or sacrificed, non-Soulless models receive -2 **Wp** until the Start Closing Phase.

Actions

(all) Abandon: Target model within 6" receives Insignificant until the end of the Encounter. The target may prevent this by discarding two Control Cards. Sacrifice this model.

(1) Blind Dedication: Draw one Control Card. This Action may be taken once per turn.

SPELLS:

(1) Magical Extension
(CC: */Rst: * /Rg: *) This Spell may be cast only once per activation. Cast one of the connected Master's **(1)** Spells. During this casting, this model may use a Soulstone to change its starting total.

Von Schill - Freikorps Leader - Henchman

Tenacious, arrogant, effective. These three words sum up the originator and leader of the mercenary band known as Von Schill's Freikorps. After a successful military career Earthside, Von Schill turned his attentions to the abundant opportunities Malifaux presented, eschewing his commissions and offering his services as a mercenary to the Guild. The Guild needed hard men to weather the early days of the second settling, and Von Schill's no-nonsense approach to just about everything ingratiated him with the men and women serving on the front lines, if not with the Guild leadership.

What should have been the crowning assignment in a distinguished career ended in disaster. When Von Schill was finally introduced to the Governor General, the two men silently decided their hatred for one another would be the last thing they'd ever agree on. Von Schill rankled the Governor General with his blunt suggestions on how security could be improved, and the Governor General made it clear he valued the veteran's advice as much as he valued crow soil on his favorite hat. Von Schill then informed the Governor General where he could put that crow soil and had his contract with the Guild promptly terminated.

Rather than return Earthside, Von Schill decided to remain in Malifaux and offer his considerable skills to the highest bidders. His time working with the Guild had garnered him a loyal following of Guardsmen and specialists who were more than happy to turn their backs on the Governor General and follow a man they respected. With this core of loyal, skilled soldiers at his command, Von Schill officially formed the Freikorps, an elite mercenary crew offering its services to those that would pay.

Von Schill's Freikorps plies its trade throughout Malifaux, owing their allegiance to their leader first, then to the employer with the deepest pockets. Von Schill's commitment to the Freikorps ensures his men are well-paid for their specialties and benefit from the best equipment to be had. Through clandestine arrangements with the Miners and Steamfitters Union, as well as other resources whose identities he chooses not to divulge, he has commissioned the development and construction of the Freikorps' signature armor, designing it to withstand the numerous threats Malifaux has to offer. When he leads his men into battle, his considerable military experience is put to use tearing down the enemy's defenses, as he bellows orders from around a well-chewed cigar. His men love him; his enemies fear him.

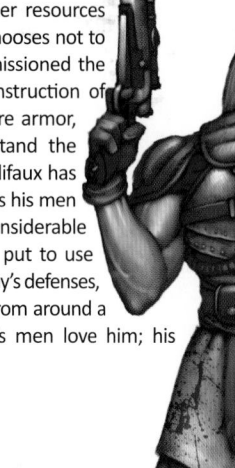

30MM BASE

SOULSTONE COST: 9

HENCHMAN 4, MERCENARY, SPECIAL FORCES (FREIKORPS)

WK/CG	HT	WP	CA	DF	WD
5/8	2	6	3	5	10

HUNTING KNIFE	
RG	///1
CB	6
DG	1/3/4

CLOCKWORK SEEKER	
RG	⌐12
CB	6
DG	3/4/5

TALENTS:

Abilities

Freikorps Armor: Armor +1. Magic Resistant 1. This model may ignore damage from (X), (◉), and (♜) effects.

Freikorps Mercenary: If a Freikorps model is hired as a Mercenary, no other model may be hired as a Mercenary unless they also have the Freikorps Characteristic.

Ruthless

Slow to Die

Special Forces Leader (Freikorps): A Crew led by this model may only hire Freikorps models and Mercenary models. A Crew containing this model may ignore the two Mercenary model limit.

Stubborn: This model receives +2 **Wp** in Duels where it is the defender.

Undead Knowledge: When attacking Undead models with a melee or ranged **Strike** or melee Spell, this model receives ⚡ to Damage Flips and ignores the **Hard to Wound** Ability.

Willing to Die: ◉6: Friendly Freikorps models gain **Slow to Die.**

Weapons

Hunting Knife: Attacks with this Weapon ignore **Armor.**

Actions

(+1) **Nimble**

(+1) **Instinctual**

(0) **Augmented Jump:** This model gains **Flight.** This model may not be blocked while disengaging.

(0) **Hard-ass:** ◉10. Friendly models receive +4 **Wp** in Morale Duels.

(0) **Leader:** Target friendly Freikorps model within 6" of Von Schill activates after this model's activation ends.

(0) **Magnetic Pulse:** (X)4. Constructs receive **Slow.**

(1) **Last Rites:** (X)6. Sacrifice all Corpse and Scrap Counters not carried by models.

Triggers

Cb (▤) **Brutal** [Hunting Knife]

Cb (🜊) **Critical Strike** [Clockwork Seeker]

Cb (♥) **Reposition** [Clockwork Seeker]: Push this model up to 3" after it damages a model with this Weapon.

Cb (X) **Skinning** [Hunting Knife]: Draw one Control Card after killing a **Ht** 1 model with this Weapon.

ASHES AND DUST - MINION

The wonders discovered by the namesake proprietor of Leveticus' Captivating Salvage and Logistics are numerous. In addition to offering his procurement services, Leveticus conducts expeditions of his own into the ruin-dotted landscape beyond the City, where he recovers relics of a bygone age he hopes will serve a purpose in his experiments. Most of these relics turn out to be little more than curios which he sells to the tourists for a few bills. Other items, however, contain pieces to a puzzle he is attempting to unlock with his blending of meat and machine.

The creation he has dubbed "Ashes and Dust" is one such relic.

Blending his talents as a Resurrectionist and artificer, Leveticus found a means by which to capture and contain souls within a relic he discovered during one of his forays outside the City. Whatever the item's original purposes, Leveticus has perverted it to his entropic ambitions, the relic absorbing the spirit energy of those who die around it. It is capable of powering and controlling other abominations and, Leveticus believes, because of the relic's properties, it possesses a malevolence that manifests as a swirling dust cloud of barely contained hatred. This entropic spirit can break itself away from the core, wreaking destruction and havoc on its own, returning to and reanimating the relic core when the need arises. Leveticus posits that his creation could function for an eternity through its ability to continually decay and regenerate itself.

50MM BASE · SOULSTONE COST: 13

CONSTRUCT, UNDEAD, UNIQUE

WK/CG	HT	WP	CA	DF	WD
5/8	2	5	5	5	8

ENTROPY CLAW

RG	𝍢 2
CB	7 ✗✗
DG	3/4/6

Ordered Chaos: ⚫6. Friendly Desolation Engines lose **Unstable Creation.**

Desolate: This model cannot be summoned.

Souleater: Each time a model is killed or sacrificed within 3" of this model it heals 1 **Wd**.

Actions
(+1) Fast

(0) Implant Decay: Kill this model.

(0) Sacrifice the Weak: Sacrifice a friendly model within 3". All friendly models within 3" of that model make a Healing Flip.

Triggers
Cb (✗✗) Desolate Warping [Entropy Claw]: After enemy defender is killed by a melee **Strike** with this Weapon, it does not generate Counters of any kind. Summon one Steampunk Abomination into base contact with the model before it is removed from play.

Df (✗) Dissolution: Models missing this model with a melee **Strike** or melee Spell suffer 2 **Dg**. If this damage kills an enemy model, Summon one Steampunk Abomination into base contact with that model before it is removed from play.

TALENTS:
Abilities
Choose Your Fate: An enemy model **Charging** this model is sacrificed at the end of its activation if the **Charge** did not inflict any damage on this model. Summon one Steampunk Abomination into base contact with the enemy model before it is removed from play.

Desolate Core: When this model is killed, Place one Ashen Core into base contact with it before it is removed from play and Place one Dust Storm in base contact with any friendly or neutral table edge. This model does not generate Counters of any kind.

Hard to Wound 2

Industrial Wasteland: ⚫6. Friendly Steampunk Abominations replace **Caustic Aura** with "**Industrial Nightmare:** At the Start Closing Phase, living models within 4" of this model must win a Df → 12 Duel or suffer 2 **Wd.**"

SPELLS:
(0) Contort
(CC: 12 / Rst: - / Rg: 10) Push this model into base contact with target friendly Steampunk Abomination or friendly Desolation Engine. This model and the target Steampunk Abomination or Desolation Engine suffer a total of 3 **Wd** split between them as this model's Controller chooses.

(1) Dominate Abomination
(CC: 10 / Rst: - / Rg: 6) Target friendly Steampunk Abomination or Desolation Engine immediately makes a melee **Strike**.

(1) Industrial Age
(CC: 10 / Rst: - / Rg: (✗)6) Living models within 3" of a friendly Steampunk Abomination must win a **Df → 10** Duel or suffer 2 **Wd**. Living models within 4" of a friendly Desolation Engine must win a **Df → 12** Duel or suffer 2 **Wd**. This Spell may be cast by this model only once per activation.

ASHEN CORE - MINION

40MM BASE

SOULSTONE COST: PLACED

CONSTRUCT, UNDEAD, UNIQUE

WK/CG	HT	WP	CA	DF	WD
-/-	2	7	7	1	6

TALENTS:

Abilities

Armor +1

Decayed: This model does not generate Counters of any kind when killed.

Desolate: This model cannot be summoned.

Hard to Wound 3

Polluted Wasteland: ⚫10. Friendly Steampunk Abominations replace **Caustic Aura** with "**Industrial Nightmare:** At the Start Closing Phase, living models within 4" of this model must win a **Df → 12** Duel or suffer 2 **Wd.**"

Ultimate Chaos: ⚫10 Friendly Desolation Engines lose **Unstable Creation.**

Actions

(0) Sacrifice the Weak: Sacrifice a friendly model within 3". All friendly models within 3" of that model make a Healing Flip.

SPELLS:

(0) Contort
(CC: 12 / Rst: - / Rg: 10) Push this model into base contact with target friendly Steampunk Abomination or friendly Desolation Engine. This model and the target Steampunk Abomination or Desolation Engine suffer a total of 3 **Wd** split between them as this model's Controller chooses.

(1) Dominate Abomination
(CC: 10 / Rst: - / Rg: 6) Target friendly Steampunk Abomination or Desolation Engine immediately makes a melee **Strike.**

(1) Industrial Age
(CC: 10 / Rst: - / Rg: (⚡)6) Living models within 3" of a friendly Steampunk Abomination must win a **Df → 10** Duel or suffer 2 **Wd.** Living models within 4" of a friendly Desolation Engine must win a **Df → 12** Duel or suffer 2 **Wd.** This Spell may be cast by this model only once per activation.

DUST STORM - MINION

40MM BASE

SOULSTONE COST: PLACED

CONSTRUCT, UNDEAD, UNIQUE

WK/CG	HT	WP	CA	DF	WD
6/-	2	5	4	7	3

CHOKE		
RG	⚔	1
CB		6
DG		2/3/4

TALENTS:

Abilities

Bulletproof 1

Desolate: This model cannot be summoned.

Float

Industrial Nightmare: ⚫4. At the Start Closing Phase, living models must win a **Df → 12** Duel or suffer 2 **Wd.**

Souleater: Each time a model is killed or sacrificed within 3" of this model it heals 1 **Wd.**

Actions

(1) Drawn to the Core: Sacrifice this model and one friendly Ashen Core within 2". Place one Ashes and Dust in base contact with the Ashen Core before it is removed from play. Activate the Ashes and Dust at the end of this Action. This Action may not be taken on the turn in which this model was Placed using **Desolate Core.**

Triggers

Df (✗) Dissolution: Models missing this model with a melee **Strike** suffer **Dg** 2. If this damage kills an enemy model, Summon one Steampunk Abomination into base contact with that model before it is removed from play.

DESPERATE MERCENARY - MINION

The trains bringing people into Malifaux carry more than just convicts, contractors, entrepreneurs, Guild employees, and volunteers; they bring in hopes, dreams, ambitions, and desires as well. For some, ambition and desire are realized, while others learn the hard way that Malifaux is an unforgiving place and that the Guild does not consider charity legal tender. For these individuals, desperation arrives when ambition and hope are lost, but their obligations remain.

Whether a Guild employee cast out of the fold, or a contractor fallen on hard times and unable to make his or her payments, there is always work for a hand quick on the draw or adept with a blade. Many seek to earn enough pay in scrip or Soulstone shards to send money back home to family who need their income to survive. These mercenaries survive day to day, forced to take jobs they might have found distasteful or horrifying not long ago. Their desperation drives them, pushing issues of morality aside as they pursue their survival and that of their loved ones.

Too often what drives these mercenaries begins to eat at them as the things they have done begin to take their toll. Eventually, the memories of their actions begin to haunt them and they question the price they have paid to sustain their families. Some fight on through it all, secure in the knowledge their actions are not in vain. Others succumb to the guilt, going out in a blaze of glory with the names of their loved ones fading on their last breath.

30MM BASE
SOULSTONE COST: 2

MERCENARY, INSIGNIFICANT, RARE 4					
WK/CG	HT	WP	CA	DF	WD
5/7	2	4	3	5	4

SWORD			SECOND-HAND PISTOL		
RG	🗡 1		RG	⌐8	
CB	4		CB	4	
DG	2/3/4		DG	2/3/4	

TALENTS:

Abilities

A Last Noble Deed: When this model is killed, but before it is removed from play, nominate a model within 4" of it. The nominated model makes a Healing Flip.

Comes Cheap

Frantic: While this model has 3 **Wd** or less, it receives ⊕ to its Attack Duels.

Making Ends Meet: Sacrifice this model at the start of the third turn's Start Closing Phase unless its Controller discards one Soulstone. If this model's Controller discards an additional Soulstone, it loses Insignificant until the end of the Encounter.

Actions

(0) For My Family: This model receives +3 to its Duel totals and ⊕⊕ to Damage Flips. Sacrifice this model in the Start Closing Phase.

(1) Uncontrolled Fire: This model takes two Second-Hand Pistol **Strike** Actions which receive -2 **Cb**. These **Strikes** may target two different targets.

Triggers

Cb (🗡) Critical Strike [Sword]

FREIKORPSMANN - MINION

Von Schill's Freikorps is filled with talented men and women who know their way around a gun. Although some are mercenaries, the majority of its membership consists of Guild Guardsmen and specialists who defected to his service when they broke ranks with the Guild. The promise of rewards that actually matched the dangers they encountered proved too much incentive for them to remain with an organization to which their loyalties were already strained to the breaking point. Even today, ex-Guard faced with the prospect of returning Earthside for work are willing to offer their skills to the Freikorps before trying to make their way back home, the respect and reward offered by Von Schill being too great to ignore.

The dangers involved in their new line of work increase exponentially, but the pay the Freikorps offers offsets the risks. All sign a contract with Von Schill personally, taking an oath of duty to the Freikorps and their fellow Freikorpsmenn. The man who breaks the contract is immediately dismissed from service, stripped of his trademark armor, and fined half of what he is currently owed. To date, none have willingly broken their agreement with Von Schill.

Freikorpsmenn do not come looking for a fight, but are well equipped to finish one. Trained by one of the most brilliant military minds to step through the Breach, Korpsmenn know how to take the fight to their opponent. They strike rapidly, their armor protecting them from attacks as they perform their duties brilliantly, proving the faith their leader has put in them is not unfounded.

30MM BASE

SOULSTONE COST: 4

MERCENARY, SPECIAL FORCES (FREIKORPS)

Wk/Cg	Ht	Wp	Ca	Df	Wd
5/7	2	5	3	4	6

HUNTING KNIFE	
Rg	1
Cb	6
Dg	1/3/4

CLOCKWORK PISTOL	
Rg	10
Cb	5
Dg	1/3/5

TALENTS:

Abilities

Freikorps Armor: Armor +1. Magic Resistant 1. This model may ignore damage from (⚡), (🌑), and (🍄) effects.

Freikorps Mercenary: If a Freikorps model is hired as a Mercenary, no other model may be hired as a Mercenary unless they also have the Freikorps Characteristic.

Scout

Stubborn: This model receives +2 **Wp** in Duels where it is the defender.

Actions

(2) Flurry

Triggers

Cb (📖) Brutal [Hunting Knife

Cb (🔫) Critical Strike [Clockwork Pistol]

FREIKORPS LIBRARIAN - MINION

A product of the axiom "a warrior's sharpest weapon is his mind", Freikorps Librarians provide clients with much needed magical support. Their abilities may not be as flashy as other spellcasters in Malifaux, but what they lack in raw unchained power, they make up for in dependability.

Most Freikorps contract teams include one Librarian. Intelligence evaluation is the Librarian's responsibility, confirming the details of the operation as explained by the employer. When that intelligence changes, the Librarian evaluates it and makes appropriate recommendations. Trained strategists, the advice Librarians provide has made the difference between victory and defeat for a number of the Freikorps' clients.

The Freikorps' mandatory training regimen keeps a Librarian's skill with a blade fresh, but most leave their knives sheathed in favor of the destructive litanies they are taught. Any Freikorps member demonstrating a knack for spellcasting is assigned to their library for evaluation and training. This well hidden repository of lore has provided the Freikorps with some of its most potent spells. Librarians can kill with a word, heal with a gentle touch, or shatter stone with a shout. Their knowledge of the arcane even allows them to interrupt the aether flowing into an opponent as she attempts a spell of her own, leaving her defenseless. With a Librarian at their side, Freikorpsmenn fear little, knowing if things get too hot, they have magical firepower standing by, ready to come to their comrades' aid at a moment's notice.

30MM BASE

SOULSTONE COST: 7

MERCENARY, SPECIAL FORCES (FREIKORPS)

WK/CG	HT	WP	CA	DF	WD
5/7	2	6	6	3	6

HUNTING KNIFE		ANCIENT WORDS	
RG	/// 1	RG	⌐8
CB	5	CB	6📖
DG	1/3/4	DG	2/3/4

TALENTS:

Abilities

Arcane Receptacle: This model's Controller discards one Control Card when it activates. Add the discarded Card's suit to this model's **Ca** until the End Closing Phase. If the model's Controller does not discard a card, this model receives **Paralyzed**.

Arcane Reservoir: Increase your Crew's maximum hand size by one while this model is in play.

Counterspell: When this model is targeted by a Spell this model's Controller may discard two Control Cards or one 📖 suit Control Card to cancel the Spell before starting totals are generated.

Elite Mercenary: This model costs +2 Soulstones when hired as a Mercenary instead of +1.

Freikorps Armor: Armor +1. Magic Resistant 1. This model may ignore damage from (X), ⬤, and ♣ effects.

Freikorps Mercenary: If a Freikorps model is hired as a Mercenary, no other model may be hired as a Mercenary unless they also have the Freikorps Characteristic.

Stubborn: This model receives +2 **Wp** in Duels where it is the defender.

Weapons

Ancient Words: This model's Attack Duels with this Weapon use **Cb → Wp**. This Weapon ignores **Armor**. Constructs may not be targeted with this Weapon.

Actions

(2) Furious Casting

Triggers

Ca (X X) Completely Blocked [Block Connection]: Defender loses all Suits associated with all of its statistics instead of one.

Ca (📖📖) Surge

Cb (📖) Brutal [Hunting Knife]

Cb (📖📖) Resonance [Ancient Words]: This Weapon's damage gains -/♣/♣♣.

SPELLS:

(1) Aetheric Theories
(CC: 12📖 / Rst: - / Rg: 8) Target friendly model gains 🎲 to its **Cast** and **Channel** Casting Flips.

(1) Block Connection
(CC: 14 X / Rst: Wp / Rg: 8) Target model loses one suit associated with one of its statistics.

(1) Healing Energy
(CC: 10👊 / Rst: - / Rg: 8) Target friendly model makes a Healing Flip.

(1) Magical Buffer
(CC: 14♞ / Rst: - / Rg: ⬤3) Friendly Freikorps models, including this model, receives +2 **Df**.

FREIKORPS SPECIALIST - MINION

The responsibility of clearing a path through dangerous quarters falls squarely on the Freikorps Specialist's shoulders. Their willingness to face threats head on, blazing a trail quite literally through the enemy to an objective, is what they are trained to do.

Skillful handling of the Specialist's signature weapon takes months to learn, training encompassing everything from basic safety to advanced tactics. Many candidates wash out of the training, unable to complete the rigorous regimen. Accidental deaths during training run high for Specialists in comparison with other Freikorps assignments. Nevertheless, the Freikorps never runs short of volunteers to wield the weapon Corpsmen have dubbed "Wyrm's Breath".

Encased in the Freikorps' armor with canisters of flammable chemicals strapped to the armor's back, a Specialist putting the weapon to work is a terrifying sight to behold. The stream of chemicals can be adjusted through the use of a nozzle, allowing the flames to be focused or spread across an area.

Gouts of flame are capable of igniting whatever they touch, mercilessly burning through wood and flesh alike. Few can withstand the horrible damage wrought by a Freikorps flamethrower, and most are willing to flee from one rather than face an agonizing death at the Specialist's hands.

30MM BASE   SOULSTONE COST: 5

MERCENARY, RARE 1, SPECIAL FORCES (FREIKORPS)

WK/CG	HT	WP	CA	DF	WD
4/-	2	5	3	4	6

HUNTING KNIFE		FLAMMENWERFER	
RG	1	RG	8
CB	5	CB	5
DG	1/3/4	DG	2/3🌳🌳/4🌳🌳🌳

TALENTS:

Abilities

Freikorps Armor: Armor +1. **Magic Resistant 1**. This model may ignore damage from (ɤ), ⚫, and 🌳 effects.

Freikorps Mercenary: If a Freikorps model is hired as a Mercenary, no other model may be hired as a Mercenary unless they also have the Freikorps Characteristic.

Hesitation: Models with **Wp** 6 or less receive ⊟ to their Attack Flips when making melee Strikes against this model.

Stubborn: This model receives +2 **Wp** in Duels when it is the defender.

Weapons

Flammenwerfer: Attacks with this Weapon ignore **Armor** and cover modifiers. When this model is killed, it generates a (ɤ)3, **Dg** 3.

Actions

(1) Detonate Tanks: (ɤ)6. This model takes a ranged **Strike** against each model. Each **Strike** causes **Dg** 2/3/4 and may activate the **Focused Burn** or **"You're Flammable"** Triggers. This model loses the Flammenwerfer Weapon for the rest of the Encounter.

Triggers

Cb (▥) Brutal [Hunting Knife]

Cb (🖋) Focused Burn [Flammenwerfer]: Defender suffers +1 **Dg**. This attack does not generate any 🌳.

Cb (▥) "You're Flammable" [Flammenwerfer]: Defender suffering damage from this Weapon must make a **Wp → 12** Morale Duel.

FREIKORPS TRAPPER - MINION

One of the Freikorps' advantages is its ability to provide the right mix of skills to complete an objective. Depending on the mission or contract, Von Schill, himself, will select the manpower necessary, flawlessly reading the tactical needs of the client. Because a contract can require a wide variety of skills Freikorps Trappers are on the payroll to provide scouting intelligence on a target. Their knowledge of using terrain to their advantage and their ability to blend into the surroundings despite wearing freikorps armor gives them an otherworldly mystique with the other men.

Trappers are also excellent hunters, bringing in extra revenue with pelts and furs. Some even go as far as to seek out local bounties on critters and hunt until the bounty is lifted. Many find the Badlands popular for bounty hunting, knowing someone, somewhere is willing to pay to clear Razorspine Rattlers from their livestock. They can track prey over rocky terrain and through streams, doggedly pursuing their quarry day and night until it collapses or is overtaken.

Because they can be depended upon for additional income, the Freikorps gives Trappers more latitude in being out of contact than they do other Freikorps members. Trappers have been known to go "a trappin'" for months without so much as a word only to return, saddlebags filled with scrip and Soulstone shards for their services.

30MM BASE   **SOULSTONE COST: 6**

GRAVEROBBER, MERCENARY, SPECIAL FORCES (FREIKORPS)

WK/CG	HT	WP	CA	DF	WD
5/8	2	5	3	5	6

HUNTING KNIFE	
RG	〣 1
CB	6
DG	1/3/4

CLOCKWORK RIFLE	
RG	⌐16
CB	5 🐾
DG	1/3/5

TALENTS:

Abilities

Freikorps Armor: Armor +1. Magic Resistant 1. This model may ignore damage from (ꓫ), (●), and (♟) effects.

Freikorps Mercenary: If a Freikorps model is hired as a Mercenary, no other model may be hired as a Mercenary unless they also have the Freikorps Characteristic.

From the Shadows: This model may be deployed after all other models. Deploy this model in or behind any terrain on the table. This model must be deployed more than 12" away from an enemy, or the objective of any Strategy or known Scheme. This model may not be targeted by **Charges** or ranged **Strikes** until it takes an Action other than **Pass** if deployed this way. If multiple models with this Ability are in play, players alternate deploying them using the deployment order for Crews.

Hunter

Ruthless

Scout

Stubborn: This model receives +2 **Wp** in Duels where it is the defender.

Weapons

Clockwork Rifle: This Weapon's Damage Flips receive 🔼 when damaging Beasts or Constructs.

Actions

(0) Guide: (ꓫ)4. Friendly models gain **Scout**.

(1) "Jerky Time!": This model discards any number of carried Corpse Counters. Heal this model 1 **Wd** per Corpse Counter discarded.

Triggers

Cb (▦) Brutal [Hunting Knife]

Cb (🐾) Reposition [Clockwork Rifle]: After damaging target model with this Weapon, Push this model up to 3".

Cb (ꓫ) Skinning [Hunting Knife]: Draw one Control Card after killing target **Ht** 1 model with this Weapon.

MALIFAUX RAT - MINION

The sight of a Malifaux rat is enough to give anyone pause. Large enough to pass for a small dog, Malifaux rats are more aggressive and territorial than their Earthside cousins. Their beady eyes betray a malevolence that is more calculating than mere animal cunning, while their sharp yellow teeth and disturbingly human paws are capable of tearing through stone and mortar given time.

Malifaux rats are filthy creatures; a mischief of them bears disease in its bite and scratch, enough to lay low the hardiest of soul. They may follow the instincts of the dominant male, but when one shows any sign of injury or weakness, they turn on it and devour it in seconds. Despite this, people will sometimes trap and attempt to tame and train these rats to guard their cellars or even keep them as pets.

More than one ambitious person has learned the hard way that a pair of those beady eyes staring at them from a crack in the cellar wall is not just a precursor to an infestation but an indication the infestation is well underway. The rats seem to know better than to show themselves until their nest is well

established, only appearing when bolstered by numbers superior to the building's occupants. They also demonstrate an unsettling ability to lie in wait and ambush their prey, as testified to by the few rat catchers who have escaped one of these crude traps. In fact, as the saying goes in Malifaux; "See a rat, run out the back."

30MM BASE   **SOULSTONE COST: 2**

INSIGNIFICANT, VERMIN

WK/CG	HT	WP	CA	DF	WD
5/8	1	4	4	4	2

YELLOW TEETH

RG	///// 1
CB	4
DG	1/2/2

TALENTS:

Abilities

Devoured: When this model is killed or sacrificed it does not generate any Counters; instead, all friendly Vermin within 3" heal 2 **Wd**.

Flock: When activating this model, simultaneously activate all friendly Malifaux Rats within 4" that have not already activated this turn.

Scout

Tiny: Ranged **Strikes** and ranged Spells targeting this model receive ⊟ to their Attack and Casting Flips. This model does not block LoS to other models.

Unfocused: This model may not block disengaging models. Models may move through this model's base, but may not stop on it.

Weapons

Yellow Teeth: Models damaged by this Weapon gain one Blight Counter.

Actions

(+1) Instinctual

(-1) Slow

(0) Hungry Rats: Sacrifice all Corpse and Scrap Counters within 6".

(0) Impetuous: This model's flips receive ⊞ during its next Action.

(0) Writhing Mass: This model suffers 1 **Wd**. Move this model into base contact with another friendly Malifaux Rat within 5".

(1) Rat Problem: Sacrifice this model and two other friendly Malifaux Rats within 3". Summon one Rat-Catcher into base contact with this model before it is removed from play.

Triggers

Cb (✗) Rabies [Yellow Teeth]: After resolving this Weapon's Damage Flip, defender receives -2 **Wp** until the end of the Encounter.

SPELLS:

(1) Overrun by Vermin
(CC: 10 / Rst: Df / Rg: 6) Target model receives Insignificant until the next Start Draw Phase.

JACK DAW - MINION

No one forgets their first trip to Malifaux. This startling world catches everyone by surprise, beginning with the macabre sight greeting them when they step off the train at Malifaux station. High in the wasted limbs of the Hanging Tree dangles Jack Daw, unofficially adopted by many in the Guild as the City's mascot. Almost nothing is known about the individual whose body hangs in the tree's limbs, bound hands and sack-covered head suggesting some sort of execution. No records have been found explaining his presence. Jack is viewed as one of hundreds of oddities in Malifaux, catalogued and contained as best the Guild can. What no human understands is that the being trapped in Jack's body has watched the comings and goings of Earthsiders since the Great Breach reopened years ago... watched and listened.

Trapped in both body and mind, Jack could only absorb the events of the world passing by until the doorway to the Grave Spirit's realm was opened at Kythera. The power that flowed into Malifaux from that doorway had an unexpected effect, stirring a creature inside Jack, breaking through the insanity which gripped its mind. It remembered nothing of its former life, only a crushing sense of guilt and a burning desire for vengeance. The two emotions warred within Jack for a time, its desire for revenge on...her...finally winning over. Jack could not remember who she was, but all it wanted was to see the life fade in her eyes. Burning deep within, this need focused what energy Jack had absorbed until its spirit broke free from its corporal prison, wandering the City seeking vengeance.

The first sightings of the ghost of Jack Daw were dismissed as drunken ramblings until their frequency began to increase. The spirit could not communicate in more than the vaguest of methods but instead seemed to be searching for something or someone, offering its services at random. Able to communicate with The Hanged, Jack shares

some spiritual connection to them. It shows particular interest in conflicts involving women, and a few of the stories tell how, in the middle of a fight, Jack lost control, switching sides when the fighting was at its thickest. Guild and Arcanist researchers have been dispatched to investigate Jack sightings, but to date, no reliable information regarding its plan has been gathered.

A visit from Jack Daw is met with a mixture of surprise, gratitude, and fear. Its motivations for appearing to aid or hamper a Crew are a mystery. Despite the benefits of having the being fighting on their side, smart Masters realize the potential threat Jack Daw could pose if it decided to change sides at the wrong moment.

MERCENARY, SPIRIT, UNDEAD, UNIQUE

WK/CG	HT	WP	CA	DF	WD
5/8	2	7	6🐾/📖	4	*

SUPPRESSED MEMORIES		SUPPRESSED MEMORIES	
RG	⚔ 1	RG	⌐12
CB	*	CB	*
DG	1/1/1	DG	1/1/1

TALENTS:

Abilities

Arcane Reservoir: Increase this model's Crew's Maximum Hand Size by one while this model is in play.

Betrayed: When determining this model's final total in a Resist Duel, reduce the value of any 🐾 Cards in the total to 0.

Betrayer: When this model or another friendly The Hanged flips the Black Joker, another random crew gains control of that model as soon as the current action is resolved. The affected model counts as friendly to the controlling crew. Control of the affected model passes back to the original player after the End Closing Phase. If the model already activated, or was in the process of activating, it receives **Reactivate**. Friendly The Hanged are unaffected by this ability if they could have been hired by your Master normally without Jack Daw.

Dual Focused: When this model uses its **Ca** it can add either suit to the total, but not both.

Float

Kill Scheme: Enemy Crews gain 1 VP when they kill this model. If this model is in play at the end of the game and has killed one or more enemy models its controlling Crew gains 1 VP.

Slow to Die

Terrifying → 13

"The Apple Never Falls…": Crews hiring this model may also hire The Hanged models. Jack Daw and all friendly The Hanged models in play increase their **Terrifying** by +2 while within 5" of a Hanging Tree special terrain feature.

The Oldest of Magics: This model is immune to **Wd** it suffers unless they are inflicted by spells, magical weapons, or **Focused Strikes**. This ability cannot be negated or removed by any means.

Undying: When this model suffers one or more **Wd**, it is killed unless the player who hired it discards one Control Card or one Soulstone. This ability cannot be negated or removed by any means.

Weapons

Suppressed Memories: Attacks with this weapon are made using **Ca → Wp**. If a model is wounded by this Weapon its controller must discard one Control Card if they have any in their Hand.

Actions

(0) Doomed: ⚡4. Models resisting spells receive -1 to the resisting stat. Models targeted by melee or ranged **Strikes** receive -1 to the defending stat.

(1) Driven by Injustices: (✗)6. Push each The Hanged model up to its **Wk** toward the Master it is closest to. If the Push ends with the Master in The Hanged's melee range it makes one Baleful Aura **Strike** targeting the Master. The **Strike's** Attack Flip receives ✚.

Triggers

Ca (📖📖📖) Repression [Suppressed Memories]: After wounding defender with this weapon, its controller must discard two Control Cards instead of one if they have more than one.

Ca (🐾🐾) Heart Stopper [Suppressed Memories, Hangman's Knot]: After hitting target model with this weapon or target fails to resist this spell, instead of flipping for damage, kill target unless target discards two Control Cards or two Soulstones. Only models with the **Use Soulstones** ability may discard Soulstones.

SPELLS:

(1) Hangman's Knot
(CC: 12🐾/Rst: Wp/Rg: 12) **Dg** 1/2/4. Push target model 4" toward this model.

(0) Severed Ties
(CC: 14📖🐾/Rst: - /Rg: ⚡6) Models may not Cheat Fate or use Soulstones to change starting Duel totals.

NIX, THE BULL TERRIER - MINION

Even gods sometimes get it wrong.

When the Tyrant Plague reanimated and took Hamelin's form, the resulting wash of energy found one other creature, Hamelin's bull terrier, Nix. The unfortunate creature had been the first to die upon Plague's awakening, and his flensed carcass lay near where Hamelin would be painfully transformed as well. The energy, which should have dissipated once Hamelin's corpse was restored and animated, flowed through Nix's remains in an attempt to reanimate him as well.

The remaining energy was not powerful enough to bring Nix back completely. Instead, it freed the bull terrier's spirit from his body, preventing it from moving on. Intrigued by this occurrence, Hamelin decided to leave the spirit to its own, knowing He could summon Nix to His side when necessary.

Nix's transformation came with a terrible cost, however. As a creation of Plague's power, Nix bears the mark of disease and pestilence and spreads them wherever he goes. He is an unwitting pawn in Plague's awful schemes.

Nix now wanders Malifaux in search of what he remembers of the real Hamelin. When called by the Plague, he is bound to come and serve. But when he is not needed, Nix roams far and wide, searching for Hamelin. His curiosity is insatiable and he sometimes aids people in need during his travels.

40MM BASE

SOULSTONE COST: 7

INSIGNIFICANT, SOULLESS, SPIRIT, UNIQUE

WK/CG	HT	WP	CA	DF	WD
5/8	2	5	5	5	6

FEED ON ANIMA	
RG	⫻ 2
CB	6
DG	4/3/2

TALENTS:

Abilities

Gorge on Pain: This model may immediately take a **(0)** Action when a model is sacrificed within 4" of it.

Hamelin's Dog: This model may only be hired by a Crew containing any Hamelin model.

Magic Resistant 2

Nihilism: While this model is in play friendly models lose Insignificant. If this model is in play at the end of the encounter, no friendly models count as Insignificant

The Sweet Taste of Failure: This model heals 1 **Wd** whenever another model within 2" loses a Duel.

Weapons

Feed on Anima: Models damaged by this Weapon gain one Blight Counter.

Actions

(0) Drain Essence: Sacrifice a friendly model within 3". This model makes a Healing Flip.

(0) Emptiness: ⚫3. All flips made by non-Soulless models in Duels receive ⊟.

(0) Herd Dog. (⚫)6. Push friendly The Stolen and Malifaux Rats up to 3".

(1) Scent of Pain: This model may Push up to 8" directly toward a model that has suffered 1 or more **Wd** this turn.

(0) Unconscious Behavior: Target another model within 6". Nominate one of target's Weapons, which receives +2 to its Weak damage, and -2 to its Severe damage.

Triggers

Cb (✗) The Stink of Death [Feed on Anima]: If this Weapon inflicts Severe damage, inflict no damage. Summon one Malifaux Rat.

Cb (♥) Submit [Feed on Anima]: After resolving this Weapon's Damage Flip, defender's Duel Flips receive ⊟. This model's Duel Flips receive ⊞. This does not stack with **Drink Spirit**.

SPELLS:

(0) Dysthemia
(CC: 10 / Rst: Wp / Rg: ⚫6) Reduce the Weak damage of all model's Weapons to 1.

(1) Bleeding Disease
(CC: 10 / Rst: Wp / Rg: 12) Target model suffers 1 **Wd** for each Blight Counter on it.

(1) Drink Spirit
(CC: 12 ✗ / Rst: Wp / Rg: 12) Target model's Duel Flips receives ⊟. This model's Duel Flips receive ⊞.

RAT-CATCHER - MINION

Nemesis of the Malifaux rat, rat-catchers ply their trade in the sewers, cellars, and alleyways of the City. Bounties offered by the Guild and resident groups for collected rat carcasses attract these men and women who are shunned and depended on in equal measures. Owners of private residences have been known to pay exorbitant fees to ensure their homes are rat free by skilled rat-catchers.

Rat-catchers belong to an exclusive brotherhood, and they do not share the tricks of their trade lightly. All bear the scars of their trade - a missing finger, ear lobe, or bit of nose attest to a hard-fought battle against their four-legged foes, and many exhibit some hint of the disease carried by the vermin. Most laugh off (albeit an often phlegmatic laugh) suggestions they have been infected with some deadly plague. They claim they're immune to whatever it is they show symptoms of up until the moment they keel over dead.

There are a number of rat-catchers who use more than their instinct and experience on the job. They are able to communicate with, or at least understand, the Malifaux rat on some level. They use their talents to lure rats into traps or to devour poison hidden in trash heaps or molding cheese, while others use their knowhow to send thrall rats against their own kind. Unscrupulous rat-catchers of the mundane and magical variety also re-infest the homes of previous clients, offering cut rates to clear them out yet again.

30MM BASE

SOULSTONE COST: 5

INSIGNIFICANT, RARE 2, VERMIN

WK/CG	HT	WP	CA	DF	WD
4/6	2	5	5	4	8

RAT TRAP

RG	///// 1
CB	5
DG	0/3/Paralyzed

TALENTS:

Abilities

Covered in Rats: This model gains **Armor +2** while it is within 2" of two or more Malifaux Rats".

Ferret: This model's **Interact** Actions cost 1 AP regardless of their listed AP cost.

Hamelin's Proxy: This model may not be hired or summoned into a Crew which does not contain Hamelin, the Plagued.

Ruffian: Ht 1, **Harmless**, **Pitiful**, and Insignificant enemy models targeting this model must win a **Wp →13** Duel or the Action fails

Voracious Rats: When this model or a model within 6" of it is killed, summon one Malifaux Rat in base contact with the model before it is removed from play. The model does not generate Counters of any kind. No other model can be summoned as a result of the model being killed.

Weapons

Rat Trap: Models damaged by this Weapon receive one Blight Counter.

Actions

(0) Slaughter Rats: (X)6. Kill any number of Malifaux Rats.

Triggers

Cb (☞) Iron Trap [Rat Trap]: The Weapon's **Dg** is 2/3/5 for this Damage Flip.

SPELLS:

(1) Bleeding Disease
(CC: 10 / Rst: Wp / Rg: 12) Target model suffers 1 **Wd** for each Blight Counter on it.

(1) Moldy Cheese
(CC: 12 / Rst: - / Rg: (X)18) Friendly Malifaux Rats may move their **Wk** directly toward this model.

(1) Vermin Frenzy
(CC: 10 / Rst: - / Rg: (✪)6) Sacrifice a friendly model within 3". Melee Strikes made by friendly Vermin inflict +1 **Dg**.

THE STOLEN - MINION

The call of Hamelin the Plagued's pan-flute is difficult to resist. It pushes against the minds of all who hear it, pushing into their thoughts and filling them with dark purpose. Those who are unable to resist the sound are drawn to Hamelin, their free will decayed by what they have heard. They become His slaves, serving Him until they succumb to the consuming sickness surrounding their new master.

Hamelin uses these individuals as a queen bee would use her drones. They fulfill menial tasks, dragging after Him with ever lessening speed as their muscles and innards are slowly eaten by disease. His only gift to them is their ability to share His bounty with others, infecting all they come into contact with. In this way, the plague is spread faster than Hamelin could hope to achieve alone.

As the stolen are devoured by Hamelin's corrupting influence, the symptoms of it begin to appear on their bodies. Weeping pustules, sores, and scabrous growths erupt on the skin, soon making them unrecognizable to even loved ones. Their suffering is short lived, however, and they quickly succumb to their affliction. Those who have the courage to put them out of their misery are crippled with guilt and horror when they realize what they thought was a zombie or other creature was, in fact, human.

30MM BASE　　　　　　　**SOULSTONE COST: 3**

INSIGNIFICANT, SOULLESS

WK/CG	HT	WP	CA	DF	WD
5/-	1	4	5	5	1

TALENTS:

Abilities
Harmless

Horrible Realization: When this model is killed or sacrificed by a non-Soulless model, that model must win a **Wp → 13** Duel or it receives **Paralyzed**.

Inevitable Fate: When this model is killed or sacrificed, summon one Malifaux Rat into base contact with it before it is removed from play.

No Humanity: (↻)6. When this model is killed or sacrificed, non-Soulless models receive -2 **Wp**.

Actions

(all) Abandon: Sacrifice this model. Target model within 6" receives Insignificant until the end of the Encounter. The model may prevent this by discarding two Control Cards.

SPELLS:

(1) Bleeding Disease
(CC: 10 / Rst: Wp / Rg: 12) Target model suffers 1 **Wd** for each Blight Counter on it.

(1) Succumb
(CC: 10 / Rst: Df / Rg: 6) Target model loses any immunities to and cannot ignore Talents and Spells requiring **Wp** Duels.

BORN ON THE BAYOU

BORN ON THE BAYOU

April 21

I cannot believe my good fortune! I have retained the services of one Silas Bullock, a local here on the bayou's edge. Silas and his men have traded regularly with several gremlin settlements for the past two years and are heading out for their monthly trade excursion on the morrow.

Having explained in detail what I hope to accomplish with this expedition, Silas was more than happy to offer the services of his trusty vessel – for a price, of course. The amount will sorely deplete my funds, but if his reputation is true, the money will be well spent, and I will have saved myself weeks of fumbling about in the muck trying to make contact with these creatures myself. The Guild documents I was able to examine before leaving the City depict gremlins as bothersome vermin; they do not consider the creatures a thinking species. I hope my hypothesis bears out, and I can disprove the mistaken classification of the gremlin and its role in Malifaux's ecosystem.

Cannot contain my excitement, I believe this is how other great men have felt upon the verge of their great discoveries in science and medicine...

April 22

The shallow drafted vessel I was directed to was, shall we say, less than confidence-inspiring. It rode low in the water, laden with trade goods packed into barrels and crates, and the rusting steam engine's clinging and clanging had me expecting it to explode the instant we pushed away from the docks. Silas greeted me warmly, extending a hand to help me aboard. He laughed at the amount of luggage I bore, especially at the camera equipment, but instructed one of the hands, Clem, to stow my materials starboard.

After a final round of haggling on price, I handed over half the money, and we pushed off, the engine's protestations quieting down once the paddlewheel was engaged, into the inhospitable bayou.

This should be the most exciting adventure of my career...either that or they'll rob me while I sleep, cut my throat, and dump me in the bayou.

April 24

My first encounter with the gremlins came our third day out. Clancy maneuvered our boat slowly through the bayou, skirting sand bars, mangroves, and shallows with a veteran's skill. Watching it all slide past us, I was struck by how inhospitable a place it was. Life, it seemed, was a constant struggle here, whether against the ever-encroaching environment or predators I had yet to see but had been assured of their existence by a vigilant Philippe, who stood at the bow, rifle in hand.

At first, I did not realize we had arrived at our destination. One moment, we were gliding around a thick stand of what could have been tall-standing junipers; the next, Silas had stopped the engine and we were drifting toward a sandy spit of land. "These'ns don't like the motor sound," he said.

The boat slid to a stop against the sand, and despite the calm demeanor of my guides, I could not completely divorce myself of the Guild reports I had read about these creatures. I noticed Philippe kept hold of his rifle and hoped we were able to affect a quick exit if things went abruptly awry. He would remain behind and guard the boat. These gremlins were more accustomed to visits from humans than some of the ones I would see later in the trip, but Silas did not trust them and wouldn't leave his vessel alone while he traded with their bosses.

The two hands, Marko and Clem, loaded the sledge with crates of dry goods, two buckets of nails, and several bolts of what I was told was cloth. Clem told me with a snort that the gremlins weren't good at much, weaving being somewhere toward the top of the list. I was even able to convince them to include my camera equipment in the load rather than being forced to drag it along or, worse, leave it behind in the boat.

The walk to the village would be a short one, they told me. Everyone, myself included, pitched in with dragging the sledge through the sand and muck. Silas said that they had tried a rolling cart, but it all too often got stuck and was impossible to keep rolling. The sledge, he said, was better for this kind of land. My aching arms and back begged to differ by the time we reached the village, but I kept my comments to myself.

Whatever I had expected to see did not prepare me for my first glimpse of a gremlin village. Shanties of varying size and shape were scattered haphazardly about, smoke curling out of several tin chimneys. A few perched above the lot on spindly wooden legs, while other stilt homes sat out over the water, a canoe or flatboat tied to rude docks at the bottom of rickety stairs.

A small gremlin, barely two years old if what I had read about their life cycle was accurate, plucked the strings of a banjo that had seen better days. His fingers froze when we came into view, but he stayed where he was on the stoop of one of the shanties, watching our antics with fascination. Other gremlins came out to see us, greeting Silas and Clancy with the broken English the traders had laughed about.

Silas returned the greeting in the gremlins' own rude language, eliciting guffaws from those within earshot. Apparently, the gremlins were not the only ones with language troubles. After the greeting, both parties settled down to haggling over the goods. I saw the gremlins had brought out their own products for trade: jerked pig, porcine and crocodile skins, several bundles of dried herbs, and jars of a mostly clear liquid.

Despite my curiosity about the trade negotiations, I wanted to see what I could of the village before they were concluded and we returned to the boat, so I gathered up my photography equipment before Silas could trade it away and went exploring. Each shanty seemed to be assembled from whatever castoff materials its owners could find. Boards of varying size and shape were the predominant material, but here and there, I saw stone shanties, shanties whose walls were sheets of fabric, even a shanty constructed from hundreds of individual pieces of scrapped metal crimped together at the edges. If nothing else, these gremlins were certainly innovative scavengers.

As I wandered, I was watched by dozens of gremlins. Some from the shelter of their shanty doorways, others glaring with malice as they fingered rusty knives and short ugly rifles. I kept moving, making sure I appeared more confident than I felt. I hoped knowing I was with Silas' crew would keep the majority of them from violence but could not be certain. Instead, I made sure I was in earshot of the trade negotiations and set up the camera, taking photographs of the more intriguing shanties and trying to photograph the locals in their natural habitat. To my surprise, many of the gremlins spoke pidgin English, and I was able to gather quite a bit of information about their family groups and social structures.

At their most common level, each village of gremlins is made up of family groups they call "kin". I was surprised by this revelation, having used the term myself in several of my own anthropological monographs pertaining to primitive cultures. Not every gremlin in the village was related by blood, I learned, but they were all related in what appeared to be their common interest in the village's survival, which was lead by a "bossman" who was the biggest and strongest of their number. Kin from other villages were not necessarily enemies, but none were safe from the occasional raid against another kin's village for food, weapons, or mates.

I was surprised by the gremlins' willingness to share their cultural information with me. A remarkable find, especially in light of the Guild's assumption that their culture and social strata are merely mimics of what human society they have encountered. Equally surprising was their intense curiosity about my camera. After taking several pictures, I was answering more questions about it than I was able to ask them. They poked and prodded at it, one very forward individual went as far as to lick the lens before I could shoo him away!

We are now on our way to the next village, where Clancy tells me I will see even more wonders of the gremlin world. I cannot wait, and even the theft of my lens cap by a little green thief cannot dampen my spirits!

April 26

Clancy was right.

During our second stop, I was able to observe not only the subtle variations in how the village functioned in comparison with our first, namely these kin were more belligerent and distrustful of strangers, but also the foundations of gremlin culture - cultivation and herding!

Gremlins in this village tended massive brutish creatures they and the crew called "pigs". Having grown up on a farm myself, I can attest to these creatures bearing a fleeting resemblance to the pigs found Earthside. Growing much larger than Earth pigs, these creatures and the gremlins share an odd synergy that I will endeavor to explain. At its simplest, both rely on the other as a food source. The pigs in the village's pen, I was told, were domesticated animals, bred by the gremlins. They were a much more docile lot than those the gremlins hunted and were hunted by out in the bayou. I shook my head in disbelief as one of the 'peaceful' creatures butted its tusked head against the fence we stood near, slamming it hard enough to crack the slats as well as stun itself for a few seconds. The gremlins used every bit of the pig. They used its meat, hide, even ground its bones to be used by their taxidermists as a curative.

I was in for a 'treat', the gremlins continued, it was feeding time. Several gremlins bearing buckets, heaped with a vile assortment of things not mentioned in polite conversation, dumped the contents of their buckets into the pig pen, nimbly dancing back to a safe distance as the beasts began to feed. I watched as one gremlin, slower than the rest, was caught and devoured messily by the fastest of the pigs. Rather than let the gremlins, who paid little attention to the noisy events in the pen, see my discomfort, I excused myself and wandered off in search of a quiet place in which to retch.

I found was a collection of crude booths, seats, and platforms at one end of the village. I was told the gremlins were holding some sort of festival the next day, something they referred to as a 'bash', where kin from the surrounding village came and participated in games and contests.

An opportunity to witness an event like the bash was too great to pass up, and after a great deal of pleading and the last of my financial reserves, I was able to convince Silas and Clancy to remain here overnight.

I do hope eating gremlin cuisine is not expected of me. After the events at the pig pen, I think I may have lost my appetite for the rest of our stay.

April 27

Amazing. Simply amazing. Apparently a 'bash' is a fair, festival, and holiday celebration combined into a day of food, drink, and rough and dangerous games to challenge a gremlin's survival skills.

Uggh, my head. I was able to avoid food for much of the day but may have imbibed one too many of the clearish liquid the gremlins refer to as 'shine'. An alcoholic beverage they brew, Marko described drinking shine to me as "drinking liquid gold filtered through the sun". He was not lying. After recovering from the first gulp I found the shine a warmly comforting feeling in my belly. If only I'd had more to eat...

My earlier romanticizing of their culture has been tempered by the events I witnessed during hours upon hours of observing gremlin 'revelry'. Games such as pig ridin' where a gremlin sees how long it can hold onto a wild pig's bristling back, where gremlins falling from the pig's back are trampled, gored, or worse. Or wildly shooting at broken bits of thrown pottery with their inaccurate boomsticks. Both activities reinforce the Guild's assertions that gremlins are a conniving and violent species. Clem said some gremlins used the bash as a way to settle old scores they could not get their kin to raid another village for. I watched as this bore out during a round of target practice where one gremlin shot dead the 'partner' throwing his targets into the air. The shooter's aim never left his partner when the last shard was tossed; he simply fired, blowing the poor soul apart. I later learned that the shooter suspected his partner of stealing his best knife in a raid earlier this year.

Toward the end of the day, the crowd's din quieted to a nervous murmur. Gremlins stepped aside as a particular group passed among them. These gremlins were led by a female, which was itself unique as all my research and conversations had led me to believe that being boss was a male-only status. These gremlins looked oddly familiar, somehow, dressed as they were in elaborate hats, ponchos, even goggles. I thought back to my time at the Guild Library and the passing glance I had of a group of Guild agents entering the building. These gremlins looked suspiciously like those agents, but how was such a thing possible?

One last thing, after the festivities died down, we returned to the boat. Philippe begged Silas to push off and put some distance between us and the village, but as Silas watched the sun dipping quickly beyond the horizon, he told Philippe it would be too dangerous to travel the swamp by night. He assured Philippe, all of us really, we would head out at first light, but there was no way he would risk the vessel this evening. Philippe cursed roundly then, mostly at me and my suggestion we stay for the bash. He wormed himself into the bow of the ship, eyes alert, hands on his rifle and said he would not sleep until we were well away from this place, cursed me once more, and took up watch on the rapidly encroaching darkness.

I hope he will accept my apology before our journey is over.

Oh my aching head...maybe some sleep will help...

Philippe will never hear my apology, and I fear none of the other crew ever will either!!

I was awakened by what I thought was a splash and opened my eyes. Philippe was GONE from his place in the bow!

I could see the faint flicker of lights through the trees, moving away from the boat. Oblivious to the danger I was in, I scooped up Philippe's discarded rifle from where it lay on the deck and slipped out of the boat in quiet pursuit of the retreating lights. I am no woodsman, and although I tried to be quiet, sneaking through the wilderness with naught but the wan moonlight and a few glimpses of torchlight to show the way resulted in me tripping over only *most* of the roots and branches along my path.

We were back at the village, a ring of torches illuminating a ring of gremlin faces as they pushed Philippe into their midst. He stood taller than the lot of them, but a nasty cut above his eye and his glass-eyed stare suggested he had been rendered senseless by a blow to the head with a cudgel or blackjack back at the boat. I wondered briefly if he had fallen asleep waiting for the dawn to arrive.

A susurrus chanting began, the circle of gremlins swaying softly from side to side. Their chanting voices rose slowly, building in intensity and volume. Philippe seemed to be caught in the chant's grip and began to sway himself. Damn me, but I could only watch, gripped in equal parts fear and academic curiosity.

After a few minutes of this, a figure emerged from the shadows. He was a gremlin dressed in a battered top hat and black coat. He paused to take a drink from the bottle he carried in one hand, pointing the onyx head of his walking stick at Philippe with the other. I could not understand his words, but as he staggered drunkenly toward the circle, the gremlins parted, never breaking the rhythm of their chanting. Another pull from the bottle and the gremlin spat at Philippe. But, instead of spewing the bottle's contents out, the gremlin spat a blaze of flame at poor Philippe. As he was engulfed, the gremlins' spell over him was broken. I still hear his screams as he fell to the ground. The gremlin smiled, his sharp teeth glinting in the firelight, and spoke a word in perfect, clear English: "Sacrifice."

I ran then, dropping the rifle and moving as fast as I could. The trees and undergrowth clutched at me, inviting me to stay and become the gremlins' next sacrifice. I don't know if they saw or heard me, but I thought we could escape. I tried to rouse Silas, Clem and the others, but to no avail. Their sleep was more than drunken slumber; they were under the sway of some powerful drug. But we all drank the same shine during the day...

Curse the conniving creatures; it was the food they drugged, not the drink! If only I'd eaten, perhaps they would have let us travel on in the morning. After all, they only came for one...

I can hear them coming, can see the lights heading this way. I do not even have Philippe's rifle to defend myself with...or to...

To: Captain Finnerty

These pages were found among the half-submerged wreckage of a vessel our scouts found floating a day's sail from Cutter's Hollow. These documents should be entered into Special Division's files and their existence forgotten by all involved.

- *Lucius*

Land!

"Heck, we got all kinds on this railcar. Them fellas over yonder come all the way from the Three Kingdoms. Those folks sittin' off a ways are escapin' whatever's goin' on in the Empire. Them over there crossed the ocean with a pass just for the Breach. Come from the King's Country, I hear. Me, I grew up down south. Heck I ain't got no kind of life hustlin' cattle or raisin' a crop, so I figure I'd try my hand in Malifaux.

"Guild's got a sweet enough deal. Can test my luck workin' my own land. They got me a few acres and heads of steer. Sold everything else I got to cover the rest settin' up a homestead and all. All I got to do is give them a quarter of what I make and swear to uphold Guild law and authority. Like we all don't just do that anyways. Hear they set up a bunch of folk the same way. Ranchers, farmers, miners, all types. From what everybody is saying, boomtowns and camps are spreading like wildfire.

"Don't reckon if it's 'Badlands Fever' or not. Spirits, demons. Hell! I'll take my chances. I got a shot at my own place and a life I never had back home. Once I learn to shoot one of them pistols, I'll be able to take care of myself against those critters that come crawling in out of the swamp or from the desert. No problem, 't all."

OPHELIA LACROIX - HENCHMAN

Gremlins are equal parts mischievous and curious creatures, when it comes to interacting with humans. For the most part, they avoid humankind despite their attraction to the "shinies" humans bring to Malifaux.

Sharing Som'er Teeth Jones' infatuation with all things human, the LaCroix kin's unhealthy attraction to human shinies has escalated to new levels. Their leader, Ophelia, has her family conducting frequent raids on humans near the Bayou in search of more.

These raids have drawn the attention of the Ortega family, whose compound is not far from the Bayou's edge. The Ortegas patrol the area between Latigo and the Bayou with orders to shoot gremlins on sight. A recent reversal of fortune Ophelia is none too happy with. She has watched the Ortega's leader, the woman with the low hat and lightning-fast *pistola*, and decided the best way to fight the humans is to copy their methods. She reasons that if the woman in the fancy hat can

put the gremlins to rout, then her fancy hat should help the gremlins do the same to the humans.

As the leader of the largest gremlin family, Ophelia's ambitions know no bounds. Until the Ortegas came, she was well on her way to gathering enough weapons to arm her gremlins for war against the other families. Now, with the Ortegas constantly harassing her raiding efforts, Ophelia knows she has no chance of becoming the next gremlin overboss unless she can get rid of them.

Taking necessary risks, Ophelia regularly joins her raiding parties now. She no longer trusts the reports brought back by the survivors of Guild attacks and wants to see how her kin are defeated so easily. She notes what she sees, careful to never make the same mistake twice. She has offered a substantial reward to the first raiding party able to bring back a live prisoner for questioning. So far, the reward remains unclaimed.

30MM BASE

SOULSTONE COST: 8

GREMLIN, HENCHMAN 6, SPECIAL FORCES (KIN)

WK/CG	HT	WP	CA	DF	WD
6/9	1	4	4	6	9

PISTOL	
RG	⌐8
CB	6
DG	2/3/4

TALENTS:

Abilities

Companion (Kin)

"Dammit, Calm Down!": ⬤4. Friendly Gremlins may ignore **"Woops!"**.

Evasive 1

Feud: This model inflicts +1 **Dg** when damaging an enemy Family model.

Gunfighter [Pistol]

Special Forces Leader (Kin): Crews led by this model can only hire Gremlin, and Kin models. In a Brawl, this model may only join Crews which contain Gremlins, Kin, Pigs, and Vermin.

"Shoot High, Boys": ⬤3. Friendly Gremlins, including this model, do not flip cards for **Ht** 1 models when determining a target while firing into melee. This Ability has no effect if the initial target of the attack is **Ht** 1.

Weapons
Pistol: Paired.

Actions
(+1) Instinctual

(+1) Reckless: This model may suffer 1 **Wd** to receive **Fast**.

(0) "Oooo! A Girl!": Push target friendly Gremlin within 8" into base contact with this model.

(0) Family Tree: One friendly Gremlin within 6" of Ophelia LaCroix may activate after this model's activation ends.

(0) Dumb and Lucky: The Weapons of one friendly Kin within 6" receive +🌕 to **Cb**.

(0) Like Herding Squirrels: ⬤6. Friendly Gremlins, including this model, receive +♥ to **Df**.

Triggers
Cb (🌕) Calculated Luck [Pistol]: Double the damage inflicted by this Weapon. This model suffers 1 **Wd**.

Df (♥) Squeel!: After this model suffers damage from an enemy melee **Strike** or melee Spell, it Pushes 4" directly away from the attacker.

SPELLS:

(0) Bent Gun Barrel
(CC: 11 / Rst: - / Rg: C) This model's Pistol **Strikes** receive -4 **Rg** and ignore **Armor**.

(1) Dirty Shot
(CC: 11 / Rst: - / Rg: C) This model immediately makes a Pistol **Strike** that receives ♣♣♣ to the Attack Flip, and ⊟ to the Damage Flip.

(1) "Right Between the Eyes"
(CC: 12 / Rst: Df / Rg: 10) **Dg** 1/2/5 that receives ♣♣♣ to the Damage Flip.

YOUNG LACROIX - TOTEM

Gremlin young'uns are a noisy, bratty bunch. They arrive into the world hungry and belligerent, looking to eat whatever is pushed in front of them and protect it with the fury of a rabid badger. They mature rapidly, ensuring they are ready to survive the dangers of the bayou once abandoned by their parents. Packs of young'uns come together in villages for mutual protection not only from the bayou's many predators, but also from their kin and their pigs.

LaCroix young'uns are little different, but they do have one advantage others do not. Where other kin treat their young as nuisances that get underfoot, the LaCroix treat them as peers, expecting them to participate and pull their weight, as if they were fully grown gremlins mere weeks after birth. They learn how to fire a gun, clean a boomstick, hunt wild pigs in the tall grass, and how to slop the village's pigs. This latter chore often ends with the gremlin child feeding the pig itself along with the slop it carried.

The sense of inclusion a young'un feels is due in part to Ophelia LaCroix's leadership of her kin. Having watched the Ortegas for some time, she saw how they treated their children and decided that if it was good enough for them, she would try it with her own kin. This has also led to many of the young following her around, trying to mimic her swagger and demeanor, with comical results.

30MM BASE

SOULSTONE COST: 2

GREMLIN, INSIGNIFICANT, SPECIAL FORCES (KIN), TOTEM (OPHELIA)

WK/CG	HT	WP	CA	DF	WD
6/-	1	3	4	5 🐗	3

PISTOL	
RG	⌐8
CB	5
DG	2/3/4

TALENTS:

Abilities

Companion (Ophelia LaCroix)

Evasive 1

Gremlin Veal: If this model is within 8" of a **Stampeding** Pig, it becomes the target of the Pig's Swine **Dash Action** even if it is not the closest non-Pig model.

Gunfighter [Pistol]

Role Model: Ophelia can connect with up to three Young LaCroix when leading a Crew.

Tiny: Ranged **Strikes** and ranged Spells targeting this model receive ⊟ to their Attack and Casting Flips. This model does not block LoS to other models.

"Woops!": When this model misses with a Pistol **Strike**, the closest other friendly model within 10" and LoS suffers an unmodifiable Damage Flip of 1/2/3.

Weapons

Pistol: This model is Pushed 1" directly away from the target when attacking with this Weapon.

Actions

(+1) Reckless: This model may suffer 1 **Wd** to receive **Fast**.

Triggers

Cb (♣) Dumb Luck [Pistol]: When damaging a defender with a **Strike** with this Weapon, double the damage inflicted. This model suffers damage equal to half the number of **Wd** inflicted.

Df (🐗) Squeel!: After this model suffers damage from an enemy melee **Strike** or melee Spell, it Pushes 4" directly away from the attacker.

SPELLS:

(1) Magical Extension
(CC: * /Rst: * /Rg: *) This Spell may be cast only once per activation. Cast one of the connected Master's **(1)** Spells. During this casting, this model may use a Soulstone to change its starting total.

FRANCOIS LACROIX - MINION

Before his encounter with Francisco Ortega, Francois LaCroix was a cowardly gremlin. He avoided conflict with the feistier members of his family (truth be told, all were feistier than Francois) and was the target of every bully in the village.

When the Ortegas swept through the Bayou, Francois watched firsthand (from the safe vantage point of some tall grass) how the elder Ortega brother stalked the gremlins, driving them off by force of will alone. He saw what power someone truly fearless possessed over his cowardly family and was in awe. After the dust settled and the Ortegas had moved on, Francois swore to himself he would never be their whipping boy again.

He secretly scavenged a rusty sword and pistol and began practicing with them out of the other LaCroix's sight. He observed his other family members and how the bullies' swagger got them what they wanted and when the threat of violence was not enough. Finally, he was ready.

At first the other gremlins laughed at him and his fancy duds. When he stood up to the first and then the second and more of the bullies who had belittled him his entire life, beating the tar out of each, he knew something would change. Pretty soon, the gremlins in the village began to look at Francois with newfound respect...or were they looking at him with fear? Either way, he did not care. He had earned his place in the village and remains one of the LaCroix's most intimidating kin, joining Ophelia's raids whenever she will have him.

30MM BASE　　**SOULSTONE COST: 5**

GREMLIN, SPECIAL FORCES (KIN), UNIQUE

WK/CG	HT	WP	CA	DF	WD
5/8	1	4	4	5	7

DUELING SWORD	
RG	///// 2
CB	6 ✋
DG	2/3/4

PISTOL	
RG	➹ 8
CB	5 🐾
DG	2/3/4

TALENTS:

Abilities

Aim High: This model does not flip cards for **Ht** 1 models when determining a target while firing into melee. This Ability has no effect if the initial target of the attack is **Ht** 1.

Feud: This model inflicts +1 **Dg** when damaging an enemy Family model.

Gremlin Kin: This model gains **Companion (Kin)** while a friendly Ophelia LaCroix is in play.

Used to it: When this model would be damaged by the **"Woops!"** Ability, the Damage Flip 0/0/1.

Actions

(+1) Reckless: This model may suffer 1 **Wd** to receive **Fast**.

Triggers

Cb (✋) Dumb Luck [Dueling Sword, Pistol]: When damaging a defender with a **Strike** with this Weapon, double the damage inflicted. This model suffers damage equal to half the number of **Wd** inflicted.

Cb (✋ 🐾) Hair Trigger [Pistol]: After resolving a Damage Flip with this Weapon, this model suffers 1 **Wd**. Make another **Strike** with this Weapon.

Df (🐾) Squeel!: After this model is damaged by an enemy melee **Strike** or melee Spell, Push it 4" directly away from the attacker.

SPELLS:

(0) Duelist

(CC: 11 / Rst: - / Rg: C) Until the Start Closing Phase, unless this model flips a Black Joker, its controller can discard a Control Card to re-flip its starting Duel card when making a melee or ranged **Strike**.

(1) Gremlin Menace

(CC: 8 / Rst: Wp / Rg: 6) Move this model 5" toward target model. Target model's Attack Flips targeting this model receive ⊟.

GREMLIN TAXIDERMIST - MINION
AND
STUFFED PIGLET - MINION

An infinitely resourceful bunch, it did not take gremlins long to turn their natural curiosity toward best adapting and using materials they could trade or steal from humans. Gremlin taxidermists were the most ambitious of the lot, combining their rudimentary understanding of chemistry and medicine with the magic black substance the humans called gunpowder to create potent yet volatile combustibles. Despite several experiments going awry and obliterating a number of villages and their residents, any taxidermists who still felt the urge to experiment after a good old fashioned beating moved their workshops to the outskirts of their villages.

No longer able to find willing gremlins to help test their creations, the taxidermists turned to their first profession, enlisting the aid of a steady stream of porcine volunteers to help gauge the results of their hard work. Stuffing the smaller piglets with different concentrations of gunpowder, swamp gas, and their own special blends of chemicals and herbs, taxidermists could light a fuse, turn the terrified critters loose, and watch the explosive results – sometimes even remembering to note them down. If a little boom was good, the taxidermists surmised, a big boom had to be better, and they strapped the piglets with as much explosive material as their little bodies could carry.

The life of a stuffed piglet is mercifully short. Stuffed full of a caustic blend of gunpowder and chemicals, and struggling under the weight of dynamite and other explosives tied haphazardly around its body, the piglet is released in the general direction of what needs "blowin' up", squealing toward it in pain and terror. When it staggers close enough to the target, the gremlin taxidermist triggers the caustic brew, detonating the unfortunate animal. This ends the piglet's miserable existence and hopefully that of the target as well.

Because the concoction is dangerously unstable, a sufficiently agitated piglet has the very real potential of exploding prematurely, sometimes taking its taxidermist tormentor with it.

30MM BASE   **SOULSTONE COST: 6**

GRAVEROBBER, GREMLIN, RARE 2

WK/CG	HT	WP	CA	DF	WD
4/6	1	4	5X	4	6

SKIN'N KNIFE	
RG	1
CB	4
DG	2/3/4

TALENTS:

Abilities

Dead Man's Switch: If this model is killed and there are no other friendly Gremlin Taxidermists in play, all friendly Stuffed Piglets are immediately sacrificed.

"Dud?": This model may take the **"Purdy Fireworks"** Action during the End Closing Phase. This may be done even if this model already took a **(0)** Action during the turn.

Lead Jacket: Reduce damage ⚫, (x), and ☘ inflict on this model by 3.

Actions

(+1) Reckless: This model may suffer 1 **Wd** to receive **Fast**.

(0) "Purdy Fireworks": ⚫12. Friendly Stuffed Piglets take the **Bacon Bomb!** Action. Stuffed Piglets may choose to conduct a **Wp →10** Duel. If they win the Duel they do not take the Action.

(1) "Load 'er Up!": Sacrifice one Piglet within 6". Summon one Stuffed Piglet.

Triggers

Ca (📖) Packed to the Gills ["It Were a Good'n"]: After successfully casting this Spell, the **Bacon Bomb!** Flip receives ⚑.

Df (🐗 or 🌀) Impulsive: After this model suffers damage, it takes the **"Purdy Fireworks"** Action.

SPELLS:

(1) "It Were a Good'n"
(CC: 11 / Rst: - / Rg: 24) Friendly Stuffed Piglet takes the **Bacon Bomb!** Action. If this model fails to cast the Spell, nominate an opponent. That opponent may nominate one of this Crew's Stuffed Piglets to take the **Bacon Bomb!** Action, which is controlled by that opponent.

(1) Piglet Roll
(CC: 10 / Rst: - / Rg: 18) Push friendly Stuffed Piglet up to its **Wk**.

(1) "Sooey!"
(CC: 10 / Rst: - / Rg: (x)18) Friendly Pigs may Push up to their **Cg** toward this model. All Pigs in range Charge this model if it loses the Casting Duel.

(1) Taxidermin'
(CC: 11 X X / Rst: - / Rg: C) Discard a Corpse Counter within 6" or sacrifice a friendly Piglet. Summon one Stuffed Piglet.

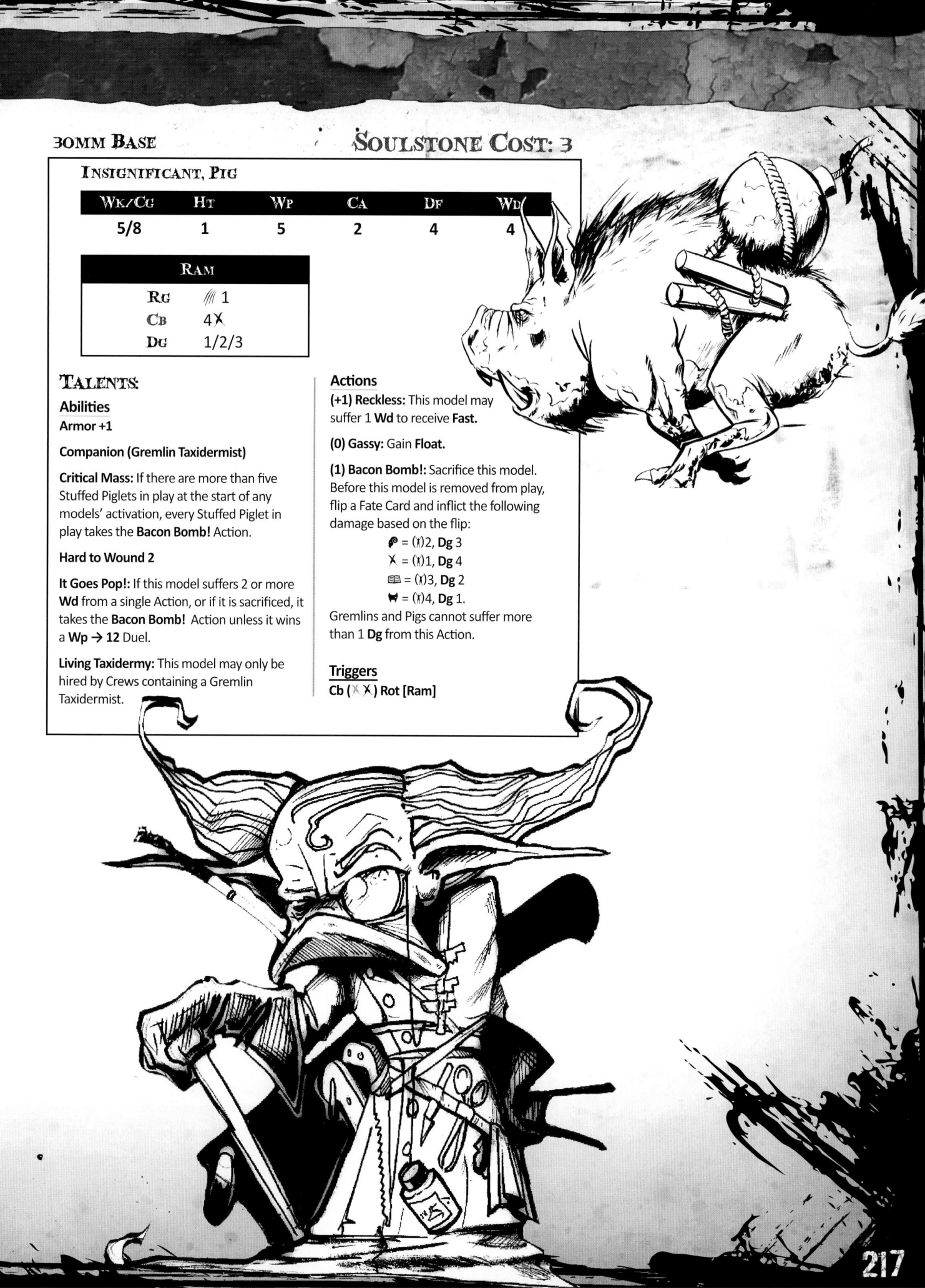

· SOULSTONE COST: 3

INSIGNIFICANT, PIG

WK/CG	HT	WP	CA	DF	WD
5/8	1	5	2	4	4

RAM	
RG	⚡ 1
CB	4✗
DG	1/2/3

TALENTS:

Abilities

Armor +1

Companion (Gremlin Taxidermist)

Critical Mass: If there are more than five Stuffed Piglets in play at the start of any models' activation, every Stuffed Piglet in play takes the **Bacon Bomb!** Action.

Hard to Wound 2

It Goes Pop!: If this model suffers 2 or more **Wd** from a single Action, or if it is sacrificed, it takes the **Bacon Bomb!** Action unless it wins a **Wp → 12** Duel.

Living Taxidermy: This model may only be hired by Crews containing a Gremlin Taxidermist.

Actions

(+1) Reckless: This model may suffer 1 **Wd** to receive **Fast.**

(0) Gassy: Gain **Float.**

(1) Bacon Bomb!: Sacrifice this model. Before this model is removed from play, flip a Fate Card and inflict the following damage based on the flip:

⚡ = (ϒ)2, **Dg** 3
✗ = (ϒ)1, **Dg** 4
▦ = (ϒ)3, **Dg** 2
🐾 = (ϒ)4, **Dg** 1.

Gremlins and Pigs cannot suffer more than 1 **Dg** from this Action.

Triggers

Cb (✗ ✗) Rot [Ram]

PERE RAVAGÉ - MINION

Pere loves fire. He loves it more than hooch, pig wrasslin', even more than his hundred young'uns back in the shanty. He loves watching the flames dance in a campfire, or consuming a Guild wagon, while his LaCroix kin loot it for all its worth. Watching reflected flames dance in Pere's goggles, one can see the small grin that tickles the corner of Pere's mouth. His breathing quickens when burning timbers collapse, scattering a thousand fireflies into the night sky, "so purdy" he whispers.

There was a time when Pere felt about fire like every other gremlin. That was before the shanty Pere was sleeping in was set alight by the Ortega family. He was trapped by the flames, certain he would never see his little ones again. Pere closed his eyes and waited for the end to come.

It never did.

When the flames subsided, Pere clambered out of the charred ruin unharmed. He could not believe his luck and thanked the Loa for protecting him through the fire. Rushing home, Pere could not wait to tell his neighbors about what happened.

As he shared his adventure with them, Pere longed for the thrill he felt while trapped in the flames. He realized he could not find the words to express how horrible and exciting it was. Instead, he closed up the doors and shutters, and as he talked, set the shack alight. While the shack burned, Pere closed his eyes. He could hear his own terrified screams in those of his neighbors and felt his pulse racing. Shocked and thrilled at what he had done, Pere convinced himself that night the feeling would go away given time.

But it never has.

40MM BASE   SOULSTONE COST: 5

GREMLIN, SPECIAL FORCES (KIN), UNIQUE

WK/CG	HT	WP	CA	DF	WD
5/8	1	3	4	4	7

BURN'N STICK	
RG	⚔ 1
CB	5
DG	2/3🟑/5🟑🟑

BREATHE FIRE	
RG	⤳8
CB	5
DG	1/3🟑/4🟑🟑

TALENTS:

Abilities

"KA-BLOOEY!": (🟑)3. **Dg** 4 when this model is killed.

Careless: This model suffers 1 **Wd** when it makes a Breathe Fire **Strike**.

Easily Influenced: This model receives -2 **Wp** in Duels when it is the defender.

Feud: This model inflicts +1 **Dg** when damaging an enemy Family model.

Gremlin Kin: This model gains **Companion (Kin)** while a friendly Ophelia LaCroix is in play.

Used to it: When this model would be damaged by the **"Woops!"** Ability, the Damage Flip 0/0/1.

Actions

(+1) Reckless: This model may suffer 1 **Wd** to receive **Fast**.

Triggers

Cb (♠) Stupid Luck [Breathe Fire]: Triple the amount of damage inflicted on the target by this Weapon. Sacrifice this model.

Df (♥) Squeel!: After this model is damaged by an enemy melee **Strike** or melee Spell, Push it 4" directly away from the attacker.

SPELLS:

(1) "Oopsie!"
(CC: 10 / Rst: Df / Rg: (🟑)6) All models, including this model suffer **Dg** 5. This model cannot make a Resist Duel to prevent this damage. **"KA-BLOOEY!"** does not activate if this model is killed by this Spell.

PIGAPULT - MINION

The first use of what would affectionately be nicknamed the "Pigapult" happened between the LaCroix and Hedfield families. Ask a gremlin, and he'll tell the story just about the same as any other, shuffling the family names around to make his kin look like the victim.

One of the two families, it makes little difference which, settled a dry patch across a deep stretch of the bayou from the other. Being a bit territorial, families typically keep to themselves, but multiple families living near one another is not unheard of. This particular stretch of murky water was a popular throughway for the different fauna in that part of the bayou. Gator, heron, even the occasional human traveled that stretch of water, making it a particularly good food source.

As expected, the one family took offense to sharing its find with the other. After a few flatboat raids between the families, one of the pair contrived a ramshackle device capable of flinging refuse and offal across the water and into the other's village. Soon after, the second village constructed one of their own and began giving as well as they received.

The violence escalated from refuse to stones, and one day, the more devious of the two families (every indication points to this being the LaCroix) loaded their device with several frantic piglets. Before the enraged animals could free themselves, they were launched deep into the Hedfield village and created a good deal of chaos for the Hedfields before they could be stopped. These barrages continued for a time before

things escalated once again, and instead of piglets, the pigapults were launching piglets stuffed with explosives at one another. These bombardments continued for several days, until the air was filled with the scent of gunpowder, porcine flatulence, and swamp gas.

When the smoke cleared, the LaCroix family stood triumphant, and such was the beating they gave the Hedfields that, to this day, no gremlin will admit to being a member of the Hedfield family.

50MM BASE   **SOULSTONE COST: 4**

GREMLIN, INSIGNIFICANT, OBJECT 5

WK/CG	HT	WP	CA	DF	WD
2/-	3	10	1	1	5

PORK BARRAGE	
RG	⌐24
CB	4
DG	2/4♠/6♠♠

TALENTS:

Abilities

Flying Pigs: While within 2" of this model, friendly Piglets and friendly Stuffed Piglets gain the Action "**(all) "Take a Ride!"**: Place this model up to 24". This model is killed if it loses a **Df → 11** Duel, which may not be Cheated, after being Placed."

Rigged: Friendly non-pig models within 2" of this model gain the Action: "**(1) Jury-rig Pigapult:** Heal target friendly Pigapult within 2" 1 **Wd**".

Weapons

Pork Barrage: This Weapon ignores LoS when declaring a target. At the start of each of this model's activations, this model must sacrifice a friendly Piglet or friendly Stuffed Piglet within 2" in order to use this Weapon durring it's activation. If a Stuffed Piglet was sacrificed, this Weapon inflicts +1♠ and + 1 **Dg**.

Actions

(+1) Reckless: This model may suffer 1 **Wd** to receive **Fast**.

(1) Launch'n: Place a target friendly **Ht** 1 model within 2" up to 24". Target model is killed if it loses a **Df → 11** Duel, which may not be Cheated, after being Placed.

RAMI LACROIX - MINION

Rami LaCroix was enamored with the boomstick from the moment he saw one. Other gremlins had trouble remembering which way the noise came out when they fired theirs, but Rami knew how to handle one, as if he was born to it, and he quickly mastered the temperamental gremlin firearm as a youngster.

As he got older, Rami's talents with gunpowder and guns convinced him there had to be a better way to shoot things than the crude boomstick the gremlins were enamored with. He had watched too many of his kin shoot off various parts of their own anatomy to consider a fate like that for himself.

After witnessing Niño Ortega and his beautiful repeating rifle, Rami knew what he had to do and set about creating his own gremlinized version of Niño's amazing weapon. His first few attempts to create his own repeating rifle met with varying degrees of failure. Although he lost a few toes, Rami's experiences convinced him that the gun simply wasn't

big enough, and he started over, looking to assemble the biggest, baddest rifle any gremlin had ever seen.

After scrapping several new designs (without any toes lost this time), Rami settled on one. The massive rifle had quite a kick, but with a counterweight, he was certain he had the rifle he wanted! The resulting weapon surprised even him when he felled a Guild messenger he ambushed at better than a thousand paces. Rami and his extra long rifle are kept busy these days by his family's leader, Ophelia. He would complain he's missing out on his naps, but the chance to do what he loves best – shooting things – is one he would never pass up.

30MM BASE

SOULSTONE COST: 6

GREMLIN, SPECIAL FORCES (KIN), UNIQUE

WK/CG	HT	WP	CA	DF	WD
5/-	1	4	4	5	6

EXTRA LONG RIFLE	
RG	⌐16
CB	5
DG	2/3/4

TALENTS:

Abilities

Aim High: This model does not flip cards for **Ht** 1 models when determining a target while firing into melee. This Ability has no effect if the initial target of the attack is **Ht** 1.

Feud: This model inflicts +1 **Dg** when damaging an enemy Family model.

Gremlin Kin: This model gains **Companion (Kin)** while a friendly Ophelia LaCroix is in play.

Hunter

Scout

Used to it: When this model would be damaged by the **"Woops!"** Ability, the Damage Flip 0/0/1.

Weapons

Extra Long Rifle: If a 1 is flipped for this Weapon's Attack Flip, this model cannot Cheat Fate. After that Flip is resolved, end this model's activation.

Actions

(+1) Reckless: This model may suffer 1 **Wd** to receive **Fast**.

Triggers

Cb (♣) Dumb Luck [Extra Long Rifle]: When damaging a defender with a **Strike** with this Weapon, double the damage inflicted. This model suffers damage equal to half the number of wounds inflicted.

Df (☙) Squeel!: After this model is damaged by an enemy melee **Strike** or melee Spell, Push it 4" directly away from the attacker.

SPELLS:

(0) Gremlin Sights
(CC: 12 / Rst: - / Rg: 18) This model's Extra Long Rifle **Strikes** receive +2 **Cb** against target model while target is further than 8" away. This Spell ends when target model is within 8" of this model, or this model casts this Spell again.

RAPHAEL LACROIX - MINION

Due to their cantankerous nature, gremlins are prone to squabbling about the slightest thing, whether it is a scrap of food or the placement of a cooking fire. A few gremlins take this squabbling to a higher level, arrogantly pushing their kin around to get what they want.

Raphael LaCroix is one of these kinds of gremlin.

Completely lacking in what few civilized manners the gremlins posses, Raphael clubs those he deems inferior into submission with his bravado. When that fails, he replaces harsh words with his rifle butt. Most gremlins avoid his eye and scatter at his approach rather than be the target of his animosity. He takes the best his family have to offer and leaves bruises and broken teeth in return. A few equally aggressive gremlins treat Raphael with the respect they reserve for their peers, a respect Raphael begrudgingly pays them as well. One of these days, he plans on showing them who the "big pig" is, but until then, playing their game seems the smartest tactic.

Only Ophelia LaCroix seems capable of keeping Raphael's rampages in check. There is something about her focused purpose and ambition he is drawn to and approves of. He is certain of one thing, when she comes calling, there will be plenty of head-cracking for him if he follows her orders. It's an arrangement he's happy to agree to, at least for now.

30MM BASE   SOULSTONE COST: 6

GREMLIN, SPECIAL FORCES (KIN), UNIQUE

WK/CG	HT	WP	CA	DF	WD
5/8	1	4	4	4	8

BIG HONKIN' STOCK	
RG	⚔ 1
CB	3
DG	1/2/4

BIG HONKIN' GUN	
RG	⌐8
CB	5
DG	2/3/5

TALENTS:

Abilities

Aim High: This model does not flip cards for **Ht** 1 models when determining a target while firing into melee. This Ability has no effect if the initial target of the attack is **Ht** 1.

Bulletproof 1

Feud: This model inflicts +1 **Dg** when damaging an enemy Family model.

Fueled by Panic: While this model has 4 **Wd** or less remaining, it may use **Reckless** without suffering a wound and receives ✚ to its Damage Flips.

Gremlin Kin: This model gains **Companion (Kin)** while a friendly Ophelia LaCroix is in play.

Hard to Kill

Used to it: When this model would be damaged by the **"Woops!"** Ability, the Damage Flip 0/0/1.

Actions

(+1) Reckless: This model may suffer 1 **Wd** to receive **Fast**.

(+1) Wade Out: This model may take an additional **Walk** Action each activation while it has 4 **Wd** or less remaining.

Triggers

Cb (🔮) Dumb Luck [Big Honkin' Gun]: When damaging a defender with a **Strike** with this Weapon, double the damage inflicted. This model suffers damage equal to half the number of **Wd** inflicted.

Df (♥) Squeel!: After this model is damaged by an enemy melee **Strike** or melee Spell, Push it 4" directly away from the attacker.

SPELLS:

(1) Gremlins Bleed Green
(CC: 10🔮 / Rst: - / Rg: C) This model makes a Healing Flip.

(2) "HOO-EEE!"
(CC: 13 / Rst: Df / Rg: ⌐(↑)6) **Dg** 3. This model suffers 1 **Wd**.

SLOP HAULER - MINION

They say an army travels on its stomach. If that is the case, the gremlin slop haulers are its chefs. These epicures of the awful use their unique scavenging skills to put together a caustic mix of offal, carrion, and whatever trash and refuse happens along to feed their always hungry pig charges. Of course, sometimes the chef becomes the main course when slopping, so good reflexes and a touch of insanity are both job requirements. Even then, a careless moment or poorly timed joke can separate a gremlin from its limb or life, depending on how voracious its customers at the trough are that day.

Despite the inherent risks in the job, slop haulin' is never short on volunteers. Haulers get the pick of the slop before it goes to the pigs, ensuring they stay well fed, which ironically slows down their reactions and makes them more appealing as food. More than one veteran hauler has had his career ended not by being devoured by its charges, but instead, by being drowned in a slop tank by another gremlin looking to take the job.

Because haulers must constantly be on the lookout for threats from both sides of the pen fence, they work together in groups of mutual self-preservation, watching out for one another, more or less, until their ambitious nature takes over and one happens to look the other way when an opportunity presents itself. Groups of haulers hold contests among one another with adorable names like "breath holdin'", "slop slingin'", and "run, Piggie's after ya!"

30MM BASE — SOULSTONE COST: 4

GREMLIN

WK/CG	HT	WP	CA	DF	WD
5/8	1	5	4	5	5

SLOP BUCKET	
RG	≋ 1
CB	5
DG	2/3/3🟤

TOSSED SLOP	
RG	↰8
CB	4
DG	1/2🟤/3🟤🟤

TALENTS:

Abilities

"Free Vittles!": When this model is killed or sacrificed, up to three friendly Pigs or Gremlins within 2" make a Healing Flip.

The Other White Meat: Push the closest Pig within 4" of this model into base contact with it when it fails a Morale Duel. Sacrifice this model. Heal all **Wd** suffered by the Pig.

"Woops!" [Tossed Slop]: When this model misses with this Weapon, the closest other friendly model within 8" and LoS suffers an unmodifiable Damage Flip of 1/2/3. If there are no other friendly models within 8" there is no effect.

Weapons

Slop Bucket: A model damaged by this Weapon reduces its **Df** to 4 until the End Closing Phase.

Tossed Slop: A model damaged by this Weapon reduces its **Df** to 4 until the End Closing Phase.

Actions

(+1) Reckless: This model may suffer 1 **Wd** to receive **Fast**.

(all) Feed Piggies: Up to four friendly Pigs or Gremlins within 3" may make a Healing Flip.

(2) Pig Frenzy: Sacrifice this model. Two friendly Pigs within 3" receive **Reactivate**.

(2) Slop Spray: (⋌)3. Non-Gremlin, non-Pig models reduce their **Df** to 4.

Triggers

Cb (🐾) "Feedin' Time!"[Slop Bucket, Tossed Slop]: After resolving the Damage Flip for this Weapon, Pigs and Gremlins attacking the defender receive +1 **Cb**.

Df (❤) Squeel!: After this model is damaged by an enemy melee **Strike** or melee Spell, Push it 4" directly away from the attacker.

SPELLS:

(1) "Betcha I C'n Hit It!"
(CC: 10 / Rst: - / Rg: C) Make a Tossed Slop **Strike** with **Rg** ↰16 and **Cb** 2.

(1) "Sooey!"
(CC: 10 / Rst: - / Rg: (⋌)18) Friendly Pigs may Push up to their **Cg** toward this model. All Pigs in range **Charge** this model if it loses the Casting Duel.

(1) "Spin 'round Real Fast!"
(CC: 12 / Rst: Df / Rg: (⋌)3) **Dg** 2. Push all models directly away from this model until each model's base is completely 3" away from it, or the model contacts impassable terrain or another model.

Driving Vengeance

A single red star shone above Malifaux. Its brightness penetrating even the frequently cloud-covered sky. Though the other stars arced across the sky nightly and with the changing of the seasons, that red star remained immobile, always hanging over the horizon in the same place. If one travelled through the swamp with the buzz of the Breach behind him and that red star before him, he would, in time, arrive at the ruins of Kythera, a temple dedicated to death. There he would find the already stagnant water of the bayou further fouled by viscous black oil that continuously bubbles up from the center of the great edifice at its center.

"It is proximity to this temple that allows for the science of necrotic reanimation and other techniques governing the manipulation of life and death," Nicodem explained, though Kirai Ankoku barely paid attention to his words. She stared at the red star through the aperture of the telescope as he had directed, though she feigned interest in that as well. Truly, she retained very little concern for anything. He continued, saying, "It is also why these techniques are of significantly reduced utility, Earthside. Malifaux has a certain…spirituality of its magic. Kythera and other such reservoirs of power allow a control over death. A corpse, here, has a lingering spiritual connection." He removed his top hat and ran those knobby fingers through wispy thin hair, matted to his pale scalp.

"I can give life to Francis?" she asked, suddenly interested.

"No, child. Not that. We may urge a corpse to walk and function, making it resemble the life you and I take for granted. But very rarely do we see anything like the life a corpse might have had before. Their personality exists beyond," and he swept his narrow fingers toward the ceiling. "Over time that connection will crumble, and even a powerful Resurrectionist may not stir its forgotten will to stand and walk."

"Then why would I want this, if not to bring Francis back to me?"

Nicodem smiled, though the corners of his lips curled down at the corners making him look even more cruel and sinister. "Your quest ended with the death of Captain Gideon?" he asked, knowing the answer. Kirai didn't answer. "No," he offered. "You are not done, are you? No, there are more."

"The Governor," she said.

"Yes."

"Why have I not assaulted him? I, I mean, the spirit? Why has it not destroyed him as it has the others?"

"The Governor is unassailable, it seems. He has wards and guards. He has many enemies. We will find a way, you and I," Nicodem said with certainty.

"But I cannot animate corpses like you've suggested."

"As I said, our control manifests differently in each of us. Though we have only heard of the animation of the once dead, their spirits are lost to us, severed

224

irrevocably. That is, it is as I supposed. Until I met you."

"Me?" she asked. "Why me?"

"Yes. Why you? Why me, for that matter? Why anything? We are, each of us, trapped in the moment of time. Fate has a way of conspiring against us. You are different. As you say, you cannot give animation to the dead. You call forth the dead – their spirits come at your call. You have a talent for such things. Knowledge of these secrets is rare, and it is my desire to take you, as an apprentice, so that I might help you master your power and fulfill the revenge you seek."

Kirai gazed through the aperture of the giant telescope within Nicodem's observatory in the heart of the forbidden Quarantine Zone. The light of that red star held her transfixed. It reminded her of the sanguine gleam in the eyes of her own manifested Ikiryo spirit. In that moment, standing over the butchered body of Gideon, her lover's murderer, the hidden vaults of her mind had been opened. She allowed herself to see the depth and power of her darkest desires and realized her own capability for violence.

As a child, she remembered attending the Kabuki Theater and seeing a play about a proud warrior laid low by terrible sickness. He blamed the illness on a visiting priest, and as the warrior sank further and further into delirium, his soul was consumed with grief that he should die such a pitiful death, withering away in bed rather than on the field of battle. His soul became fractured by this grief and that most jealous and hateful part of him left to seek vengeance for this crime. The warrior's grudge became a curse, a spirit that plagued the priest incessantly. It eventually caused the holy man to drown himself to escape the torture. The tale was intended to warn against jealous and hateful thoughts as the deaths of both men were mourned by the village. Both the warrior and the priest had brought many blessings to the village, and both were greatly honored in a shrine dedicated to their memory and the virtue of morality.

For Kirai, there was no redeeming virtue in those responsible for Francis' murder. Her desire for revenge was justified; it was a matter of honor to see his death avenged. The cold certainty of this truth had steeled her heart. The time for mourning had passed. Like the old stories she enjoyed seeing performed as a girl, she would stay here and adopt Nicodem as her mentor and learn the esoteric techniques that would prepare her for an inevitable confrontation with the Governor General, empowering her to exact justice.

It was as she gazed upon the Red Star of Kythera that she contemplated these truths.

"Vengeance? That is my only motivation? All for me to live for?" She was apathetic at best.

Nicodem was perplexed and grew irritated with her pathetic melancholy. He had always imagined that the training of a new practitioner in the art of a Resurrectionist would require elaborate steps of stripping a person of her humanity, breaking her down into something submissive and non-empathetic. Kirai was the opposite of those expectations. She was so filled with grief that her pitiful demeanor gave her no hope at all. "Perhaps not," he said. "Though you have much to learn on the path to mastery, you have the power to summon spirits, do you not?"

She looked at him quizzically, thinking. "You think I can summon Francis? His spirit?" Her eyes widened, and she beamed with newfound hope. Nicodem had found the angle by which he might manipulate the girl, but he would proceed cautiously, keeping her between hope and desperation, lest he lose her too quickly and his plans unravel.

"Perhaps, girl. Have hope, but know that my guidance will provide only direction. Spirituality is not a common ability among my order." She nodded, though her darting eyes and only partially waning smile revealed her newfound hope. "And the work will be arduous for us both," he continued. "Time consuming and daunting. My work will suffer as well. My research-"

"I will work hard," she said, interrupting him. "I will do it."

He continued, ignoring her. "The longer it takes for you to master the Summoning, the more difficult it will be to locate your one disjoint soul in the maelstrom."

"Then we must begin!" she said. "I will not be a burden upon you. I will follow your teaching. I can help you with your research, I can be helpful," she pauses for a moment, looking down and away, "... in many ways." Her last words gave a rehearsed hint of seduction, but her eyes were emotionless and dead. Nicodem did not show much emotion but his eyes grew vaguely thoughtful and his gaze lingered on her for a moment. His eyes circled her round face and roved across her lithe body. She recognized the lewd stare despite the gentlemanly persona he presented. She was disheartened. Still, Francis was disembodied, and their reunion would be of the spirit. Her flesh mattered little now, so long as they might rejoin in the spirit as they were always truly united.

Nicodem nodded and said, "We'll speak of what you can offer me in the future. Let us begin."

He gestured for Kirai to follow him, and he led her from his observatory into the chambers below. It was a quick tour through his fantastic library, a giant vault containing a seemingly uncountable volume of books. The library's scale awed her, and she was certain she would spend much time exploring its many stacks. Various sculptures depicting a variety of unbelievable monsters were placed throughout the vast chamber. Nicodem explained that these creatures were identified by the people of Old Malifaux in constellations in the night sky.

Still lower into the tower they travelled, and Nicodem opened a large, barred door into a vast chamber. This place was filled with a complex assortment of arcane machinery, devices which Kirai could not divine the purpose of. Still stranger, the chamber was occupied by a host of desiccated men shambling about, mindlessly fulfilling mundane chores of moving crates or large burlap bags filled with machinery or lifeless bodies. Following Nicodem into an adjoining lab, she had to move through dried corpses hanging vertically upon hooks as if cattle at a butcher. Still others were upon tables, in various stages of dissection. Kirai found that she was not frightened of them, only curious. Nicodem moved to a steel slab where a corpse had been laid out.

"Your study will involve, beyond the development of your own unique power, the proper preparation of a body and the production of this serum which must be uniquely tailored to the subject. With research, I will perfect the agents administered to these corpses, increasing their durability and flexibility.

Resurrecting those with talents in a particular arena has proven fruitless, as I've explained. A master of swordsmanship in life, for example, has forgotten all but simple gestures of weapon recognition in animated rebirth. Mental faculties suffer too greatly by the trauma of death and rebirth for the raised to be able to recall whatever feats they were capable of in life. We've learned various alchemical processes, however, by which we have created individuals inspired to cause harm to others and appear to enjoy inflicting despicable pain upon our enemies. We may yet unlock darker secrets. Our order seeks mastery of the dead to create ever stronger, smarter weapons. Your goal and mine are the same, Kirai: the dethroning of the Governor General and justice for the crimes he has committed. For this, we will need an army to combat him and his agents. If you, Kirai, can infuse a corpse with a willful spirit of its own, we may together unlock that weapon. When the moment is right, we will lead this army to raze the Guild District and strip them of the control they wield."

"And kill the Governor," she said with more venom than he would have expected.

He smiled that same downturned smile that conveyed his malice well. "Yes, and kill the Governor." Nicodem moved beside Kirai and pushed the needle of his syringe into the chest of the corpse. He injected a highly reflective silver fluid into the body.

Examining the body as Nicodem administered the fluid, she said, "This man; he is Nipponese," as she turned her eyes up to look at Nicodem. "Of the Three Kingdoms."

Nicodem nodded. "It is said that there is no other nation in which its warriors fears death less than Nippon. Though this quality is perhaps irrelevant in their reanimation, I prefer the use of Nipponese corpses. At the least, they are often buried with their daisho and retain a familiarity with it." Nicodem's eyes turned to the corpse, again, and noted the progress of the serum. "In a moment, this body will reanimate. The solution I've developed returns superior function to the body's nervous system. A voice spoken while it wakes will imprint itself upon the crude intellect of the corpse and take the place of the brain's decision making processes, which are not able to be salvaged."

"The voice will become its Master?

"Correct. Now, you will greet this corpse as it wakes. He will serve you. As he stirs, focus your attention upon him. Do not think of it. Think as though you are just falling into a gentle slumber. Call a spirit to this corpse. Think of a warrior that would fight for you; obey you. Think of that warrior and this warrior as one."

Kirai returned her focus to the body, and indeed, she noticed small spasms of minute movement in the corpse's limbs. In a sudden flicker, its eyes flashed open, and Kirai saw that the silver fluid had rehydrated the corpse's eyes, giving it a strange, reflective gaze. She did not shrink from that gaze. She did not fear the unnatural process that took place before her. With a confident voice, she greeted the corpse just as she was instructed, commanding, "Arise good soldier, your battles have not yet ended."

As it rose, picking up the two katana near it, Nicodem whispered, "Very good. Very good."

But she had nothing to do with the reanimation of the corpse. She hadn't even been able to reach into that vague place where she had touched the wailing spirits. The memory of such an event was fleeting and vague, like a dream many days forgotten. But then, as she thought of her own Ikiryo spirit pulling from her to enact the vengeance she desperately wanted for herself, she saw herself, as if from above, looking down. She lifted her hands and there, below her, they lifted. Now, the Ikiryo was free but not fully manifest. Nicodem was aware of nothing as his nose wrinkled and he scowled at a sudden rancid smell that permeated the room.

She commanded the Ikiryo to summon a spirit, but it was more a plea than an order. It moved invisibly through a barrier, invisible even to her, into a void, empty of anything. It was a blank whiteness, tinged lilac, silent and still.

Through the vision of the Ikiryo she could not see that her small body, standing before Nicodem, still had her hands uplifted. Her head bent back as a ghostly wind billowed forth from the tear in the fabric between this world and the aether where the Ikiryo had gone. Her eyes rolled into her skull and the sultry air blew upon Nicodem, tiny drops of condensation forming on his spectacles. The Ikiryo returned, and with it, a strange beastly shape formed beside her. It was dark and wispy, created of a smoky shadow and vaguely feminine, with long hair of billowing darkness falling across her face and before her gaunt body.

The Ikiryo had done as she asked, and she suddenly knew that she was the key to anchoring this new spirit to this world. Though she could see it, Nicodem could not, looking upon his risen zombie as if it now housed a spiritual warrior she had summoned and imbedded within it. But she had not connected the Shikome spirit to this fragile form. She did not care. She knew that for the first time, she had drawn an angry spirit back from beyond this world. Just as Nicodem could feel the presence of a corpse awaiting his will to walk again, Kirai could follow the path this spiritual creature took to find her. In her awakening mind, she saw it flow from a powerful void filled with spiritual magic and beasts like it. They awaited a release to enact vengeance upon those they harbored great resentment and jealousy: the living. It had found the Gorgon and through it, this world. Like that beacon calling it forth, the Shikome found her through the serpentine ring now hanging by a thin copper chain around her neck. Hidden beneath her black kimono, it pulsed and throbbed in the presence of this terrible spirit, hovering silently nearby, waiting for her to command it.

She held it there, between worlds, not giving it tangibility, waiting. The room returned to normal, and Nicodem smiled at his zombie warrior and his young apprentice.

Dark Discovery

When the garrison at the Gallows Street Checkpoint was attacked by the strange man and the gang that followed him, attacking the Guardsmen with a strange and detached apathy, one Guardsman broke ranks and retreated, defying orders to hold his ground and fight. Matthew Longfellow, a veteran Guard, aspired to join the higher ranks of the Death Marshals one day soon. He was no coward, though the fear he felt at the vacant obedience of the young teens fighting and dying for that strange man-creature sent shivers through him. It was the leader of the gang that chilled him most, and he knew that images of this night would always haunt him. He felt no discernable fear in fighting them. Officer Longfellow, himself, fired multiple Peacebringer rounds into the chest of that creature, standing resolute against the Guild officers, unconcerned. Each strike of a bullet was met with similar lack of interest, resulting only in a brief groan from within him.

Hoffman moved meticulously through the Slum District on his quest from the Governor General, questioning residents that might travel through the shadowed evening streets for possible sightings of a man that might match the brief description he had amassed of the new murderer.

It was no more than an element of fate, an accident at best, that his Hunter construct carried him around the corner of a crumbling building, the unique sound of multiple Peacebringer rounds in the distance carried to him through the chill evening air and above the heavy footfalls of the Hunter upon the worn stones of the city street. With a thought, his Hunter rose higher so that he might see above a fallen wall nearby. As his vantage cleared the debris, he could see down the gently sloping street to the checkpoint into the Quarantine Zone. At this distance, he could not discern the nature of the combatants, yet the flashes of yellow flame accompanying the crack of each gun and the great mob moving against those guns allowed no question that the checkpoint garrison was being overrun.

He sighed and gnashed his teeth. Though recently promoted to a Guild Officer in charge of a whole new division, he had no practical combat training. He was a mechanic, and the only thought he had regarding combat was perhaps that of a combat engineer. Perhaps a strategist at best.

He patted the armor plating on the thick forearm before him, and he commanded it to stoke its boiler and build some steam. "Okay, girl. Let's see what you can do." As if having a conversation with the machine, he waited a moment, then nodded. "Yes. I wish we had brought along a Guardian or two, also. Even a Peacekeeper. At least we have the new Watcher we've worked up," and he nodded to the vaguely batlike construct. He gave a silent command to the Watcher, and it came alive, the hundreds of tiny gears spinning madly within its tiny frame, a brief whistle of steam expelled as it launched into the air. He made a note to move that exhaust port away from its backside as it did resemble a living bat too much, and the comical expulsion of steam was not exactly in line with the formidable image the Guild intended to convey. The original ornithopter design of his former colleague and friend, Victor Ramos, had been redesigned and refined but odd elements remained, needing attention. He made a note of it.

He shook aside the intuitive redesign thoughts as he looked upon every machine and focused on the battle to be waged. His first battle. He swallowed hard and commanded the Hunter into a full run, the pistons and gears moving in fluid precision. "Another design flaw," he thought. The Hunter was designed as a forward strike construct, not as a transportation unit. As such, he based its design on more feline quadrupeds. Modifying it on the fly to move upright, in order to haul him around, left it clumsy and more vulnerable. "Like me," he thought. "Quite a team." The construct had some shortcomings when pushed for combat, and he felt different pistons loosening as the construct achieved its full two-legged gait, and screws flew loose as one strap across his upper thigh broke free from its attachment to the Hunter. His hand, resting upon that forearm before him, felt the shaky connection of the outer plate to the articulated machinery beneath. Still, he urged it on, hoping the machine and he might make it to the conflict in one piece. He couldn't help himself and pulled an adjustable wrench from an inner pocket on his vest and began repairing it even as it bore him toward the battle. "Dammit," he said. "I didn't even remember to bring that bloody Peacebringer they assigned me." He rolled his eyes, chastising himself as a true amateur.

As the Hunter ran, Hoffman busied himself with repairs while dangling from the machine's chest and hardly noticed Deputy Longfellow rounding the corner before him, his own weapon at the ready even as he ran. Longfellow ground to a halt, driving the heel of his boot into a cobblestone joint and dropping to one knee, shouting "Halt!" as he leveled the Peacebringer upon Hoffman, eyes wide in fear and confusion. Hoffman looked up and realized quickly that most Guards wouldn't have seen him yet and certainly not out on patrol. Stopping the Hunter in full movement was no easy task, however, and the Guardsman clearly demonstrated his intent to fire upon him first and ask questions second as Hoffman descended upon him. The Hunter shielded him as it could with its many arms, and he slowed it as best he could, bellowing, "Stand down, Guardsman! I am Officer Hoffman!"

Longfellow, ready for the fight of his life, nearly pulled the trigger but realized at the last moment that neither the thin man dangling and bouncing at the center of the lumbering machine, nor the machine itself, seemed intent upon combat.

He rose to his feet, lowering the pistol as Hoffman brought the Hunter to a stop. The Guard's breathing came laboriously while the burners within the construct, the release of steam through automatic valves, and the release of hydraulic pressure on the various pistons came to a rest. Hoffman, far more comfortable with machines than people, still understood the emotional conflict upon the Guard's face. "Easy, deputy," he said calmly. Longfellow looked up at him nervously, still questioning the validity of his identity, though Hoffman believed his reliance upon the construct for any mobility made him appear as little threat to anyone. "Catch your breath." The sound of gunfire from several blocks distant waned. "What happened down there, deputy?"

Mathew Longfellow looked up at him, still struggling to reclaim his breath. "You'll never believe me," he said.

"Chap," Hoffman said, the formal English accent more severe and commanding. "You'll need to have out with it, I insist."

The Guard nodded. "We were overrun at the garrison." He paused, looking for the right words.

"Your enemy, soldier?"

"Sir?"

"With whom did you wage battle?" he asked. "Ill advised Arcanist conjurer? Resurrectionist mongrel digging up bones?"

The accent and odd descriptive style of speech confused poor Officer Longfellow even more. "Neither. I don't know. Resurrectionist, if anything, sir. Only — well, they weren't exactly dead. Not physically." He became urgent once more. "We must gather reinforcements. The Guild offices, sir, are-"

Hoffman cut him short. "Are too far away. That is, if there are survivors in need of our aid." The Guardsman very clearly did not like the idea of returning even so much as a look back toward the garrison and maintained a steady look toward the heart of the city that housed the Guild militia. Hoffman drove the Hunter toward the barracks, expecting Longfellow to continue toward the Guild offices. He was relieved to see the Guard reluctantly fall in beside him, his pistol gripped in slightly shaking hands. Together, they strode back toward the assault. The gunfire ahead of them abruptly ceased, but they continued more slowly as Longfellow reported what had happened.

Hoffman inspected the carnage around the Quarantine Zone checkpoint in confusion. In just a matter of several short weeks, he had gone from crippled machinist to deputized expert overseeing the new Flesh-Construct Grafting Charter. Determining illegalities surrounding the merger of biological and mechanical seemed quite daunting enough; analyzing a battle scene, however, was several steps beyond his pay grade.

The Hunter took several crashing steps toward another dead body, the thunderous footfalls of the large construct jarring him at every step. Pistons in his Hunter's midsection released excess pressure in a low whistle, and gears in its chest clicked together as it recalibrated its internal balance. Hoffman no longer noticed those constant mechanical sounds. As the darkness embraced them, he appreciated the Hunter's boiler and commanded it to stoke up.

The Watcher, circling the area, dutifully following Hoffman's unspoken orders, suddenly froze on a low stone wall and sounded its alarm. The warbling klaxon droned until Hoffman silenced it with a thought.

"Deputy," he said to Longfellow. "Come with me." The Watcher faced the bare pavement, orange and black in the gaslight too far away for Hoffman's liking. He could see nothing to set off the construct's alarm, though he knew better than to question it.

Back inside the slum, near the spot where Hoffman and Longfellow had come, they found what might have been the remains of two Guardsmen. Unlike the battered and torn flesh of those murdered at the barracks, Hoffman could only stare at the empty uniforms soaked in a black sludge, wet and glistening in the faint light. He had the Hunter bend to inspect the sludge closer, and as it bent, his eye caught the faintest movement between the flattened cobblestones near him. His eyes slowly focused, and he ordered the Hunter to step back. "Don't touch it!" he ordered Longfellow.

"You don't have to worry about that, sir, I swear. What is it?" he asked, stepping back.

"Maggots. On the ground. They're coming right at us." He bent as best he could with a body broken from the midsection down and strapped to an eight hundred pound construct. He pulled an acetylene torch from his kit and a dark Soulstone from his front pocket. Though he had forgotten his Peacebringer, he was a man that thrived on improvisation. He looked quickly upon the bodies all around them. More than thirty, bodies of Guardsmen lay among scuttlers, and other settlers, whose faces were frozen in death with blank disregard. The infection was here, and it was potent beyond nature, Hoffman knew. "Guardsman," he said sternly. "I have no time to notarize an official request, so you must be emphatic. Return to the Guild offices. Demand to speak to Lady Justice, immediately. My Watcher construct will accompany you to validate my presence here. Inform her at once of my whereabouts and the condition of our adventure. Mind you, now! Be emphatic."

The Guard saluted. "Believe me, sir. Emphatic will not be a problem." Hesitating no further, he hastily ran to carry out his orders.

Hoffman set the Soulstone into a makeshift brass cage attached to the hose of the torch. He would need its power. He lit the torch and began with the maggots charging him. They burned and popped in the great belch of heat of his Soulstone torch. He burned the black liquid, once Guardsmen, before turning the torch on the recently killed around the barracks. "May you rest," he prayed quietly, engulfing their bodies in the white Soulstone flame. For good measure, he burned the checkpoint building, too, razing the whole area, purging it of the pestilence.

Pestilence

The dim light through the nearby window signaled the coming dawn. While Nicodem withdrew to attend to matters in another part of the tower, Kirai retired to the enormous library, reluctant to spend more time with him than necessary. She was nervous that he would follow through with her end of their bargain, and she needed time to process the incredible turn of events that had befallen her. With no great interest in reading and certainly not prepared to begin research, she merely sought isolation. Still, she browsed the volumes, most of them ancient by her reckoning, and the titles on the spine written in the alien script of the Neverborn. She moved slowly past the many books, touching them gingerly, absently, as her mind wandered.

The serpent ring at her neck pulsed against her throat, startling her, as a faint whisper to her right said what might have been the single word, "Gorgon." Her head jerked toward the sound, though there was no one there. Her wide eyes stared intently. The ring throbbed again, and one book among the great multitude in her field of vision seemed to beat at the same moment as the ring.

Pressing the coiled serpent against her throat, she approached that book and pulled it from the shelf. It was small and thin, completely unremarkable amidst its fellows. On its olive leather cover, it bore the same fluid, spiraling script as the others. Finding a desk, she looked through the book filled with the strange, spidery, alien script. She could read nothing within. These were from a different world, written by a people not at all human. Still, the manner of the script was unlike anything she could have expected. Symbols crawled across the page.

She flipped through the passages curiously, but with no comprehension. Deep in the heart of the book, a single character seemed to jump at her, as the circular symbols separated, overlapping one another. She flipped the pages more frantically, seeing the same effect – alien characters jumping off the page. As she thumbed through the book, an image formed, twisting, winding, uncoiling. It became a serpent. She became frantic, gasping as the serpent head formed, rose upon the flashing pages, ready to strike.

"Don't strain your eyes too much on those, girl," Mortimer said, his grating voice behind her. She looked up from the book, her heart racing. "You'll learn to see through the table before you figure those letters out. There's plenty for you to read, though. The Master's transcribed a number of books into English if'n you can read. Never had much call fer it mahself. You can find them in the shelves beneath the statue, there," he said gruffly.

His clothes were soiled with fresh earth, but that scent was ubiquitous in this tower populated by the freshly risen dead. The smell of fresh soil amidst decaying flesh was merely stronger while Mortimer was near. Indeed, as Kirai sat there and considered this man, a host of animated dead followed him into the chamber, carrying several large wooden boxes filled with more books. They dutifully unpacked and stacked them as commanded and attended to a variety of other chores about the library. To her, they seemed merely automatons. If she were to walk by them or even bump into them, they did not seem to be aware of her, but simply walked around her to continue with their tasks.

She pushed the book aside though it seemed to call to her, compelling her to continue reading. She resisted the lure, afraid of it. Instead, she considered the events that led her to this towering observatory and the tutelage of a Resurrectionist. The group, she had thought, might be mere superstition to scare newcomers to this world. Now, apparently, she was one.

In the relative silence of the library, Kirai experienced a peace she hadn't felt for some time, since the death of her lover. The certain knowledge that her revenge would come in time had filled her with a contentment. The purpose granted by her new life in this macabre tower filled her with a sense of confidence and comfort that she was entering an exciting new world.

A distant bell resounded above them, breaking her from her reverie. It came not from the observatory, but from an adjoining tower. The animated dead in the library's chamber issued an eerie chorus of moans and abandoned their labors. In unison, they shambled quickly from the room, and Kirai became aware of the scent of smoke. Though quite rotund, Mortimer acted with surprising speed. He knocked over the newly stacked books, racing toward the exit. Pausing momentarily at the door, he looked back at Kirai's expression of bewilderment. "Come on girl, that's the alarm. We've uninvited guests!"

Kirai leapt after him. Racing out to a balcony, both leaned over the railing and gazed into the courtyard below. The bell tower stood alone in the center of a large expanse. The space between the building and a perimeter of reinforced barriers was filled with a small militia of Nicodem's walking dead, more than fifty strong. Nicodem had explained that it was necessary to guard against the dangers of the Quarantine Zone, wandering covens of Neverborn and patrolling Guild Guards. She knew, too, of another purpose for the protection – to keep safe the growing army intended to invade and raze the Guild's center of power in Malifaux.

The zombie militia, however, did not struggle against a horde of nightmarish Neverborn or a Guild contingency that had discovered them. Kirai was surprised to see a raid by what appeared to be a typical street gang, though larger in number than she might have imagined. The scuttlers breached the courtyard's barriers and fell against the waiting zombies.

Mortimer called out and leaning over the rail, pointed toward a distant alley. There, behind the churning melee was a single man dressed in a rough leather coat. He had a flute at his lips and the dirge he played reached even into the heights of the tower overhead. The song inspired a sudden tremor that shook the ground, and suddenly, the streets began to flood with a tide of sewer rats. The storm drains and manhole covers burst, and countless vermin boiled up from beneath the streets. The tide crashed against the melee and swept through the struggling scuttlers. Pouring through combatants, the legion of voracious vermin overwhelmed the defenders who seemed to melt as their flesh was rent and consumed.

A stream of vermin stretched from the perimeter and into the gates of the tower itself. With the defenders pushed back, the gangers rushed forward and crashed against the vaulted doors of the tower. With their chains, clubs, and knives, they beat upon the door to bring it down. Behind them, the piper

casually strode forward, the tide of rats and gang members parting before him to make a clear path to the tower. Though Mortimer and Kirai craned forward, the man and his entourage of ruffians disappeared from sight below.

She turned from the railing and darted back into the tower to climb the stairs. Mortimer called after her, but the lithe girl was far faster than his own meaty body. Still he chased after her, holding his hat to his head. It was up to him to hold the tower and keep the girl alive until Nicodem appeared. As he clambered up the stairs, he muttered a short prayer that Nicodem arrive soon.

As if on cue, Nicodem strode around a corner above them and descended the stairs with three katana wielding zombies behind him. All were in various degrees of decomposition though their clothing marked them as unmistakable descendants of the Three Kingdoms. "Kirai. Upstairs," he commanded tersely. "Mortimer. With me." They quickly descended the stairs.

Kirai was tempted to follow, both curious and anxious to help. Should the defense of Nicodem's sanctuary fall, she would, too. Now, with urgency to live, and hope to reunite spiritually with Francis, she

could not accept defeat after coming to embrace hope. Reluctantly, she ascended the broad staircase, seeking shelter in a room far to the back of the great structure.

Hamelin the Plagued surveyed the foyer and up the winding stairs as his swarming army poured around him. Great stone columns stretched upwards to support lofty rafters. He offered no fear for his own safety, though Nicodem directed all of his sword-wielding zombies upon him. As each sprang toward Hamelin, nearly tearing itself apart in its ardent fervor to fulfill its command, one of the scuttlers intercepted the attack and dragged the zombie aside to be overwhelmed by rats.

For his part, Nicodem would quickly raise any of the boys that fell to a zombie's attack, replenishing his own ranks even as Hamelin's continued to worm their way into the conflict. It was a grotesque balance of power.

Nicodem realized the grim truth that the balance would eventually tip in Hamelin's favor as he would run out of both zombies and the vessels by which he might replenish them, while Hamelin had a seemingly endless horde of rats. Being outnumbered and overwhelmed by the opposition was a feeling wholly unique to Nicodem, and he loathed it. Before the inevitable tide could turn against him, he crushed the fragile outer crust of a Soulstone, basking momentarily in the milky white cloud that enveloped him before harnessing its power as his own. He absorbed it, twisting it within him, tying it to his own spiritual manifestation. Settlers upon Malifaux knew him as the undertaker, but his understanding of the dead went far beyond that mere act of preparing a body for its final rest. He also had the ability to give a corpse the will to walk again; he was powerful in that regard. Nicodem commanded the very power of death and decay.

One of his katana-wielding zombies, swarmed by voracious rats, would soon fall. He released the dark energy teeming within him, centering it upon two youths converging upon one of the remaining Nipponese zombies, itself wounded and battered. Oddly similar to Hamelin's plague, Nicodem's spell of decay set into their flesh, devouring it as if seconds were years. The boys aged and withered, eyes rolling into their skulls as the skin around them grew pallid, gaunt, and finally desiccated in a death that looked decades old. All of the rats nearest the boys suffered the same fate, drawing away from their prey, shaking violently before expelling their last breath. The effect upon his zombie, already dead and suffering the effects of a natural decay, found itself suddenly renewed and stood defiantly against the still growing horde of vermin beyond the battered doors.

Hamelin strode forward, humming loudly as he now simply carried the flute at his side. Where he walked, scuttler and rat stepped quickly aside, though neither made any indication of acknowledging the presence of the other. Hamelin's throng was an extension of his vast will. He stared intently upon Nicodem, unconcerned of the melee around him as he waded through it unscathed. "Where is it?" Hamelin asked above the din of combat, his voice hollow and echoing more from within him than about the cavernous chamber.

"Where is what?" Nicodem asked, spreading his arms in exaggerated innocence. "This is about some trinket, perhaps?" he asked, though he knew it must be much more. "Some artifact? I am a collector of rare finds and curious, I admit." He tried to sound dismissive of the danger mounting below him. He whispered to Mortimer on the step just behind and above him, "second floor escape." Mortimer knew the path and the plan and waited for his cue to bolt. Nicodem addressed Hamelin still on the foyer below. "Have your...well, shall we say, 'colleagues' wait outside and we can discuss the return of this item you seek."

"I've come for the key," Hamelin said in that disconcerting vibration. His mouth stood agape, the lips unnecessary in the forming of the words.

"Then you've made a small mistake, I'm afraid, though one that can be easily forgiven. You see I have no--"

Hamelin ignored him. "The Gorgon stirs. It will finish what it began centuries before. My ascension must come first. The time is nigh." He strode forward, staring still upon Nicodem while the battle waged around him. Moths fluttered about his face and neck, and a beetle crawled from beneath the exposed collar of his shirt to turn back once it hit the light. As he walked, an occasional maggot or other carrion insect fell from him. Though clearly an agent of death, Nicodem knew the stranger was no Resurrectionist. He was something quite different.

"Earth is dead," Hamelin said. "This world is dying. I've come to claim the keys of another."

The sound of gunfire beyond the walls and outer walls carried to both Masters, and they turned toward it.

Mortimer tugged on Nicodem's shoulder. "Guild."

"Yes," Nicodem agreed. "Prime the charges. Quickly! We must retrieve Ankoku if possible. On the upper level if I can buy us the time!" Mortimer grunted and bound up the stairs.

Nicodem turned back to his unearthly foe below. "The conquering arrows of your Pestilence may herald the final days of this world, but it is Death who marshals the legions of the damned." Nicodem spoke with foreboding as he urged the dead bodies of the settlers to rise to his command. They gathered quickly around Hamelin. The mass of undead rushed upon him at the same moment a booming blast struck high upon the foyer's wall opposite Nicodem. The wall broke open and two fluttering mechanical constructs shot through the hole to survey the battleground. Nicodem made a final command to the remaining zombie mob below to block the staircase as he turned and hobbled away in search of Kirai.

The Watcher constructs focused upon the battle. They saw Hamelin ignore the undead standing before him, inflicting upon them the blight at his command. Even in death, the plague consumed their rotting flesh.

Nicodem reached the second floor landing and turned in time to see the buxom form of Lady Justice climb into the hole made above them.

She was blind, or at least blindfolded with a dark red handkerchief strapped tightly across her eyes, though her head scanned back and forth across the conflict below her. Strawberry blonde hair billowed into his fortress, falling in thick curls around the immense sword she held by its sheath before her. The tight corset about her torso displayed her ample curves though anyone having an opportunity to watch her work came to understand that her clothing fulfilled a need of function, never fashion.

Hesitating no longer, she leapt straight out and fell more than thirty feet. As she descended, her sword

came free of its sheath, and she somersaulted in a tucked position with her knees against her chest and her sword thrust behind her. As her feet came up over her head, her body jerked around, gaining momentum. The long sword came up and over, following her movement, cleaving a zombie in half as her boots hit the ground. The sword dug deep into the stone tile and the two halves of the zombie fell to either side. She rose from the crouch, pulling the sword from the stone with a tug that left loose pebbles across the great scar on its surface.

Nicodem gnashed his teeth. Even with her combat prowess, no human could cut bone and body in half with a blow. And if he had somersaulted more than thirty feet through the air, he would have simply broken something. He hated the woman. Her sword struck out and beheaded, or literally disarmed, one zombie after another while deftly avoiding the damned gang members that followed Hamelin. She no doubt mistook them as innocent.

Hamelin ignored it all, pressing toward the staircase.

Nicodem turned to flee but stopped short as the rapid clanking of metal sounded from below. He turned in time to see the narrow blade of the accursed Judge fly straight like an arrow, the quick clinking from the attached chain trailing after it. The sword sank through the back of Hamelin and out through his chest, sticky remains of various vermin staining the glistening metal.

"You are under arrest, Resurrectionist!" the Judge said from beyond the entry.

Nicodem fled. 'Maybe those Death Marshals will be good for something, after all,' he thought. Mistaking Hamelin for the Resurrectionist commanding the zombies was a fortuitous twist of fate and a great mistake that might garner him invaluable time. He still hated the lot of them and hoped the whole observatory came down to consume them all.

Hamelin ignored the blade protruding from his chest and continued walking. His humming brought more boys and rats to fill in behind him, and they swarmed Lady Justice and the Judge. Hamelin ascended the stairs unimpeded.

Kirai Ankoku had found an abandoned room at the far end of the vast building. The door's hinges barely gave, and she pulled and pulled against the long rusted iron until a small gap allowed her to squeeze through. 'Nothing but a rat could squeeze through there,' she thought, unknowingly foreshadowing the swarm assembled in the round foyer below her.

She closed her eyes. Kirai stood only a few dozen yards from the door, poised defiantly against the intrusion. Her hands were balled into fists, and her nails had cut into the palms of her own hands so that a slight trickle of blood dripped through her tightly clenched fingers. Her little body shook but not with fear. There was no fear left in this girl. She shook with anger, and that fury manifested itself as an intense heat that radiated from her. It was unnatural, the manifestation of something magical, something frightening.

She had to summon her Ikiryo – her own spirit. Only it could protect her. She saw it in her mind. She saw the memory of it killing Gideon in his cell. She saw it kill all of the Guardsmen that had been in the room that morning at the Qi and Gong – the morning they

had come to kill her but had taken Francis instead. She saw the memory of her own spirit hunt and kill those that had hunted her, that had led Gideon to her and Francis. She grew agitated, both at the memory and pain inflicted upon her and by her inability to call forth the great vengeful spirit that should be hers to command. She had felt the power to summon lost spirits in the nether regions between worlds just hours before, with Nicodem, but now could not feel even a strand of that intoxicating power.

She trembled, impotent and desperate. The Ikiryo was her spirit, but it was a spirit of vengeance and did not come to her.

Her fists beat against her upper thighs in frustration. The sound of the conflict grew close as footsteps approached down the hall. He came straight toward her, spending no time checking any other room. She sobbed at the futility and inability to carry out her destiny. Here, on the precipice of calling Francis back, this strange man had come to strike her down. She felt the great weight of that inevitability and grew enraged.

A hand, soft and fleshy, grasped the open edge of the door. Several flies droned about the fingers, and a long centipede crawled around the door and down to the floor.

"Francis," she whispered pitifully. "Take me with you," she pleaded. In answer, an image of something dark worked at the back of her mind. She thought of release and the crossing of the Great River into the valley of Death. It was a horrible story about death told since she was very young: the innocent dead would be preyed upon by the great Datsue-Ba spirit, fierce and terrible. Those who sinned, however, received a more terrible fate. The Datsue-Ba would cut the clothing from the body, exposing the sinner. Then she would cut small layers of flesh from the body, flaying swaths of flesh in payment for each sin committed. She saw her sins play out in her mind as she could see the memory of her Ikiryo enact her revenge. She saw each act of prostitution she had succumbed to. All the weight of her sins. She would not be allowed to cross the Great River. She would never rejoin Francis.

The fleshy fingers at the door heaved, and its hinges groaned reluctantly. He whistled absently as he stepped into the room.

His song and his demeanor were in complete contrast to Kirai's own. He was cool and stoic, and where Kirai's rage was so obvious in the visible soulflame burning about her head like an unholy halo. Hamelin gave no sign of emotion or stress.

Kirai lifted her head, and her eyes were possessed of that same raging fire. Her voice sounded as if it were a demon's roar from deep out of the belly of Hell. It was a single word, a word foreign to Hamelin who was born in the silent darkness that followed this world's spiritual decay. Hers was a word and an ideal honored for thousands of years by the fearless people of the Three Kingdoms. In the heat of that moment, she lifted her eyes to heaven and called out with a voice far larger than her tiny body would suggest, "*Fukushuu!*" With the word, revenge, the fire that wreathed her burst forward, taking the shape of an old woman bent and twisted. She shuffled forward with heavy feet and claws that held a long, thin skinning knife. She cackled softly as she walked, saying, "Oh, the sins are a great weight. We'll take some weight from you," and the Datsue-Ba spirit giggled shrilly. "Oh, this one's weight is great, indeed!" Its quickly shuffling feet took her closer to Hamelin, still disregarding the spirit's presence.

"The Gorgon is here," he said, more to himself than to Kirai or the Datsue-Ba. "I sense it."

The spirit lunged forward, easily slicing into the flesh of Hamelin's arm. In swift jerks of her gossamer arms, the clothing and outer flesh were cut away. Maggots poured from the exposed and gaping wound. Beetles, centipedes, and small carrion insects writhed across the Datsue-Ba's long knife. Hamelin pressed his staff against its forehead. It stabbed at him as the black plague consumed even its spiritual form.

Hamelin lurched forward, grasping Kirai's arm before she could react. Before she realized it, she was staring into the eyes of this intruder. Where her eyes burned with rage-fueled fire, his were hollow and empty, devoid of soul or emotion. They were dark passages into the vacant recesses of his being, a being that held no redeemable virtue or humane concern. She saw, though, that even that emptiness was an illusion, that he was no man at all, but a crawling mass of vermin that crawled within the sockets of his eyes and across the open wound on his arm. He held her to the wall by the wrist as the pests within him moved from his open wound and across her skin. His song ended, but the room continued its throbbing pulse, every item and every surface possessed of this carnal cadence. He spoke softly, nonchalantly, "At last I have found you. The key had wandered far, it seems."

It all happened in the span of a heartbeat. That man grasped her arm and the illusion of his humanity disappeared. From the swarm of vermin that created his shape, three white grubs burrowed into her flesh. She gasped and wrenched her arm away but already the sickness in those worms had taken hold. The joints of her fingers and wrist swelled with black bulbs of puss before her whole hand was consumed in black. She screamed in agony as her hand died, sending daggers of pain coursing through her arm.

One hand held her to the wall and the other went around her neck. She could not focus upon the summoning of more spirits but wasn't sure she even knew how to. Instead of choking her, his hand wrapped around the dainty chain and jerked it free of her neck. As the silver band with the winding snake of emeralds slowly spun on the chain he held before his grotesque face, she saw the gemstone snake-head pulse brightly.

Smiling, intent now only upon the ring, he discarded Kirai, tossing her to the corner. She writhed in pain, screaming as the pestilence consumed her.

Hamelin reached into his coat and drew out the device that had lain in a necropolis beneath Malifaux for hundreds of years. It was a flat, thick piece of lacquered metal inlaid with a myriad of interconnected delicate gears, similar to the inner workings of a watch and decorated with a crescent moon and a collection of stars. The hinges at the side of the metal plate allowed Hamelin to open the device like a book.

Inside was similarly clustered with gears and levers and springs. More gems were set in the workings of the device, and these suggested the motion of the stars in the night sky. Set in the orbit of the largest gear was a red stone to match a red star that never moved in the sky above Malifaux.

It was as she howled in terrible pain, as the grip of pestilence claimed her arm, that Nicodem's commanding voice filled the chamber. "Come!" he called, and it was like the blast of a trumpet in the final days of the world. He saw the blackness of her arm and ran to her, wary of Hamelin turning upon them, but the strange creature was too intent upon the device before him. Nicodem saw the grotesque blackness devouring Kirai's arm, knowing she had only moments to live. He pulled his last Soulstone from a pocket within his coat and began to teach his young Resurrectionist apprentice the most non-intuitive and complex uses of Soulstone power. Consumed by death-bearing decay, the powerful creature intent upon their demise mere arm-spans away, and the Guild fighting their way to them, he slapped her smartly as she screamed. "Stop it!" he bellowed. "Focus, and we may save you!" He shook her violently and she stopped screaming though she stared at the blackness, quickly racing up her arm. "Look at me!" he said, shaking her again. "You must do this. I cannot do it for you." He held the Soulstone and pressed it into her other hand. "As you crush it you will feel the spiritual energy coalesce around you. It will urge you to bind it to your will, to release it in focused arcana. Magic," he corrected, seeing her confusion. "Do not bind it to a spell! As tempting and easy as it will feel. You must resist that compulsion or you will be lost. Bind it not to your will, but to your form. Your body." He touched her chest. "Bind it within. Absorb it!" He could spare no more time as the blackness had reached her shoulder and he squeezed her hand against the stone. With a crack, the Soulstone energy was released, and he stepped back.

Even in the best, most controlled circumstances, use of a Soulstone to heal took many attempts to master. He waited for her unfortunate, but inevitable failure and death.

What he could not have predicted, was the great control she had over the Soulstone. Kirai was the Master of Spirits, and Soulstones embodied the spiritual energy that fueled them all. In an elaborate twist of fate, she not only absorbed the Soulstone energy, binding it to her body, but dispelled the blight from within her. Immediately, the blackened color receded and was replaced by the pink flesh of a grizzly wound. The fibers of her putrefied tissues lashed out to reform her forearm. Kirai watched in amazement as the flesh stitched itself into a whole limb and feeling returned to her wiggling fingers.

"That son of a bitch has my ring," she said vehemently. Nicodem smiled approvingly at her incredible control and recovery despite the inane obsession with the trinket.

Behind the Master and his Student, Mortimer emerged from the hall. "Sir! Preparations are complete. The charges are primed. Are we leavin' or fightin'?"

Nicodem saw the anger well up in Kirai again and her eagerness to return to the battle. He sharply grasped her chin, however, and forced her eyes to consider his own. "This tower is lost." He pointed over his shoulder at the gunfire closing upon them. "Those are Guild officers. A battle against this powerful creature and the Guild forces cannot be easily won. We will win your revenge, another day." He pulled her to her feet and forcefully took her from the room while Hamelin worked, ignoring their every action.

Near the bottom right corner of the mechanical device was an orbit that was missing its cog. Kirai's ring fit neatly into the empty space as he slid it into place with a satisfying click. Then, producing a Soulstone he'd recovered from the abandoned carts in the sewer, he touched the stone against the device and a cloudy energy poured from it. Energized, Kirai's ring began to slowly turn on its spindle; the emeralds along its circumference acted as a gear's teeth and manipulated neighboring cogs to spin. The device rang with a metallic song as the gears moved and the gemstone stars began to dance in their orbits. Hamelin was most focused on the motion of the red gemstone, and when it began to move, he leapt from where he crouched and went to the window to observe the morning sky.

As he adjusted the knobs on the device, he saw the red star streak from the heavens. He watched the falling star in its arc toward the City.

Far from the towering buildings and narrow streets of Malifaux, Seamus conducted his own research into this world's past. His encounter with the Grave Spirit at Kythera had galvanized his sense of purpose. The coded and mystical nature of Old Malifaux's texts had been revealed, and the forces they described were real, tangible things that offered a power to be leveraged against reality itself.

It was a dank cave that had called to him from some repeated metaphor scattered throughout some forgotten set of books. He held a gas-light lamp against the glassy walls of the cavern and saw the evidence of a previous presence scratched in elaborate but barely recognizable text in an unknown language.

As he studied the aged message, he could hear the sloshing of Molly, his clumsy assistant, working behind him. He had dressed his undead associate as a caricature of an Imperial explorer with canvas shorts, a pith helmet, and a terrible plaid sport coat. The sloshing paused long enough for the creature to cough up a lungful of blood, and she spat it into a well-stained bloody cloth.

"Molly-girl, please. A man needs silence, occasionally, in his life," Seamus remarked without turning his head from the writing on the wall.

"Seamus," Molly spoke with a momentary wheeze. "Something's happening. The Gate is open, Seamus," she said cryptically.

"Gate? What gate are you jabbering about? Just pipe down, now, Molly-girl. I haven't the patience for your rambling." He rolled his eyes and continued scanning the spiraling web-like script faintly etched upon the stone.

Molly turned her head and looked out of the mouth of the cave. The sky lit up red as the fiery comet sped across the firmament. She said no more. Seamus would be aware of that Gate's opening momentarily.

The Event

Samael stood guard just outside the tiny one room library, abandoned for many years despite its relative close proximity to Malifaux. Although the badlands south of the great City were a desert landscape, they did not retain the heat of the bayou to the east. He pulled his buffalo-hide hat closer to his eyes and drew the oiled duster tight about his torso to combat the biting wind.

Sonnia sat at the same makeshift desk she had been at since late the previous afternoon, a small stack of books on either side of her and a larger stack piled haphazardly on the floor. Those were her "irrelevant" books, skimmed through and discarded.

She sat on the edge of exhaustion, writing frantically in her log book, the official record of her position. Samael knew that her notes were of a considerably different nature than the formal documents they were expected to keep and turn in.

"...many texts relating to astrology," she wrote. "The culture of Old Malifaux attached a great amount of mysticism to the night sky, and each constellation was attributed a vast mythology. The final days of Old Malifaux were heralded by the appearance of a red star hovering over the horizon.

"The heavens were held in high esteem by this ancient people. It was when the coven of powerful tyrants that ruled that world dared to subject the night sky to their meddling that the people of Old Malifaux were inspired to revolt. The ultimate result of their rebellion was the artificial breach located within the Kythera Ruins.

"It was the activation of this breach that brought about the cataclysm that would doom this world's people. Subjected to the very substance of death, survivors of the cataclysm were forced to adapt in dramatic ways. These divergent adaptations are manifested today by the variety of native creatures we call Neverborn.

"Activities pursued by particular covens of Neverborn, and particularly by those known as Nephilim are extremely puzzling. It has been the opinion of the Guild that these creatures possess an alien, primitive, and unknowable intellect and that their activities lack any logical motivation. These Neverborn pursue unknown agendas that have their roots in the days of Old Malifaux.

"That they have managed to survive in the days after Kythera suggests that members of the tyrant coven might also survive. This research suggests that the Nephilim continue to pursue their campaign against these tyrant-entities, ancient creatures with spectral connections to life and vast in power. Fortunately, their ability to interact and influence the tangible world is, as yet, very limited. One of these tyrants is referred to in text by a particular ideogram: an eye surrounded by a coiled serpent. This symbol is also used to name the red star that hangs over Kythera."

Samael sipped his morning coffee, turning the brim of his hat against the cold wind blowing desert sand in his tired eyes. His head cocked slightly, his eye caught the glint of red light illuminating the indigo sky of early morning. It was far larger than a mere shooting star. "Uh, Sonnia," he called. "Any idea what the hell that is?"

Deep in the bayou, a hard day's ride far to the southeast of Malifaux city, Perdita and her family stood before the towering serpent statue. Many bones were scattered around the base, and the deeply weathered remains of stone-carved walls were found just beyond it, mostly consumed by weather and lush vegetation over many years.

"What the hell you think it is?" Francisco asked.

Santiago, typically charging into the thick of things before thinking, said, "Let's pull those vines off it and see what we got. Don't seem nearly as worn down as the rest of the building o'er there."

Perdita shook her head. "I don't know, hermano. Sonnia warned us to stay away from it and I'm inclined to agree. It is strange that the rest of those ruins you and Niño found are so weathered. This isn't."

"Just don't seem like much." He picked up a short stick and hefted it at the statue. It sailed up and struck the head of the snake and fell, with nothing at all extraordinary. Looking up at that moment, following the trajectory of the stick, they each saw the glowing red meteor plummeting from the sky. It looked like it was coming straight at them.

Francisco growled. "Dammit, Santiago!" he said. "What have you done now?"

The halo of bright fire descended with frightening speed.

Each member of the Ortega clan fled from the summit of that hill as the fiery meteor filled the sky overhead, clearly falling directly upon their location. Each ran as far as they dared before diving for cover behind trees or fallen logs.

The falling star struck directly upon the snake statue as if it were an angry fist punching through paper with a deep "Whoomph" each could feel rattle his chest. It moved too quickly to see what it was, though it took up as much space as a small house. The passing of the red mass left no physical mark upon the statue, save the blowing of the vine's leaves like a breeze.

The Ortegas looked around at each other, confused. Santiago snorted and Niño shrugged. They stepped from behind their respective hiding places and

She looked up and went to the open entry of the building behind Samael, seeing the red star streak across the sky, the fiery light hurtling toward the ground. "Oh, shit," she muttered. "Samael," she whispered in a tone of fear and urgency he was unaccustomed to hearing from her. He turned quickly to her as she said, "I don't know what's going to happen next."

"Sonnia?"

"Just be ready. And, Sam--" She hesitated, looking beyond him thoughtfully. She looked into his eyes. "If things don't go well, I want you to know that it was an honor working with you."

The blazing red meteor descended, drawing closer. It would strike just beyond the city, he figured, probably near the bayou.

approached the statue cautiously. Francisco pushed his sombrero from his head, and it rested upon his upper back as he scratched his head in bewilderment. He said, "That was sure strange. Thought we were dead for a minute."

Perdita nodded. "Si." She squinted at the thing. She said, "Its eyes."

The eyes of the statue were hidden by thick vegetation, but a faint azure light slowly rose from the deep recesses. It intensified and changed, quickly growing bright, shifting into a bright green, all before they could say anything about it.

A deep ringing chime issued from within the monolith. A violent eruption of energy burst from its head. Like a circular wave rippling away from a stone dropped into a still pond, a great wave of screaming energy. Thick and opaque, the glowing purple eddies of countless spiritual forces unleashed upon the world at once. No physical indication marked its passing save a brief swaying of the vegetation in its wake. Towering well over fifty feet, the great wave moved out from the hill.

It struck the Ortegas faster than they could perceive what was happening and threw them to the ground as screaming voices howled in their minds, forcing Santiago, Niño, and Papa to press open palms against the raging pain of their head.

The wave spread swiftly, radiating beyond them through the bayou and toward the city in several blinks of the eye. Everyone it washed over felt the great screaming energy within their minds. Every animal, too, felt its crippling pain as even the frogs around them ceased their chirping and cowered for a moment in pain. Every settler at the mining camps and within Malifaux was struck by the unexpected lashing of power, and each would later recount this shared pain as "the Event". People staggered, confused and nauseous, all to varying degrees of intensity, some much more violent than others. Some temporarily lost their vision and everyone saw flashing spots before their eyes for the remainder of the day and into the next. They could all see the same strange purple wall barrel upon them and pass through like the wind, leaving only that splitting headache.

Not everyone understood that the wall of energy that struck them affected people in greater degrees than others because of their various strength and control of the magical forces that drew them to Malifaux in the first place. While most men and women felt a spiritual affinity, most never felt the true control and mastery of the invisible and imperceptible magical forces around them. Some were strong in the arcane arts without ever knowing it, and those were reduced to retching and whimpering through the pain in their minds.

Francisco might have been one of those powerful men, more attuned to the magical forces around him than he ever realized. As the great wave passed over him, so intense at the epicenter of the blast, he fell back, groaning as he clutched his head, rolling in agony in the wet grasses of the swamp. Shaking his own debilitating pain away, Santiago went to his aid. Though he could do nothing to help, with a protective instinct, he cradled his elder brother's head in his lap while he whimpered uncontrollably.

Niño, still rubbing the pain from his flashing eyes, caught sight of Perdita. Gasping, he bolted upright, exclaiming, "*Dios mío!*"

Perdita was floating three feet off the ground, arms outstretched and back arched so that her face pointed toward the sky. Her mouth was open in a silent scream. She was frozen in the air, hovering and unmoving.

Pandora and Candy walked alone through the narrow alleys between shops on Malifaux's west side. Candy skipped beside the elder Neverborn who carried the small box of Woes in the crook of her arm. She was jubilant while Pandora merely smiled, keeping a vigilant eye upon the cobblestones before them, twisting around buildings and out of sight.

The sun rose, but the alleys maintained the depth of darkness they needed to retreat from the city. At night they could easily pass as humans, allowing them to infiltrate the city with ease and terrorize the outlanders that took their new homes for granted. In full light of day, however, their skin took on that pale translucency that the humans could identify as too cool and white to be exactly right.

Hidden in that alley, neither could see the red meteor descend upon Malifaux, nor could they see the circular wave of energy wash across the landscape from the point of impact.

"Did you see that woman scream?" Candy asked. "The mother," and she grimaced at the word, closing her eyes and shuddering as though it were too foul and despicable. "Did you even get that 'Dad' to scream? I wanted to see you make him cry."

Pandora shushed the other, even as she chuckled. "Not the father this time. He –" Pandora never finished her sentence. At that moment, the inescapable purple wave passed intangibly through the building beside them and engulfed the girls as it raced on, unimpeded by the stone buildings.

Candy, like many others struck by the wave, shrieked in pain, clutching her head. She moaned and shook.

Pandora suffered a different fate. The box fell from her hip and much of the energy of the mystical wave lingered upon her. The Soul-energy bombarded her, pouring in and out of her magical box, becoming great and terrible Woes she had never imagined. They struck through her like small versions of the great wave and became a torrent of wailing voices.

Anguish and trauma she had inflicted upon others rebounded upon her as the memory of each painful act she had ever caused another raced through her mind as disembodied glowing forms, with vague humanoid faces drove into her. Some pawed at her back, crawling across her, while others swirled around her body. Those that stayed upon her sought to imprint themselves upon her flesh and clothing, the moaning faces clear as they writhed about her coat and pale skin. The Woes drew her into the air, buffeting her with hate and sadness and distress.

Candy could barely see Pandora through the great column of glowing entities and covered her eyes against the bright light.

Pandora could take no more. Candy heard her voice bellow thunderously from within the great swirling column, "Suffer!" The Woes rose up from her and arced down, seeking a human host to torment, snaking around Candy to disappear through the walls of the building beside her.

Screams quickly followed from all around them.

Rasputina left the comfort of December's temple, far north of Malifaux. Hidden in the side of a mountain, it was well constructed and furnished, allowing a person to forget it was part of a very large mountain. She stepped into the rough cave that served as its entrance, dark and cold, though she no longer felt the pangs of the bitter wind that swept through the mouth of the cave and struck against her exposed skin.

Rasputina spoke to one of the three Silent Ones attending her. The woman had no tongue, of course, as all women's tongues are removed by December's priests to prevent Him from choosing them as vessels as his interests and power grow. Perhaps fortunate, Rasputina had escaped a similar fate, though the events leading to the conflict at Kythera left her questioning how fortunate she might truly be. This girl had been particularly abused by the higher priests before Rasputina had arrived to realign the hierarchy, elevating the Silent Ones to their proper station. The few male acolytes standing guard on either side of the temple entrance beyond the rough rock grew fearful in the presence of both Rasputina and the three Silent Ones and discreetly withdrew into the warm chambers hidden within. The girl had great resolve, Rasputina sensed, and defiance in her young face. Unlike the others, she refused to communicate to any save Rasputina. Without a name, they all called her 'Snow' because, similar to Rasputina, the girl demonstrated little awareness of the suffering cold.

"The Guild have abandoned the miners and intend to send them no aid?" she asked the girl.

Snow pulled her fur hood away from her head and nodded agreement, grunting quietly. "Then we're out of food, too. I needed them to send reinforcements and try to re-establish the mines up here."

The mouth of the cave blew with the bite of an unnatural winter she had intensified and reinforced, shrouding them from pursuit and cutting off the supply lines with a perpetual drive of snow and ice. "I'm out of Stones. The storm will dissipate by mid-day," she said to the young girl who merely nodded, helpless to change their circumstance.

The two Silent Ones at the entrance to the cave, keeping watch on the rocky path up the side of the mountain, leapt forward, animated and urgent. One motioned frantically with a hand bound in a thick fur mitten. She made guttural "Ungh!" sounds, trying to speak. Rasputina and the other young Silent One ran to the mouth of the cave. The rock face fell away sharply below them, but the slope evened out some allowing her three Ice Gamin and a towering Golem to stand guard, immobile as statues but ever vigilant. Far beyond the mountain's edge and into the hills to the south, she could see a large purple wall of roiling energy spread further away from an epicenter like a great tidal wave. It moved quickly across the hills and approached the mountain.

Faster than she could imagine, it ascended the mountain, the rocky vertical terrain doing nothing to slow it, passing through everything as if it were not even there. It struck her Gamin, and as it passed, they shook with a faintly audible high pitched ring and exploded in shards of ice. The Golem, too,

erupted as the wave passed through it, sending sharp shards of icy daggers and large blocks of ice against the face of the mountain.

Rasputina lifted her arm to her face, instinctively trying to ward off the glowing wall that consumed her effortlessly.

She screamed as her body, mind, and soul was inundated with a great surge of magical energy, very similar to the effect of a Soulstone but magnified a hundredfold. The three Silent Ones around her groaned mutely, their heads thrown back. Their arms stretched out and backs bent so their mouths, agape, faced the ceiling of the cave. They were lifted by the spiritual energy consuming them, rising above the cold stone, their thick fur covered feet dangling as they slowly revolved around Rasputina, also lifted from the ground by the deeply magical forces burrowing within her. Together, the four women rotated slowly and left the cave, hovering above the rocks and supported by the magical energy and a sharply intensified gale of wind and sleet.

The purple wave had moved on, continuing to rage across the land, but the influx of magic within them would not abate. The swirling storm above drew together, as the wind and dark clouds pulled inward, directly above Rasputina until it was a small cloud, dense and angry, spinning in a black tempest of sleet and wind as lightning cracked within it.

It unleashed its full wintry fury in a pillar of wind down upon Rasputina. Her upturned face took the gale, and it lashed against her flesh. Her arms were pinned to her sides as she was buffeted, but still, she was held aloft as were the three girls, beaten madly by the supernatural storm.

The Wind howled and they heard the rising intonation of a great voice made of the gale. "The Key Has Been Found. The Gateway is Open," it said. "The Red Prison Has Fallen. We Will Ascend. The Ritual is Nearly Complete."

Samael, struggled against the pain, gasping and sick. Every small movement he made throbbed against his skull, yet he staggered away from the consuming fire. It raged and growled. Vague faces of fire, moaning in apparent anguish, circled her, obscuring her in flame.

Every Master of Soulstone in Malifaux experienced the same transcendence. The power infused them, changing them, drawing their natural power out and embodying it in an external manifestation of their control and abilities.

Far from the northern mountains to south of Malifaux, the ring of energy struck the abandoned town Sonnia and Samael had found where she continued her research into the very phenomenon about to befall her. Alone among the living settlers on Malifaux, she had a vague understanding of the portents about this day and thought she would be in a position to stop it. As the purple wave could be seen through gaps between the small buildings of the town, and then towering over them, she wondered then if she would live beyond the day.

It struck her and Samael.

As she had so many times before focused her power to burn the souls of those violating the dark magic of this world, the Soul-energy burned deep within her. Consumed by the magical flame, she screamed as she left the ground, her arms outstretched. Containing it, trying to master it and stifle it would burn her out, she knew, reducing her to a shell of thought and emotion. She let the infusion of magic have its way with her, and she exploded in a great column of fire, engulfed within the great conflagration.

The wave struck Nicodem and Kirai while they retreated through the back of his observatory fortress. Much like the others in Malifaux, Nicodem cried out, dropping his cane. He clutched his chest and head as he was lifted to the heavens and moaned in agony. His eyes glowed with the same purple as the unnatural wave of energy.

Kirai doubled over, arms futilely protecting her head while Mortimer, confused and suddenly fighting a painful headache of his own, stumbled back against the wall of the building, which was about to explode any minute.

They stood upon a grassy garden, untended for centuries. Mortimer felt a slight tremor, and the earth moaned faintly. Suddenly, a skeletal hand burst from the ground before him, then more and more, all around. Arms, long decayed beyond the ability of any Resurrectionist master to reanimate, clawed at the surface, pulling forgotten bodies from the packed soil. The garden had perhaps never been a graveyard, but over the vast history of the planet, countless bodies had fallen and fully decomposed. The intensified power of Nicodem, unleashed, called those pieces together enough so that they would rise and serve him. He reveled in the power as whole bodies clambered to the surface, twisted, broken, incomplete, yet desperate to serve him. They found him, groping their leathery flesh and bone hands upon him, raising him up and clambering upon one another to touch him in a kind of reverence.

Kirai, unlike all of the others, succumbed to the deep pain within her mind. Perhaps if she had more experience with Soulstone and the mastery of the arcane art Nicodem hoped to instill upon her, her ascension at the passing of the spiritual wave might have called forth a veritable army of spirits to pay homage to her power as the undead horde had come at Nicodem's subconscious calling.

Her own great spirit, the Ikiryo, however, was dragged out of Kirai as it heard the call of the innumerable wave of spirits bombarding her. Its ethereal presence grew strong and tangible, her hair billowing around her head like fire on the wind. It was that part of her soul, that portion fractured from the rest that contained her hate, her desire for revenge, her grudge. It burned with a terrible heat that communicated well its carnal nature. It was the image of the woman's spirit but twisted with disgust into a monster capable of gruesome carnage.

She surveyed the risen dead and dismissed the pillar of bodies surrounding Nicodem, irrelevant and miniscule. The Ikiryo spun upon Mortimer, and he felt that unnatural heat emanating from her, sweat beading on his flesh as she growled and a ghostly wind breathed hot and wet upon him. It felt the pangs of anger and hatred from Kirai. The sense of retribution struck deep. But the fat man cowering before it was not part of Kirai's hatred. "Where?" his own voice asked in his mind. His eyes were as wide as his open mouth, and he could not form the words. He didn't know what it was talking about, but he hitched a thumb toward the building they had just abandoned.

It lunged toward him, howling in rage only inches from his face. He closed his eyes, sure she was about to eat him or drag him to hell or some other unpleasant thing. Mortimer was nothing to her and she looked up to the tower at the source of the unlocking and this puncture between worlds. She passed through Mortimer and flew madly through the tower, seeking the source of the atrocity committed.

Mortimer, having another mighty wave of spiritual energy pass through him only moments after the first, simply sighed. Then he fainted, falling beside Kirai.

The Ikiryo found him easily, drawn to the origin of her own physical manifestation, the ring given to Kirai.

She entered the chamber and howled in rage.

Hamelin stood upon a roiling mass of vermin that enveloped his lower limbs, lifting him from the ground. His arms outstretched, his mouth turned upward and agape, as dark breath emanated in a fog of pestilence and decay that grew as his power intensified. Soon it would be too strong to stop, and he would breathe it upon the world, sending out his decay to consume every living thing. The blackness would devour them all, and he would thrive on the power of the pests that fed upon the lingering Soul-energy the decaying world provided.

The ancient Lock stood open at his feet, the delicate gears spinning frantically with her ring twirling in the middle, whistling in its wild rotation. The Red Cage had fallen, unleashing the Gate between worlds, but the red gem in the device had not completed the rotation to the bottom of the device that would signify the completion of the ceremony. She hurtled toward her adversary, the despicable creature wearing the guise of a human.

Her unearthly claws reached out for the spinning ring when Hamelin's black staff, glowing at the end in deepest purple, waved toward her and a torrent of rats, maggots, and other vermin splashed forward at her, following the arc of his arm. They struck her physically despite her intangible form and drove her backward, striking her upon the wall. "YOU THINK YOU CAN STOP ME NOW?" He asked, the voice just a disembodied and vibrating echo caused by the grinding and buzzing bodies of the vermin against one another throughout the room. The black death, gaseous and filled with tiny gnats, swarmed toward her, and she knew, even in her deathly state, it would consume even her. She clawed at the vermin surrounding her, killing everything she touched, but, even as she did, more rats and insects filled the void.

Hamelin resumed his meditation, summoning more and more of the Soul-energy from the plane between worlds. He would ascend after eons of planning and waiting, imprisoned in a vague semblance of life, never truly immortal and nearly impotent. Now, feeling the release of that endless power of death, he would be the one to ascend and would be allowed to move on to master the next world; a world rife with power enough to sustain even him. The death energy enveloped him, filling him and thrilling every fiber of his tangible existence and beyond. He felt the elation as the red gem dropped in the Lock mechanism, bringing him closer to the inevitable end of this world and the beginning of his next. The power grew and his mind barely registered the world of Malifaux and its living creatures.

He would not have registered the quick sound of a click of a gear before him if not for the accompanying collapse of power, akin to being struck in the stomach, taking the wind from him so violently. He staggered from the mound of vermin that lost the strength to sustain him. "What?" he gasped. Before him stood the Ikiryo, the green serpent ring in her ghostly claw. "How?" he asked, alarmed and disbelieving.

She smiled wickedly and motioned behind her at the creatures she summoned, vaguely human-like and frantically gorging. Their once human mouths opened wider than the circumference of their heads and their great mummified bellies distended beyond them abnormally as they scooped great handfuls of maggots and squirming rats into their snapping maws. "GAKI," she said with his own voice inside his own mind. "INSATIABLE."

Hamelin, stunned, and powerless from the moment the ring was pulled from the device, raised his staff to strike her, but she sprang forward, grabbing him with both claws. She flew through the room in a rush, shrieking in anger. Not slowing, she struck the far wall. Though her intangible form flew effortlessly through the brickwork, Hamelin's physical form struck it with a resounding crash, cracking the mortar. His false body ruptured, sending the internal contents splashing away in an explosion of vermin and insects. The Ikiryo flew from the building and doubled back,

knowing that the great being would only be temporarily slowed. He must be destroyed, finally. As she descended, however, the charges set by Mortimer in the boilers beneath the observatory and around the structure began the sequence of detonations, destroying the building in rapidly exploding bursts.

The fires of spiritual energy engulfing Sonnia lost the Soul-energy that fueled them when the Ikiryo pulled the ring from the ceremonial device that had loosed the containment of the puncture between worlds. She fell, exhausted as those fires dissipated, her eyes blinking rapidly in the confusion and pain that wracked her mind and body.

"You okay?" Samael asked nervously as he reached her side. She was in too much pain to answer, but stared up at him, a weak smile reassuring him.

Marcus leapt through the air, the power of many beasts urging him to hunt in a way he had never before experienced. The energy that fueled him quickly waned as the ring was pulled from the mechanism many miles away. He fell bodily, rolling as he returned to normal, the beast energy drawn from him.

The new Woes bombarding Pandora, who was held aloft by their assault, circled her and moved through her tangible form. Some, unable to breach the greater mass of spirits, sought out Candy and struck similarly against her. The wailing in her head intensified, and she staggered backward against the wall.

Unexpectedly, the passing of the wave twisted not only her mind, but caused her body to spasm, wracking her against the stonework. Her limbs and torso twisted and elongated with the same celerity as a quickly grown Nephilim might experience after consuming enough blood. For Candy, she was one moment a young girl, and the next, she had become a young woman, much the peer of Pandora, and the small skirt that once stretched to her knees now barely covered her.

She clutched the sides of her head, feeling as though her very skull might split. The voices laughed and whispered in her mind. The pain was unbearable. Pandora, too, moaned as the Woes dissipated, returning to their box.

Candy laughed through the pain. She reveled in it. Hearing Pandora whimpering near her brought a strange titillation to the changed young woman. As the shrieking of people echoed through the back alley, Candy's laughter rose to an equal shriek, hideous and full of animosity.

Pandora could barely lift herself from the cobblestones. She struggled to look upon the changed girl, concern mounting as Candy, still clutching the sides of her head, shrieked in pain and glee.

Doctor McMourning's gloved fingers clawed at the dissection table, and he pulled himself upright from the tile floor of his lab. He shook his head, dispelling the confusion. Around him were the strange amalgamations of body parts, assembled and animated at his whim into powerful and amazing creatures, all extensions of his own will and encompassing the unique strengths of their original

hosts. He sighed. They were not stitched together but merely held in place by his own unlocked potential. Losing that newfound strength so abruptly, however, he watched as the body parts fell from one another like a tower of children's blocks suddenly toppled.

Rasputina was mute as the storm raged down upon her, but not because her tongue had been severed by December's priests. She hovered in the midst of the great entity, December, basking in great warmth of her spirit even as her body froze in the blasting of His wintry might. It was illusory warmth, however, as her heart had long been frozen by the rites that claimed her as December's. She saw His plan of ascension, though she marveled at the calm in His mind upon hers as it stood in such great contrast to the fury he exhibited upon her flesh.

"He Does Not Have My Piece Of The Key." She wanted to ask more, but could not even form the words in her mind. "You Must Be Protected," he said. The wind and ice cutting into her flesh since He had been summoned gathered on the mountain face below her. It swirled and tossed the smaller rocks and debris about. His presence pushed against her will, and the girls revolving around her fell down the sheer cliff face and into the heart of the density of the storm raging now upon the mountain. She was still held aloft, carried back to the edge of the cave's mouth.

The wind below her took shape and held together as the last of the clouds above poured down into it. Wind, snow, and daggers of ice shot out of the great mass and circled back to become part of the dense storm. It struck her, pressing her own identity aside so that December could claim her as his own. She would be lost, forever, and December would rise again in reincarnation through her. It was the moment He had chosen her for, to be lost as Fate decreed.

Rasputina could barely think as her own frail mind was consumed by the tyrant entity. She felt the pummeling wind from the sphere. It was only a chaotic ball of dense winter storm, yet it leapt toward her, up the mountainside. Amidst the gale and ice she saw the vague form of a great white lion, the bulk of the sleeting wind about its indistinct head like a mane. It rose up on its back legs made of dense snow and it took on a slightly humanoid form. It howled at her, and the wind drove her back, but her own icy spirit withstood it, and she stared it down. She had been a pawn for too long, and her strength and will had grown considerably since December had chosen her. She pushed back against His domination, knowing that she could never beat Him. Rather than deny him a host, with a will much greater than even she was aware, she pressed it out and away, and down into the Silent One called Snow. The girl was more than fifty feet below, her body broken from the fall. In the great cold of the mountainside, intensified tenfold by the presence of December, her dead flesh and blood was frozen so that she was translucent white and blue. Rasputina devoured the last of the great Spirit-energy and tied December's will to Snow even as He became the Storm. He had chosen her, though, and withdrew lest he be confined in a weaker vessel. Part of Him lingered within the storm and the girl. Snow rose, emotionless and chilled, alive once more, but her flesh still frozen. Snow turned to the Storm, bound to her will as she was bound to Rasputina's. It howled again like a hurricane ravaging everything around it, but it knew she was its master. The creature might have originally been a mighty spirit unleashed by the Unlocking of the Gate, used by December to take his first step toward the ascension he had prepared for, but it was bound to Rasputina who commanded it now.

"Snow Storm," she said of the two. The spiritual beast howled again above the icy figure of the pale girl and the wind blew cold against the rock face. "You are mine." It snorted angrily, knowing that it must obey her.

Zoraida stood amidst frogs, silurids, and other bayou creatures that had heeded her unspoken call, ready to serve and obey. The power of the great wave left her and they did, too.

She returned to her hut and readied a scrying pot and the essential elements necessary for a divination. She first consulted the deck of cards she kept in her sewing kit. She pulled it from beneath scraps of tightly woven burlap, leftovers from the puppets she made. Focusing upon the deck, attaching her magical will to the divination, she flipped the first card.

A two of Tomes. Two books needed to find the answer.

Queen of Rams. A female warrior. Face cards needed a following flip to denote their meaning and she flipped the Black Joker. Death. Another card turned revealing the Ten of Crows. The Necropolis.

More cards flipped, some with meanings too obscure for her to make out, and the odd connections they foretold made less and less sense. Even when she thought she had the understanding of a set, the next would either contradict it or carry the interaction of fate in a path that could not be discerned.

Why would the female warrior die and find physical power at the Necropolis? The divination, she was sure, would hold true. She continued to examine the cards, looking for the interaction of the Neverborn in the scheme of their unfolding destiny.

The magical charge waned in all of them, returning the inhabitants of Malifaux to their normal state, though disoriented, confused, and in deep exhaustion and mental pain.

Perdita, the first to be hit, at the very epicenter of the mystical blast, fell to the ground, her arms outstretched.

Santiago and Francisco were at her side in an instant and Niño held Papa, bewildered and dazed, just paces away.

"'Cisco," Santiago whispered urgently. "She's not breathing."

Francisco shook her. "Perdita!" he yelled, shaking her again. "Perdita!" He slapped her face, hoping the strike might awaken her from the ordeal.

Only moments had passed since the red object had struck the statue and the purple wave had been unleashed. A rumbling in the ground beneath them quickly intensified. "You've got to be kidding," Santiago muttered. "What the hell?"

"Go!" Francisco said, lifting her and running. He hauled her away as the ground around the serpent gave way, falling into a sinkhole in an expanding circle. The mud and trees fell just paces behind them as they ran. Neither Francisco nor Santiago bothered to look back though Niño was wide eyed and scared. The rumbling subsided, and they were able to stop, looking back on the hole that spanned more than fifty yards. Cautiously, they stepped to the edge of the great pit that descended beyond the depth of light. The large snake statue still stood at the center of the hole, a thick pillar supporting it down into the blackness. It looked like polished black marble or obsidian with lighter veins of pink, green, and pale lavender. After a moment, they could see the veins slowly moving around the massive column, swirling across one another very similar to the glowing wave that had struck each of them. A foul smell of long-stagnant air hit them, and they recoiled. It was unique and identifiable to each of them as the smell of death.

Perdita suddenly coughed, and her body shook in Francisco's arms. He hugged her tightly and set her down, cradling her in his arms. She smiled weakly and looked up at him. He nearly dropped her and fought against the urge to jump back. Her eyes were pools of black with faint strands of silver and purple moving across them. Flecks of red popped faintly as little dots of color that faded into the black to be replaced by more.

She coughed again and slumped against Francisco's chest. He held her tightly, but looked to his family, clearly distressed. "We're in trouble," she whispered.

The stench of old death wafted thicker from the pit. The sound of a high screeching rose in echoes from its depth. A large hand, bigger than a grown man's chest, grabbed hold of the edge near them. Its long black claws sank into the soil as it pulled itself from the hole.

Hoffman pressed his torso upright as the energy within him dissipated. The Hunter had merged with all the metal fragments from around the area, whether wrought iron gates or simple metal hinges torn from their framework, making it a towering new construct, no doubt an extension of his will while under the influence of the strange Spirit-energy that had overwhelmed him. Now, however, it stood immobile, unable to function after his subconscious will twisted and deformed it.

He didn't have time to consider the ramifications of its loss, for at that moment, a series of timed detonations blew out the first floor of the tower before him. The colossal structure imploded and fell. The collapse sent out a violent shockwave and shower of dust and debris that consumed the city blocks around it.

Shielding his eyes with one hand, the other could not support his weight, and he fell to an elbow, his legs limp behind him. "No," he gasped. "Justice! The Judge!" They were still within the structure, under the debris. He called out with his mind for the Hunter to pick him up, forgetting it had been destroyed by his will. He searched the area with his mind for a connection to the constructs brought with Justice, but he had sent them in as support for the Lady and the Judge. They were gone.

He realized that the loss of the constructs and Justice was the harbinger of his own doom. He was alone there in the Quarantine Zone, crippled and defenseless.

The remains of the great observatory burned in the morning light, sending smoke and ash far into the sky.

"WE RE IN TROUBLE," SHE WHISPERED.

THE STENCH OF OLD DEATH WAFTED THICKER FROM THE PIT. THE SOUND OF A HIGH SCREECHING ROSE IN ECHOES FROM ITS DEPTH.

Epilogue

"What the hell happened in here anyway?" Franklin Derrick, the youngest of the hastily assembled carpenters asked, a bit too brazenly, too loud for the other men in the room whose eyes stared at him intently.

He had a smile on his face, thinking he would bring some levity to the arduous work of cleaning and repairing the Governor General's study. The foreman, Milo Holmes, grabbed his arm from behind, spinning him with a heavy grip. The boy was aghast at the vehemence behind Milo's cold gray eyes and the deep sneer of his lips behind the sparse white whiskers on his face. "You stay focused on this job, boy!" he growled in a tight whisper, his eyes darting beyond the large room to the light pouring in through the open door wall and the two figures standing on the balcony. He nearly spat at the boy as he cursed, "Damn you if he hears!" He released Franklin's arm with a thrust and silently motioned for him to resume work.

Holmes turned from him and pushed his flat shovel through debris of fallen plaster and splintered wood, seeming to have been torn apart by a bomb blast though there was no evidence of burning or other use of explosives. Franklin looked to the other workmen for support, motioning to Milo as if the old man were crazy. He received no support from them as they simply shook their heads and refocused on the task of digging through the debris. Two of the men moved apart from the journeyman carpenter, and Franklin Derrick soon felt exposed and vulnerable, alone in the middle of the room, shoving around some debris, glowering at the others for his rejection and chastisement, still perplexed by their cold behavior. Having worked with them for several weeks on other projects, they were typically a boisterous and jovial crew.

The two men that had moved away from the young Franklin busied themselves with the remains of what used to be a large open fireplace. The quarried stones of granite were rare in these parts and only a few of the sparkling stones could be re-used. The majority were shattered, crushed as if between the molars of an old Nephilim, as the saying goes. The smaller remains of the once large stones were piled with the granite dust but the larger pieces were hefted in heavy sacks. The two men looked to the balcony where they had previously carried them to dump over the railing, to be cleaned from where they fell, later. The workmen paused, remembering that they were no longer alone in the repair of the devastated study and actually carried them through the mansion and down the stairs, all to avoid the presence of the Governor General and his secretary upon the balcony.

Neither Franklin, Milo, nor the other men working in the chamber could hear the two men upon the balcony speak in their atypically quiet conversation.

"Any report on specific details of the Event?" the Governor General asked of his secretary, Lucius Matheson.

Lucius adjusted the wire rim pince-nez glasses resting upon the bridge of his thin nose, the bright light of the noonday sun striking opaque upon the lenses. "Not as yet, sir," the small man said. "Scholars are working on it. Specific books on the subject of this energy wave are missing from the library archives," he said, stoically.

"Criid?"

"Unknown. They were not checked out appropriately. Although, these key tomes were accessible only by a select few. The highest ranking officials in each branch, myself, and a handful of your top advisors."

"Criid," the Governor growled, sure it was her without doubt. "She's still not returned to her post?"

"She has not. Whereabouts unknown."

"Be sure I'm aware of her return the moment she sets foot in Malifaux."

"Certainly."

The bright light of the sun beating down upon them did not cause the Governor to so much as squint against its harsh light, but he inquired, "The special glasses I requested?" Lucius withdrew the black-lensed spectacles from the pocket of his vest and handed them to the Governor. Turning to take them, the swirling purple and faintly silver bands that roiled in the black fields that dominated what were once normal eyes were visible to his secretary. "How long until this fades completely?" he asked.

Lucius had the rare courage to look intently upon the Governor, to stare directly into his eyes without turning away. "The glowing has subsided significantly in just the past twenty-four hours. The swirling eddies are still quite visible and the black depth has not abated. I'll have a better idea in the next day. Perhaps four or five days, estimated."

The Governor's lips drew down in a scowl and he cursed. Hooking the iron arms of the spectacles over his ears, he hid his eyes behind the dark lenses. He glanced at the men working on repairing the devastated remains of his study. "The scholars that witnessed your transformation during the Event?"

"Disposed of. Sorry," he said, correcting his terminology. "Missing, Sir. Missing."

The Governor nodded, turning back to stare down the long sloping hill to Malifaux, a mile distant. "When these men have finished repairing the study, they will find themselves missing, too."

"Of course."

"And you will take care of it yourself. No other agents will be involved."

"Naturally. It is a pleasure to evoke my will again; at your discretion, of course."

"Yes. The time of your slinking in the darkness nears an end. Remain patient. Remain vigilant."

Secretary Lucius Matheson strode through the debris that was once an ornate and beautiful study. He stepped past the carpenters working with eyes turned submissively away. They would soon be among the few to see his power manifest. As with everyone who bore witness to his secret abilities, they, too, would be unable to share his secret.

The Governor General, with his arms behind his back, surveyed his city from the balcony that granted him a view of every district.

Sonnia Criid might not be controllable now, he speculated. If she had grown aware of his own machinations, she would have to face Lucius, too, or worse. His plans were finally coming to fruition. The days of sedition by the insignificant rabble neared an end.

STANDARD ABILITIES

Models in Malifaux possess a wide range of abilities, specific Actions, and triggers, collectively called talents.

ABILITIES

Models in Malifaux may possess one or more Abilities. Abilities are not considered Actions and do not require AP to use. Unless otherwise mentioned, an ability is always active. While most abilities are unique to specific models, some are common enough across models that only their name is listed in the model's statistics with their full descriptions listed here.

Common Abilities List

Arachnid: This model ignores severe terrain movement penalties and climbs 1 **Ht** for each 1" of movement it spends.

Armor +#: A model suffering damage reduces the damage by the indicated number down to a minimum of 1.

Black Blood: All non-Neverborn models within 1" suffer 1 **Wd** when this model suffers damage from a melee **Strike** or melee Spell.

Bulletproof #: Reduce the amount of damage this model suffers from ranged **Strikes** or ranged Spells by the indicated number to a minimum of 1. This is cumulative with any other **Armor**.

Comes Cheap: This model's Soulstone Cost is not increased when hired by another Faction.

Companion (model): If this model and the companion (model) are within 6" of one another at the start of either model's activation, both models may activate simultaneously. Complete the acting model's activation first.

Easy to Wound #: Damage Flips against this model receive one ✚ per #.

Evasive #: Reduce the amount of damage this model suffers from ☻ by the indicated number to a minimum of 1. This is cumulative with any other **Armor**.

Float: This model may move over terrain and over other models without penalty, and can end its movement over impassable terrain but cannot end its movement over another model's base.

Fly: This model may move over terrain and over other models without penalty but cannot end its movement in or on impassable terrain or another model's base.

Gunfighter [Weapon]: This model can make melee **Strikes** up to 2" away with this weapon. The weapon gains /// and loses ☞ when making these **Strikes**.

Hard to Kill: While this model has 2 or more **Wd** remaining when it suffers damage, it can only be reduced to 1 **Wd** by a single damage source.

Hard to Wound #: Damage flips against this model receive one ⊟ per #.

Harmless: Enemy models must win a **Wp →12** Duel when targeting this model with an attack or the Action immediately fails. Harmless ends when the model performs an Action other than **Walk** or **Pass**. **Terrifying** models ignore **Harmless**.

Hunter: This model ignores cover and increases its LoS through obscuring terrain to 6".

Immune to Influence: This model is immune to **Wp** Duels when it is the defender."

Magic Resistant #: Reduce the damage this model suffers from spells by the indicated number to a minimum of 1.

Pass Through: This model may move through intervening models.

Poison #: The affected model receives the indicated number of Poison Counters if it has no Poison Counters on it. The affected model replaces any Poison Counters on it with the indicated number if that number is greater than the number of Poison Counters it currently has. The model suffers 1 **Wd** per Poison Counter on it at the start of its activation, and then discards 1 Poison Counter.

Regeneration #: Heal this model the indicated number of **Wd** at the start of its activation.

Ruthless: This model ignores **Harmless** and **Pitiful** when targeting enemy models.

Scout: This model ignores severe movement penalties.

Slow to Die: When this model is killed, it immediately takes a 1 AP Action before being removed from play.

Terrifying #: Living models who are engaged in melee with this model, or who wish to **Charge** this model, must win a Morale Duel or fall back (Morale, Book I, p 77).

Use Soulstones: This model may use game effects that require Soulstones. All Masters and Henchmen automatically have this Ability.

ACTIONS

Models in Malifaux may possess one or more Actions. Actions either require AP to use or provide additional specific or general AP. A action must be used to active unless it adjusts a models AP during its action, in which case it is always active on the model. While most actions are unique to specific models, some are common enough across models that only their name is listed in the model's statistics with their full descriptions listed here.

Common Actions List

(+1) Casting Expert: This model receives one additional **Cast** Action during its activation.

(+2) Casting Master: This model receives two additional **Cast** Actions during its activation.

(2) Flurry: Discard a Control Card. This model immediately makes up to three melee **Strikes** against a single model.

(2) Furious Casting: Discard a Control Card. This model receives 3 AP that must immediately be used on **Cast** Actions.

(+1) Instinctual: This model may perform two different (0) Actions during its activation.

(0) Link: This model and target model in base contact with it are Linked. After the model this model is Linked to completes a Walk Action or ends its activation, Push this model into base contact with the Linked model. A model can be Linked to one model at any time.

(+1) Melee Expert: This model receives one additional Melee **Strike** Action during its activation.

(+2) Melee Master: This model receives two additional Melee **Strike** Actions during its activation.

(+1) Nimble: This model receives one additional **Walk** Action during its activation.

(+1) Ranged Expert: This model receives one additional Ranged **Strike** Action during its activation.

(+2) Ranged Master: This model receives two additional Ranged **Strike** Actions during its activation.

(2) Rapid Fire: Discard a Control Card. This model immediately takes up to three **Strike** Actions with this Weapon against a single model.

TRIGGERS

A Trigger is a Talent that requires certain conditions to occur, including an activating event and one or more suits in the model's Duel total, before its game effect begins. When the Trigger is reached, the Controller declares his intent to use the Trigger then applies its effects at the appropriate time. A model can only activate one Trigger during an Action or in response to an event, regardless of the number of eligible Triggers that the model possesses. The model's Controller chooses which Trigger to activate. Actions generated by Triggers do not cost AP to use.

A Trigger with more than one activating event listed can be activated when any of those events are met, but the Trigger must meet the suit requirements as normal.

Remember: Only one Trigger per model can be activated per Action or event, regardless of how many of a model's Triggers may have their requirements met.

While most triggers are unique to specific models, some are common enough across models that only their name is listed in the model's statistics with their full descriptions listed here.

Common Triggers List

Cb (🗡) Critical Strike: When damaging defender with a melee or ranged weapon **Strike**, defender suffers +1 **Dg** for each 🗡 in this model's attack Duel total. The weapon the model may apply the Critical Strike trigger to will be listed in the models statistics.

Cb (♥♥) Flay: When damaging defender with a melee Strike, defender suffers +2 **Dg**.

Cb (✗✗) Rot: When damaging defender with a melee Strike, the damage flip receives ♣.

Ca (▦▦) Surge: After successfully casting a Spell, discard 1 Control Card. Draw 1 Control Card.

Cb (▦) Brutal [Weapon]: When damaged by this Weapon, defender suffers +1 **Dg** for each ▦ in this model's Duel total.

Run Nineteen

" What do I remember different about Run Nineteen? Not a damn thing. You'd think I'd remember something that stands out. It was a typical passenger run through the Breach. Something like two hundred Earthsiders due to start a new life in Malifaux. By what I heard, the locomotive had been serviced just recently, and most of the cars were straight off the steel presses. Who'd call it a mechanical problem anyway? Not me.

" What I do remember about Run Nineteen, son, was out of those two hundred souls who boarded that cursed train from Earthside, not one, not a single one made it to Malifaux. I remember we were just standing at the station when the train pulled in. Yeah that's right, didn't come crashing or screeching in; rode down the track just like it always would and came to a slow stop, nice and easy. To this day, I think that scares me the most - who or what brought that train in? We all just waited, and nobody got off. Nobody. I trust my own two eyes, and I know what I saw. Eventually somebody decided to take a look inside. Nothing prepared us for what we found.

" See, son, what chills me still is nobody was on that train. Not a soul. It was searched and searched again along with every square foot of track right back to the Breach. Witnesses Earthside said they saw passengers through the car windows as the train hit the portal. Not one person, not a scrap of person - just empty car after empty car.

" What happened to the train that made Run Nineteen? Well, it's still in service. Surprising isn't it? Not half as surprising as some of what I've heard. You see, passengers on that train now report whispers for help coming from out'a nowhere. People sometimes see reflections not their own when looking out its glass windows, too. I heard of at least a dozen people who have gone mad while looking in the mirror in the number seven car, but nobody knows what they seen. By all accounts, they don't speak anymore, just scream themselves raw all day, every day.

" I tell you this, boy. I thought about going back Earthside a while back, but I was there the day Run Nineteen came through. And, to be honest, I think I'll take my chances in Malifaux."